C. S. Lewis

FIVE BEST BOOKS
IN ONE VOLUME

C. S. Lewis

THE SCREWTAPE LETTERS

THE GREAT DIVORCE

MIRACLES

THE CASE FOR CHRISTIANITY

CHRISTIAN BEHAVIOUR

Christianity Today, Inc.
produced by
The Iversen Associates • New York 1969

Acknowledgement is made to The Macmillan Company for permission to reprint the following titles by C. S. Lewis:

THE SCREWTAPE LETTERS from *The Screwtape Letters* and *Screwtape Proposes a Toast*; THE GREAT DIVORCE; MIRACLES; THE CASE FOR CHRISTIANITY and CHRISTIAN BEHAVIOUR from *Mere Christianity*. Copyright 1943, 1945, 1946, 1947, 1952 by The Macmillan Company.

Produced by The Iversen Associates, Inc.
New York, N.Y. 1969

Printed in U.S.A.

Library of Congress catalog card number: 72-93142

Contents

Foreword

In Ecclesiastes it is said: "Of making many books there is no end." In our day tens of thousands of new titles flow from the presses annually. But few are remembered for more than a year or two, and only a fraction of all books that are published become classics. Long after most books have been forgotten, the works of C. S. Lewis will be not only remembered but read by multiplied thousands of people. Why is this so?

Lewis was a gifted writer. From a literary viewpoint he was certainly one of Christianity's greatest twentieth-century craftsmen. But he was more than that. He was a profound thinker and a hard-headed logician. He followed the trail to its end, courageously and persistently, never afraid of where truth would take him. He reinforced his premises with substantial evidence and gained for his efforts great skill as a Christian apologist. There is nothing shoddy about his product; each of his books bears the marks of his genius, his labors, and his polish.

Lewis became a Christian only after he had subjected the Christian faith to the toughest intellectual tests. His was a life based on a reasoned faith. He did not hesitate to embrace the supernatural, nor did he shrink from distinguishing between Christianity and the cultural overhang that so often accompanies it. He had a rare gift of being able to separate the primary from the secondary and had neither time nor patience for sham and hypocrisy.

There are places at which I disagree with C. S. Lewis, but I respect him most at those very points. For his work is marked by humility. He was a teachable person who would have been the first to acknowledge his finitude and change his opinions. Even those who might oppose him most vigorously would have to say that he was an able scholar and a true Christian gentleman.

It is with great pleasure that *Christianity Today* makes available this C. S. Lewis reader, a volume that is certain to be welcomed by many and read with eagerness and enduring profit.

HAROLD LINDSELL, *Editor*

CHRISTIANITY TODAY
Washington, D.C.

THE SCREWTAPE LETTERS
by
C. S. Lewis
FELLOW OF MAGDALEN COLLEGE, OXFORD

THE MACMILLAN COMPANY, NEW YORK

Preface

It was during the second German War that the letters of Screwtape appeared in the (now extinct) *Guardian*. I hope they did not hasten its death, but they certainly lost it one reader. A country clergyman wrote to the editor, withdrawing his subscription on the ground that "much of the advice given in these letters seemed to him not only erroneous but positively diabolical."

In general, however, they had a reception I had never dreamed of. Reviews were either laudatory or filled with that sort of anger which tells an author that he has hit his target; sales were at first (by my standards) prodigious, and have continued steady.

Of course, sales do not always mean what authors hope. If you gauged the amount of Bible reading in England by the number of Bibles sold, you would go far astray. Sales of *The Screwtape Letters*, in their own little way, suffer from a similar ambiguity. It is the sort of book that gets given to godchildren, the sort that gets read aloud at retreats. It is even, as I have noticed with a chastened smile, the sort that gravitates towards spare bedrooms, there to live a life of undisturbed tranquillity in company with

The Road Mender, John Inglesant, and *The Life of the Bee.*
Sometimes it is bought for even more humiliating reasons. A lady
whom I knew discovered that the pretty little probationer who
filled her hot-water bottle in the hospital had read *Screwtape.*
She also discovered why.

"You see," said the girl, "we were warned that at interviews,
after the real, technical questions are over, matrons and people
sometimes ask about your general interests. The best thing is to
say you've read something. So they gave us a list of about ten
books that usually go down pretty well and said we ought to read
at least one of them."

"And you chose *Screwtape?*"

"Well, of course; it was the shortest."

Still, when all allowances have been made, the book has had
readers of the genuine sort sufficiently numerous to make it
worthwhile answering some of the questions it has raised in their
minds.

The commonest question is whether I really "believe in the
Devil."

Now, if by "the Devil" you mean a power opposite to God and,
like God, self-existent from all eternity, the answer is certainly
No. There is no uncreated being except God. God has no opposite. No being could attain a "perfect badness" opposite to the
perfect goodness of God; for when you have taken away every
kind of good thing (intelligence, will, memory, energy, and existence itself) there would be none of him left.

The proper question is whether I believe in devils. I do. That
is to say, I believe in angels, and I believe that some of these, by
the abuse of their free will, have become enemies to God and, as
a corollary, to us. These we may call devils. They do not differ
in nature from good angels, but their nature is depraved. *Devil*
is the opposite of *angel* only as Bad Man is the opposite of Good
Man. Satan, the leader or dictator of devils, is the opposite, not
of God, but of Michael.

I believe this not in the sense that it is part of my creed, but
in the sense that it is one of my opinions. My religion would not
be in ruins if this opinion were shown to be false. Till that happens—and proofs of a negative are hard to come by—I shall re-

tain it. It seems to me to explain a good many facts. It agrees with the plain sense of Scripture, the tradition of Christendom, and the beliefs of most men at most times. And it conflicts with nothing that any of the sciences has shown to be true.

It should be (but it is not) unnecessary to add that a belief in angels, whether good or evil, does not mean a belief in either as they are represented in art and literature. Devils are depicted with bats' wings and good angels with birds' wings, not because anyone holds that moral deterioration would be likely to turn feathers into membrane, but because most men like birds better than bats. They are given wings at all in order to suggest the swiftness of unimpeded intellectual energy. They are given human form because man is the only rational creature we know. Creatures higher in the natural order than ourselves, either incorporeal or animating bodies of a sort we cannot experience, must be represented symbolically if they are to be represented at all.

These forms are not only symbolical but were always known to be symbolical by reflective people. The Greeks did not believe that the gods were really like the beautiful human shapes their sculptors gave them. In their poetry a god who wishes to "appear" to a mortal temporarily assumes the likeness of a man. Christian theology has nearly always explained the "appearance" of an angel in the same way. It is only the ignorant, said Dionysius in the fifth century, who dream that spirits are really winged men.

In the plastic arts these symbols have steadily degenerated. Fra Angelico's angels carry in their face and gesture the peace and authority of Heaven. Later come the chubby infantile nudes of Raphael; finally the soft, slim, girlish, and consolatory angels of nineteenth century art, shapes so feminine that they avoid being voluptuous only by their total insipidity—the frigid houris of a teatable paradise. They are a pernicious symbol. In Scripture the visitation of an angel is always alarming; it has to begin by saying "Fear not." The Victorian angel looks as if it were going to say, "There, there."

The literary symbols are more dangerous because they are not so easily recognized as symbolical. Those of Dante are the best.

Before his angels we sink in awe. His devils, as Ruskin rightly remarked, in their rage, spite, and obscenity, are far more like what the reality must be than anything in Milton. Milton's devils, by their grandeur and high poetry, have done great harm, and his angels owe too much to Homer and Raphael. But the really pernicious image is Goethe's Mephistopheles. It is Faust, not he, who really exhibits the ruthless, sleepless, unsmiling concentration upon self which is the mark of Hell. The humorous, civilised, sensible, adaptable Mephistopheles has helped to strengthen the illusion that evil is liberating.

A little man may sometimes avoid some single error made by a great one, and I was determined that my own symbolism should at least not err in Goethe's way. For humor involves a sense of proportion and a power of seeing yourself from the outside. Whatever else we attribute to beings who sinned through pride, we must not attribute this. Satan, said Chesterton, fell through force of gravity. We must picture Hell as a state where everyone is perpetually concerned about his own dignity and advancement, where everyone has a grievance, and where everyone lives the deadly serious passions of envy, self-importance, and resentment. This, to begin with. For the rest, my own choice of symbols depended, I suppose, on temperament and on the age.

I like bats much better than bureaucrats. I live in the Managerial Age, in a world of "Admin." The greatest evil is not now done in those sordid "dens of crime" that Dickens loved to paint. It is not done even in concentration camps and labour camps. In those we see its final result. But it is conceived and ordered (moved, seconded, carried, and minuted) in clean, carpeted, warmed, and well-lighted offices, by quiet men with white collars and cut fingernails and smooth-shaven cheeks who do not need to raise their voices. Hence, naturally enough, my symbol for Hell is something like the bureaucracy of a police state or the offices of a thoroughly nasty business concern.

Milton has told us that "devil with devil damned Firm concord holds." But how? Certainly not by friendship. A being which can still love is not yet a devil. Here again my symbol seemed to me useful. It enabled me, by earthly parallels, to picture an official society held together entirely by fear and greed. On the surface, manners are normally suave. Rudeness to one's superiors would obviously be suicidal; rudeness to one's equals might put them on their guard before you were ready to spring your mine. For of course "Dog eat dog" is the principle of the whole organisation. Everyone wishes everyone else's discrediting, demotion, and ruin; everyone is an expert in the confidential report, the pretended alliance, the stab in the back. Over all this their good manners, their expressions of grave respect, their "tributes" to one another's invaluable services form a thin crust. Every now and then it gets punctured, and the scalding lava of their hatred spurts out.

This symbol also enabled me to get rid of the absurd fancy that devils are engaged in the disinterested pursuit of something called Evil (the capital is essential). Mine have no use for any such turnip ghost. Bad angels, like bad men, are entirely practical. They have two motives. The first is fear of punishment: for as totalitarian countries have their camps for torture, so my Hell contains deeper Hells, its "houses of correction." Their second motive is a kind of hunger. I feign that devils can, in a spiritual sense, eat one another; and us. Even in human life we have seen the passion to dominate, almost to digest, one's fellow; to make his whole intellectual and emotional life merely an extension of one's own—to hate one's hatreds and resent one's grievances and indulge one's egoism through him as well as through oneself. His own little store of passion must of course be suppressed to make room for ours. If he resists this suppression he is being very selfish.

On Earth this desire is often called "love." In Hell I feign that they recognize it as hunger. But there the hunger is more ravenous, and a fuller satisfaction is possible. There, I suggest, the stronger spirit—there are perhaps no bodies to impede the operation—can really and irrevocably suck the weaker into itself and permanently gorge its own being on the weaker's outraged individuality. It is (I feign) for this that devils desire human souls and the souls of one another. It is for this that Satan desires all his own followers and all the sons of Eve and all the host of Heaven. His dream is of the day when all shall be inside him and all that says "I" can say it only through him. This, I surmise, is the bloated-spider parody, the only imitation he can understand, of that unfathomed bounty whereby God turns tools into servants and servants into sons, so that they may be at last reunited to Him in the perfect freedom of a love offered from the height of the utter individualities which he has liberated them to be.

But, as in Grimm's story,* *des träumte mir nur,* this is all only myth and symbol. That is why the question of my own opinion about devils, though proper to be answered when once it was raised, is really of very minor importance for a reader of *Screwtape.* To those who share that opinion, my devils will be symbols of a concrete reality: to others, they will be personifications of abstractions, and the book will be an allegory. But it makes little difference which way you read it. For of course its purpose was not to speculate about diabolical life but to throw light from a new angle on the life of men.

I am told that I was not first in the field and that someone in the seventeenth century wrote letters from a devil. I have not seen that book. I believe its slant was mainly political. But I gladly acknowledge a debt to Stephen McKenna's *The Confessions of a Well-Meaning Woman.* The connection may not be obvious, but you will find there the same moral inversion—the blacks all white and the whites all black—and the humour which comes of speaking through a totally humourless *presonna.* I think my idea of spiritual cannibalism probably owes something to the horrible scenes of "absorbing" in David Lindsay's neglected *Voyage to Arcturus.*

The names of my devils have excited a good deal of curiosity, and there have been many explanations, all wrong. The truth is that I aimed merely at making them nasty—and here too I am perhaps indebted to Lindsay—by the sound. Once a name was invented, I might speculate like anyone else (and with no more authority than anyone else) as to the phonetic associations which caused the unpleasant effect. I fancy that *Scrooge, screw, thumbscrew, tapeworm,* and *red tape* all do some work in my hero's name, and that *slob, slobber, slubber,* and *gob* have all gone into *slubgob.*

Some have paid me an undeserved compliment by supposing

* *Der Raüberbräutigam.*

that my *Letters* were the ripe fruit of many years' study in moral and ascetic theology. They forgot that there is an equally reliable, though less creditable, way of learning how temptation works. "My heart"—I need no other's—"showeth me the wickedness of the ungodly."

I was often asked or advised to add to the original *Letters*, but for many years I felt not the least inclination to do it. Though I had never written anything more easily, I never wrote with less enjoyment. The ease came, no doubt, from the fact that the device of diabolical letters, once you have thought of it, exploits itself spontaneously, like Swift's big and little men, or the medical and ethical philosophy of *Erewhon,* or Anstey's Garuda Stone. It would run away with you for a thousand pages if you gave it its head. But though it was easy to twist one's mind into the diabolical attitude, it was not fun, or not for long. The strain produced a sort of spiritual cramp. The work into which I had to project myself while I spoke through Screwtape was all dust, grit, thirst, and itch. Every trace of beauty, freshness, and geniality had to be excluded. It almost smothered me before I was done. It would have smothered my readers if I had prolonged it.

I had, moreover, a sort of grudge against my book for not being a different book which no one could write. Ideally, Screwtape's advice to Wormwood should have been balanced by archangelical advice to the patient's guardian angel. Without this the picture of human life is lopsided. But who could supply the deficiency? Even if a man—and he would have to be a far better man than I—could scale the spiritual heights required, what "answerable style" could he use? For the style would really be part of the content. Mere advice would be no good; every sentence would have to smell of Heaven. And nowadays even if you could write a prose like Traherne's, you wouldn't be allowed to, for the canon of "functionalism" has disabled literature for half its functions. (At bottom, every ideal of style dictates not only how we should say things but what sort of things we may say.)

Then, as years went on and the stifling experience of writing the *Letters* became a weaker memory, reflections on this and that which seemed somehow to demand Screwtapian treatment began to occur to me. I was resolved never to write another *Letter*. The idea of something like a lecture or "address" hovered vaguely in my mind, now forgotten, now recalled, never written. Then came an invitation from the *Saturday Evening Post,* and that pressed the trigger.

"The best way to drive out the devil, if he will not yield to texts of Scripture, is to jeer and flout him, for he cannot bear scorn."—*Luther*

"The devill . . the prowde spirite . . cannot endure to be mocked."—*Thomas More*

TO
J. R. R. TOLKIEN

Preface

I have no intention of explaining how the correspondence which I now offer to the public fell into my hands.

There are two equal and opposite errors into which our race can fall about the devils. One is to disbelieve in their existence. The other is to believe, and to feel an excessive and unhealthy interest in them. They themselves are equally pleased by both errors and hail a materialist or a magician with the same delight. The sort of script which is used in this book can be very easily obtained by anyone who has once learned the knack; but ill-disposed or excitable people who might make a bad use of it shall not learn it from me.

Readers are advised to remember that the devil is a liar. Not everything that Screwtape says should be assumed to be true even from his own angle. I have made no attempt to identify any of the human beings mentioned in the letters; but I think it very unlikely that the portraits, say, of Fr. Spike or the patient's mother, are wholly just. There is wishful thinking in Hell as well as on Earth.

In conclusion, I ought to add that no effort has been made to clear up the chronology of the letters. Number XVII appears to have been composed before rationing became serious; but in general the diabolical method of dating seems to bear no relation to terrestrial time and I have not attempted to reproduce it. The history of the European War, except in so far as it happens now and then to impinge upon the spiritual condition of one human being, was obviously of no interest to Screwtape.

C. S. LEWIS

MAGDALEN COLLEGE
July 5, 1941

I.

My Dear Wormwood,

I note what you say about guiding your patient's reading and taking care that he sees a good deal of his materialist friend. But are you not being a trifle *naïf*? It sounds as if you supposed that *argument* was the way to keep him out of the Enemy's clutches. That might have been so if he had lived a few centuries earlier. At that time the humans still knew pretty well when a thing was proved and when it was not; and if it was proved they really believed it. They still connected thinking with doing and were prepared to alter their way of life as the result of a chain of reasoning. But what with the weekly press and other such weapons we have largely altered that. Your man has been accustomed, ever since he was a boy, to have a dozen incompatible philosophies dancing about together inside his head. He doesn't think of doctrines as primarily "true" or "false," but as "academic" or "practical," "outworn" or "contemporary," "conventional" or "ruthless." Jargon, not argument, is your best ally in keeping him from the Church. Don't waste time trying to make him think that materialism is *true!* Make him think it is strong, or stark, or courageous—that it is the philosophy of the future. That's the sort of thing he cares about.

The trouble about argument is that it moves the whole struggle onto the Enemy's own ground. He can argue too; whereas in really practical propaganda of the kind I am suggesting He has been shown for centuries to be greatly the inferior of Our Father Below. By the very act of arguing, you awake the patient's reason; and once it is awake, who can foresee the result? Even if a particular train of thought can be twisted so as to end in our favour, you will find that you have been strengthening in your patient the fatal habit of attending to universal issues and withdrawing his attention from the stream of immediate sense experiences. Your business is to fix his attention on the stream. Teach him to call it "real life" and don't let him ask what he means by "real."

Remember, he is not, like you, a pure spirit. Never having been a human (Oh that abominable advantage of the Enemy's!) you don't realise how enslaved they are to the pressure of the ordinary. I once had a patient, a sound atheist, who used to read in the British Museum. One day, as he sat reading, I saw a train of thought in his mind beginning to go the wrong way. The Enemy, of course, was at his elbow in a moment. Before I knew where I was I saw my twenty years' work beginning to totter. If I had lost my head and begun to attempt a defence by argument I should have been undone. But I was not such a fool. I struck instantly at the part of the man which I had best under my control and suggested that it was just about time he had some lunch. The Enemy presumably made the counter-suggestion (you know how one can never *quite* overhear what He says to them?) that this was more important than lunch. At least I think that must have been His line for when I said "Quite. In fact much *too* important to tackle at the end of a morning," the patient brightened up considerably; and by the time I had added "Much better come back after lunch and go into it with a fresh mind," he was already half way to the door. Once he was in the street the battle was won. I showed him a newsboy shouting the midday paper, and a No. 73 bus going past, and before he reached the bottom of the steps I had got into him an unalterable conviction that, whatever odd ideas might come into a man's head when he was shut up alone with his books, a healthy dose of "real life" (by which he meant the bus and the newsboy) was enough to show him that all "that sort of thing" just couldn't be true. He knew he'd had a narrow escape and in later years was fond of talking about "that inarticulate sense for actuality which is our ultimate safeguard against the aberrations of mere logic." He is now safe in Our Father's house.

You begin to see the point? Thanks to processes which we set at work in them centuries ago, they find it all but impossible to believe in the unfamiliar while the familiar is before their eyes. Keep pressing home on him the *ordinariness* of things. Above all, do not attempt to use science (I mean, the real sciences) as a defence against Christianity. They will positively encourage him to think about realities he can't touch and see. There have been sad cases among the modern physicists. If he must dabble in science, keep him on economics and sociology; don't let him get away from that invaluable "real life". But the best of all is to let him read no science but to give him a grand general idea that he knows it all and that everything he happens to have picked up in casual talk and reading is "the results of modern investigation." Do remember you are there to fuddle him. From the way some of you young fiends talk, anyone would suppose it was our job to *teach!*

Your affectionate uncle
SCREWTAPE

2.

MY DEAR WORMWOOD,

I note with grave displeasure that your patient has become a Christian. Do not indulge the hope that you will escape the usual penalties; indeed, in your better moments, I trust you would hardly even wish to do so. In the meantime we must make the best of the situation. There is no need to despair; hundreds of these adult converts have been reclaimed after a brief sojourn in the Enemy's camp and are now with us. All the *habits* of the patient, both mental and bodily, are still in our favour.

One of our great allies at present is the Church itself. Do not misunderstand me. I do not mean the Church as we see her spread out through all time and space and rooted in eternity, terrible as an army with banners. That, I confess, is a spectacle which makes our boldest tempters uneasy. But fortunately it is quite invisible to these humans. All your patient sees is the half-finished, sham Gothic erection on the new building estate. When he goes inside, he sees the local grocer with rather an oily expression on his face bustling up to offer him one shiny little book containing a liturgy which neither of them understands, and one shabby little book containing corrupt texts of a number of religious lyrics, mostly bad, and in very small print. When he gets to his pew and looks round him he sees just that selection of his neighbours whom he has hitherto avoided. You want to lean pretty heavily on those neighbours. Make his mind flit to and fro between an expression like "the body of Christ" and the actual faces in the next pew. It matters very little, of course, what kind of people that next pew really contains. You may know one of them to be a great warrior on the Enemy's side. No matter.

18

Your patient, thanks to Our Father Below, is a fool. Provided that any of those neighbours sing out of tune, or have boots that squeak, or double chins, or odd clothes, the patient will quite easily believe that their religion must therefore be somehow ridiculous. At his present stage, you see, he has an idea of "Christians" in his mind which he supposes to be spiritual but which, in fact, is largely pictorial. His mind is full of togas and sandals and armour and bare legs and the mere fact that the other people in church wear modern clothes is a real—though of course an unconscious—difficulty to him. Never let it come to the surface; never let him ask what he expected them to look like. Keep everything hazy in his mind now, and you will have all eternity wherein to amuse yourself by producing in him the peculiar kind of clarity which Hell affords.

Work hard, then, on the disappointment or anticlimax which is certainly coming to the patient during his first few weeks as a churchman. The Enemy allows this disappointment to occur on the threshold of every human endeavour. It occurs when the boy who has been enchanted in the nursery by *Stories from the Odyssey* buckles down to really learning Greek. It occurs when lovers have got married and begin the real task of learning to live together. In every department of life it marks the transition from dreaming aspiration to laborious doing. The Enemy takes this risk because He has a curious fantasy of making all these disgusting little human vermin into what He calls His "free" lovers and servants—"sons" is the word He uses, with His inveterate love of degrading the whole spiritual world by unnatural liaisons with the two-legged animals. Desiring their freedom, He therefore refuses to carry them, by their mere affections and habits, to any of the goals which He sets before them: He leaves them to "do it on their own". And there lies our opportunity. But also, remember, there lies our danger. If once they get through this intial dryness successfully, they become much less dependent on emotion and therefore much harder to tempt.

I have been writing hitherto on the assumption that the people in the next pew afford no *rational* ground for disappointment. Of course if they do—if the patient knows that the woman with the absurd hat is a fanatical bridgeplayer or the man with squeaky boots a miser and an extortioner—then your task is so much the easier. All you then have to do is to keep out of his mind the question "If I, being what I am, can consider that I am in some sense a Christian, why should the different vices of those people in the next pew prove that their religion is mere hypocrisy and convention?" You may ask whether it is possible to keep such an obvious thought from occurring even to a human mind. It is, Wormwood, it is! Handle him properly and it simply won't come into his head. He has not been anything like long enough with the Enemy to have any real humility yet. What he says, even on his knees, about his own sinfulness is all parrot talk. At bottom, he still believes he has run up a very favourable credit-balance in the Enemy's ledger by allowing hmself to be converted, and thinks that he is showing great humility and condescension in going to church with these "smug," commonplace neighbours at all. Keep him in that state of mind as long as you can.

Your affectionate uncle

SCREWTAPE

3.

My dear Wormwood,

I am very pleased by what you tell me about this man's relations with his mother. But you must press your advantage. The Enemy will be working from the centre outwards, gradually bringing more and more of the patient's conduct under the new standard, and may reach his behaviour to the old lady at any moment. You want to get in first. Keep in close touch with our colleague Glubose who is in charge of the mother, and build up between you in that house a good settled habit of mutal annoyance; daily pinpricks. The following methods are useful.

1. Keep his mind on the inner life. He thinks his conversion is something *inside* him and his attention is therefore chiefly turned at present to the states of his own mind—or rather to that very expurgated version of them which is all you should allow him to see. Encourage this. Keep his mind off the most elementary duties by directing it to the most advanced and spiritual ones. Aggravate that most useful human characteristic, the horror and neglect of the obvious. You must bring him to a condition in which he can practise self-examination for an hour without discovering any of those facts about himself which are perfectly clear to anyone who has ever lived in the same house with him or worked in the same office.

2. It is, no doubt, impossible to prevent his praying for his mother, but we have means of rendering the prayers innocuous. Make sure that they are always very "spiritual", that he is always concerned with the state of her soul and never with her rheumatism. Two advantages will follow. In the first place, his attention will be kept on what he regards as her sins, by

which, with a little guidance from you, he can be induced to mean any of her actions which are inconvenient or irritating to himself. Thus you can keep rubbing the wounds of the day a little sorer even while he is on his knees; the operation is not at all difficult and you will find it very entertaining. In the second place, since his ideas about her soul will be very crude and often erroneous, he will, in some degree, be praying for an imaginary person, and it will be your task to make that imaginary person daily less and less like the real mother—the sharp-tongued old lady at the breakfast table. In time, you may get the cleavage so wide that no thought or feeling from his prayers for the imagined mother will ever flow over into his treatment of the real one. I have had patients of my own so well in hand that they could be turned at a moment's notice from impassioned prayer for a wife's or son's "soul" to beating or insulting the real wife or son without a qualm.

3. When two humans have lived together for many years it usually happens that each has tones of voice and expressions of face which are almost unendurably irritating to the other. Work on that. Bring fully into the consciousness of your patient that particular lift of his mother's eyebrows which he learned to dislike in the nursery, and let him think how much he dislikes it. Let him assume that she knows how annoying it is and does it to annoy—if you know your job he will not notice the immense improbability of the assumption. And, of course, never let him suspect that he has tones and looks which similarly annoy her. As he cannot see or hear himself, this is easily managed.

4. In civilised life domestic hatred usually expresses itself by saying things which would appear quite harmless on paper (the *words* are not offensive) but in such a voice, or at such a moment, that they are not far short of a blow in the face. To keep this game up you and Glubose must see to it that each of these two fools has a sort of double standard. Your patient must demand that all his own utterances are to be taken at their face value and judged simply on the actual words, while at the same time judging all his mother's utterances with the fullest and most oversensitive interpretation of the tone and the context and the suspected intention. She must be encouraged to do the same to him.

Hence from every quarrel they can both go away convinced, or very nearly convinced, that they are quite innocent. You know the kind of thing: "I simply ask her what time dinner will be and she flies into a temper." Once this habit is well established you have the delightful situation of a human saying things with the express purpose of offending and yet having a grievance when offence is taken.

Finally, tell me something about the old lady's religious position. Is she at all jealous of the new factor in her son's life?—at all piqued that he should have learned from others, and so late, what she considers she gave him such good opportunity of learning in childhood? Does she feel he is making a great deal of "fuss" about it—or that he's getting in on very easy terms? Remember the elder brother in the Enemy's story,

Your affectionate uncle

SCREWTAPE

4.

My Dear Wormwood,

The amateurish suggestions in your last letter warn me that it is high time for me to write to you fully on the painful subject of prayer. You might have spared the comment that my advice about his prayers for his mother "proved singularly unfortunate". That is not the sort of thing that a nephew should write to his uncle—nor a junior tempter to the under-secretary of a department. It also reveals an unpleasant desire to shift responsibility; you must learn to pay for your own blunders.

The best thing, where it is possible, is to keep the patient from the serious intention of praying altogether. When the patient is an adult recently re-converted to the Enemy's party, like your man, this is best done by encouraging him to remember, or to think he remembers, the parrot-like nature of his prayers in childhood. In reaction against that, he may be persuaded to aim at something entirely spontaneous, inward, informal, and unregularised; and what this will actually mean to a beginner will be an effort to produce in himself a vaguely devotional *mood* in which real concentration of will and intelligence have no part. One of their poets, Coleridge, has recorded that he did not pray "with moving lips and bended knees" but merely "composed his spirit to love" and indulged "a sense of supplication." That is exactly the sort of prayer we want; and since it bears a superficial resemblance to the prayer of silence as practised by those who are very far advanced in the Enemy's service, clever and lazy patients can be taken in by it for quite a long time. At the very least, they can be persuaded that the bodily position makes no difference to their prayers; for they constantly forget, what you must always remember, that they are animals and that whatever their bodies do affects their souls. It is funny how mortals always picture us as putting things into their minds: in reality our best work is done by keeping things out.

If this fails, you must fall back on a subtler misdirection of his intention. Whenever they are attending to the Enemy Himself we are defeated, but there are ways of preventing them from doing so. The simplest is to turn their gaze away from Him towards themselves. Keep them watching their own minds and trying to produce *feelings* there by the action of their own wills. When they meant to ask Him for charity, let them, instead, start trying to manufacture charitable feelings for themselves and not notice that this is what they are doing. When they meant to pray for courage, let them really be trying to feel brave. When they say they are praying for forgiveness, let them be trying to feel forgiven. Teach them to estimate the value of each prayer by their success in producing the desired feeling; and never let them suspect how much success or failure of that kind depends on whether they are well or ill, fresh or tired, at the moment.

But of course the Enemy will not meantime be idle. Wherever there is prayer, there is danger of His own immediate action. He is cynically indifferent to the dignity of His position, and ours, as pure spirits, and to human animals on their knees. He pours out self-knowledge in a quite shameless fashion. But even if He defeats your first attempt at misdirection, we have a subtler weapon. The humans do not start from that direct perception of Him which we, unhappily, cannot avoid. They have never known that ghastly luminosity, that stabbing and searing glare which makes the background of permanent pain to our lives. If you look into your patient's mind when he is praying, you will not find *that*. If you examine the object to which he is attending, you will find that it is a composite object containing many quite ridiculous ingredients. There will be images derived from pictures of the Enemy as He appeared during the discreditable episode known as the Incarnation: there will be vaguer—perhaps quite savage and puerile—images associated with the other two Persons. There will even be some of his own reverence (and of bodily sensations accompanying it) objectified and attributed to the object revered. I have known cases where what the patient called his "God" was actually *located* up and to the left at the corner of the bedroom ceiling, or inside his own head, or in a crucifix on the wall. But whatever the nature of the composite object, you must keep him praying to *it*—to the thing that he has made, not to the Person who has made him. You may even encourage him to attach great importance to the correction and improvement of his composite object, and to keeping it steadily before his imagination during the whole prayer. For if he ever comes to make the distinction, if ever he consciously directs his prayers, "Not to what I think thou art but to what thou knowest thyself to be," our situation is, for the moment, desperate. Once all his thoughts and images have been flung aside or, if retained, retained with a full recognition of their merely subjective nature, and the man trusts himself to the completely real, external, invisible Presence, there with him in the room and never knowable by him as he is known by it—why, then it is that the incalculable may occur. In avoiding this situation—this real nakedness of the soul in prayer—you will be helped by the fact that the humans themselves do not desire it as much as they suppose. There's such a thing as getting more than they bargained for!

Your affectionate uncle

SCREWTAPE

5.

MY DEAR WORMWOOD,

It is a little bit disappointing to expect a detailed report on your work and to receive instead such a vague rhapsody as your last letter. You say you are "delirious with joy" because the European humans have started another of their wars. I see very well what has happened to you. You are not delirious; you are only drunk. Reading between the lines in your very unbalanced account of the patient's sleepless night, I can reconstruct your state of mind fairly accurately. For the first time in your career you have tasted that wine which is the reward of all our labours—the anguish and bewilderment of a human soul—and it has gone to your head. I can hardly blame you. I do not expect old heads on young shoulders. Did the patient respond to some of your terror-pictures of the future? Did you work in some good self-pitying glances at the happy past?—some fine thrills in the pit of his stomach, were there? You played your violin prettily, did you? Well, well, it's all very natural. But do remember, Wormwood, that duty comes before pleasure. If any present self-indulgence on your part leads to the ultimate loss of the prey, you will be left eternally thirsting for that draught of which you are now so much enjoying your first sip. If, on the other hand, by steady and cool-headed application here and now you can finally secure his soul, he will then be yours forever—a brim-full living chalice of despair and horror and astonishment which you can raise to your lips as often as you please. So do not allow any temporary excitement to distract you from the real business of undermining faith and preventing the formation of virtues. Give me without fail in your next letter a full account of the patient's reactions to the war, so that we can consider whether you are likely to do more good by making him an extreme patriot or an ardent pacifist. There are all sorts of possibilities. In the meantime, I must warn you not to hope too much from a war.

Of course a war is entertaining. The immediate fear and suffering of the humans is a legitimate and pleasing refreshment for our myriads of toiling workers. But what permanent good does it do us unless we make use of it for bringing souls to Our Father Below? When I see the temporal suffering of humans who finally escape us, I feel as if I had been allowed to taste the first course of a rich banquet and then denied the rest. It is worse than not to have tasted it at all. The Enemy, true to His barbarous methods of warfare, allows us to see the short misery of His favourites only to tantalise and torment us—to mock the incessant hunger which, during this present phase of the great conflict, His blockade is admittedly imposing. Let us therefore think rather how to use, than how to enjoy, this European war. For it has certain tendencies inherent in it which are, in themselves, by no means in our favour. We may hope for a good deal of cruelty and unchastity. But, if we are not careful, we shall see thousands turning in this tribulation to the Enemy, while tens of thousands who do not go so far as that will nevertheless have their attention diverted from themselves to values and causes which they believe to be higher than the self. I know that the Enemy disapproves many of these causes. But that is where He is so unfair. He often makes prizes of humans who have given their lives for causes. He thinks bad on the monstrously sophistical ground that the humans thought them good and were following the best they knew. Consider too what undesirable deaths occur in wartime. Men are killed in places where they knew they might be killed and to which they go, if they are at all of the Enemy's party, prepared. How much better for us if *all* humans died in costly nursing homes amid doctors who lie, nurses who lie, friends who lie, as we have trained them, promising life to the dying, encouraging the belief that sickness excuses every indulgence, and even, if our workers know their job, withholding all suggestion of a priest lest it should betray to the sick man his true condition! And how disastrous for us is the continual remembrance of death which war enforces. One of our best weapons, contented worldliness, is rendered useless. In wartime not even a human can believe that he is going to live forever.

I know that Scabtree and others have seen in wars a great opportunity for attacks on faith, but I think that view was exaggerated. The Enemy's human partisans have all been plainly told by Him that suffering is an essential part of what He calls Redemption; so that a faith which is destroyed by a war or a pestilence cannot really have been worth the trouble of destroying. I am speaking now of diffused suffering over a long period such as the war will produce. Of course, at the precise moment of terror, bereavement, or physical pain, you may catch your man when his reason is temporarily suspended. But even then, if he applies to Enemy headquarters, I have found that the post is nearly always defended,

Your affectionate uncle
SCREWTAPE

6.

My dear Wormwood,

I am delighted to hear that your patient's age and profession make it possible, but by no means certain, that he will be called up for military service. We want him to be in the maximum uncertainty, so that his mind will be filled with contradictory pictures of the future, every one of which arouses hope or fear. There is nothing like suspense and anxiety for barricading a human's mind against the Enemy. He wants men to be concerned with what they do; our business is to keep them thinking about what will happen to them.

Your patient will, of course, have picked up the notion that he must submit with patience to the Enemy's will. What the Enemy means by this is primarily that he should accept with patience the tribulation which has actually been dealt out to him— the present anxiety and suspense. It is about *this* that he is to say "Thy will be done", and for the daily task of bearing *this* that the daily bread will be provided. It is your business to see that the patient never thinks of the present fear as his appointed cross but only of the things he is afraid of. Let him regard them as his crosses: let him forget that, since they are incompatible, they cannot all happen to him, and let him try to practise fortitude and patience to them all in advance. For real resignation, at the same moment, to a dozen different and hypothetical fates, is almost impossible, and the Enemy does not greatly assist those who are trying to attain it: resignation to present and actual suffering, even where that suffering consists of fear, is far easier and is usually helped by this direct action.

An important spiritual law is here involved. I have explained that you can weaken his prayers by diverting his attention from the Enemy Himself to his own states of mind about the Enemy. On the other hand fear becomes easier to master when the patient's mind is diverted from the thing feared to the fear itself, considered as a present and undesirable state of his own mind; and when he regards the fear as his appointed cross he will inevitably think of it as a state of mind. One can therefore formulate the general rule; in all activities of mind which favour our cause, encourage the patient to be un-selfconscious and to concentrate on the object, but in all activities favourable to the Enemy bend his mind back on itself. Let an insult or a woman's body so fix his attention outward that he does not reflect "I am now entering into the state called Anger—or the state called Lust". Contrariwise let the reflection "My feelings are now growing more devout, or more charitable" so fix his attention inward that he no longer looks beyond himself to see our Enemy or his own neighbours.

As regards his more general attitude to the war, you must not rely too much on those feelings of hatred which the humans are so fond of discussing in Christian, or anti-Christian, periodicals. In his anguish, the patient can, of course, be encouraged to revenge himself by some vindictive feelings directed towards the German leaders, and that is good so far as it goes. But it is usually a sort of melodramatic or mythical hatred directed against imaginary scapegoats. He has never met these people in real life— they are lay figures modelled on what he gets from newspapers. The results of such fanciful hatred are often most disappointing, and of all humans the English are in this respect the most deplorable milksops. They are creatures of that miserable sort who loudly proclaim that torture is too good for their enemies and then give tea and cigarettes to the first wounded German pilot who turns up at the back door.

Do what you will, there is going to be some benevolence, as well as some malice, in your patient's soul. The great thing is to direct the malice to his immediate neighbours whom he meets every day and to thrust his benevolence out to the remote circumference, to people he does not know. The malice thus becomes wholly real and the benevolence largely imaginary. There is no good at all in inflaming his hatred of Germans if, at the same time, a pernicious habit of charity is growing up between him and his mother, his employer, and the man he meets in the train. Think of your man as a series of concentric circles, his will being the innermost, his intellect coming next, and finally his fantasy. You can hardly hope, at once, to exclude from all the circles everything that smells of the Enemy: but you must keep on shoving all the virtues outward till they are finally located in the circle of fantasy, and all the desirable qualities inward into the Will. It is only in so far as they reach the will and are there embodied in habits that the virtues are really fatal to us. (I don't, of course, mean what the patient mistakes for his will, the conscious fume and fret of resolutions and clenched teeth, but the real centre, what the Enemy calls the Heart.) All sorts of virtues painted in the fantasy or approved by the intellect or even, in some measure, loved and admired, will not keep a man from our Father's house: indeed they may make him more amusing when he gets there,

Your affectionate uncle
SCREWTAPE

7.

My Dear Wormwood,

I wonder you should ask me whether it is essential to keep the patient in ignorance of your own existence. That question, at least for the present phase of the struggle, has been answered for us by the High Command. Our policy, for the moment, is to conceal ourselves. Of course this has not always been so. We are really faced with a cruel dilemma. When the humans disbelieve in our existence we lose all the pleasing results of direct terrorism and we make no magicians. On the other hand, when they believe in us, we cannot make them materialists and sceptics. At least, not yet. I have great hopes that we shall learn in due time how to emotionalise and mythologise their science to such an extent that what is, in effect, a belief in us, (though not under that name) will creep in while the human mind remains closed to belief in the Enemy. The "Life Force," the worship of sex, and some aspects of Psychoanalysis, may here prove useful. If once we can produce our perfect work—the Materialist Magician, the man, not using, but veritably worshipping, what he vaguely calls "Forces" while denying the existence of "spirits"—then the end of the war will be in sight. But in the meantime we must obey our orders. I do not think you will have much difficulty in keeping the patient in the dark. The fact that "devils" are predominantly *comic* figures in the modern imagination will help you. If any faint suspicion of your existence begins to arise in his mind, suggest to him a picture of something in red tights, and persuade him that since he cannot believe in that (it is an old textbook method of confusing them) he therefore cannot believe in you.

I had not forgotten my promise to consider whether we should make the patient an extreme patriot or an extreme pacifist. All extremes, except extreme devotion to the Enemy, are to be encouraged. Not always, of course, but at this period. Some ages are lukewarm and complacent, and then it is our business to soothe them yet faster asleep. Other ages, of which the present is one, are unbalanced and prone to faction, and it is our business to inflame them. Any small coterie, bound together by some interest which other men dislike or ignore, tends to develop inside itself a hothouse mutual admiration, and towards the outer world, a great deal of pride and hatred which is entertained without shame because the "Cause" is its sponsor and it is thought to be impersonal. Even when the little group exists originally for the Enemy's own purposes, this remains true. We want the Church to be small not only that fewer men may know the Enemy but also that those who do may acquire the uneasy intensity and the defensive self-righteousness of a secret society or a clique. The Church herself is, of course, heavily defended and we have never yet quite succeeded in giving her *all* the characteristics of a faction; but subordinate factions within her have often produced admirable results, from the parties of Paul and of Apollos at Corinth down to the High and Low parties in the Church of England.

If your patient can be induced to become a conscientious objector he will automatically find himself one of a small, vocal, organised, and unpopular society, and the effects of this, on one so new to Christianity, will almost certainly be good. But only *almost* certainly. Has he had serious doubts about the lawfulness of serving in a just war before this present war began? Is he a man of great physical courage—so great that he will have no half-conscious misgivings about the real motives of his pacifism? Can he, when nearest to honesty (no human is ever *very* near), feel fully convinced that he is actuated wholly by the desire to obey the Enemy? If he is that sort of man, his pacifism will probably not do us much good, and the Enemy will probably protect him from the usual consequences of belonging to a sect. Your best plan, in that case, would be to attempt a sudden, confused, emotional crisis from which he might emerge as an uneasy convert to patriotism. Such things can often be managed. But if he is the man I take him to be, try Pacifism.

Whichever he adopts, your main task will be the same. Let him begin by treating the Patriotism or the Pacifism as a part of his religion. Then let him, under the influence of partisan spirit, come to regard it as the most important part. Then quietly and gradually nurse him on to the stage at which the religion becomes merely part of the "cause", in which Christianity is valued chiefly because of the excellent arguments it can produce in favour of the British war-effort or of Pacifism. The attitude which you want to guard against is that in which temporal affairs are treated primarily as material for obedience. Once you have made the World an end, and faith a means, you have almost won your man, and it makes very little difference what kind of worldly end he is pursuing. Provided that meetings, pamphlets, policies, movements, causes, and crusades, matter more to him than prayers and sacraments and charity, he is ours—and the more "religious" (on those terms) the more securely ours. I could show you a pretty cageful down here,

Your affectionate uncle

SCREWTAPE

8.

My Dear Wormwood,

So you "have great hopes that the patient's religious phase is dying away," have you? I always thought the Training College had gone to pieces since they put old Slubgob at the head of it, and now I am sure. Has no one ever told you about the law of Undulation?

Humans are amphibians—half spirit and half animal. (The Enemy's determination to produce such a revolting hybrid was one of the things that determined Our Father to withdraw his support from Him.) As spirits they belong to the eternal world, but as animals they inhabit time. This means that while their spirit can be directed to an eternal object, their bodies, passions, and imaginations are in continual change, for to be in time means to change. Their nearest approach to constancy, therefore, is undulation—the repeated return to a level from which they repeatedly fall back, a series of troughs and peaks. If you had watched your patient carefully you would have seen this undulation in every department of his life—his interest in his work, his affection for his friends, his physical appetites, all go up and down. As long as he lives on earth periods of emotional and bodily richness and liveliness will alternate with periods of numbness and poverty. The dryness and dulness through which your patient is now going are not, as you fondly suppose, your workmanship; they are merely a natural phenomenon which will do us no good unless you make a good use of it.

To decide what the best use of it is, you must ask what use the Enemy wants to make of it, and then do the opposite. Now it may surprise you to learn that in His efforts to get permanent possession of a soul, He relies on the troughs even more than on the peaks; some of His special favourites have gone through longer and deeper troughs than anyone else. The reason is this. To us a human is primarily food; our aim is the absorption of its will into ours, the increase of our own area of selfhood at its expense. But the obedience which the Enemy demands of men is quite a different thing. One must face the fact that all the talk about His love for men, and His service being perfect freedom, is not (as one would gladly believe) mere propaganda, but an appalling truth. He really *does* want to fill the universe with a lot of loathsome little replicas of Himself—creatures whose life, on its miniature scale, will be qualitatively like His own, not because He has absorbed them but because their wills freely conform to His. We want cattle who can finally become food; He wants servants who can finally become sons. We want to suck in, He wants to give out. We are empty and would be filled; He is full and flows over. Our war aim is a world in which Our Father Below has drawn all other beings into himself: the Enemy wants a world full of beings united to Him but still distinct.

And that is where the troughs come in. You must have often wondered why the Enemy does not make more use of His power to be sensibly present to human souls in any degree He chooses and at any moment. But you now see that the Irresistible and the Indisputable are the two weapons which the very nature of His scheme forbids Him to use. Merely to over-ride a human will (as His felt presence in any but the faintest and most mitigated degree would certainly do) would be for Him useless. He cannot ravish. He can only woo. For His ignoble idea is to eat the cake and have it; the creatures are to be one with Him, but yet themselves; merely to cancel them, or assimilate them, will not serve. He is prepared to do a little over-riding at the beginning. He will set them off with communications of His presence which, though faint, seem great to them, with emotional sweetness, and easy conquest over temptation. But He never allows this state of affairs to last long. Sooner or later He withdraws, if not in fact, at least from their conscious experience, all those supports and incentives. He leaves the creature to stand up on its own legs—to carry out from the will alone duties which have lost all relish. It is during such trough periods, much more than during the peak periods, that it is growing into the sort of creature He wants it to be. Hence the prayers offered in the state of dryness are those which pleases Him best. We can drag our patients along by continual tempting, because we design them only for the table, and the more their will is interfered with the better. He cannot "tempt" to virtue as we do to vice. He wants them to learn to walk and must therefore take away His hand; and if only the will to walk is really there He is pleased even with their stumbles. Do not be deceived, Wormwood. Our cause is never more in danger than when a human, no longer desiring, but still intending, to do our Enemy's will, looks round upon a universe from which every trace of Him seems to have vanished, and asks why he has been forsaken, and still obeys.

But of course the troughs afford opportunities to our side also. Next week I will give you some hints on how to exploit them,

Your affectionate uncle

SCREWTAPE

9.

MY DEAR WORMWOOD,

I hope my last letter has convinced you that the trough of dulness or "dryness" through which your patient is going at present will not, of itself, give you his soul, but needs to be properly exploited. What forms the exploitation should take I will now consider.

In the first place I have always found that the Trough periods of the human undulation provide excellent opportunity for all sensual temptations, particularly those of sex. This may surprise you, because, of course, there is more physical energy, and therefore more potential appetite, at the Peak periods; but you must remember that the powers of resistance are then also at their highest. The health and spirits which you want to use in producing lust can also, alas, be very easily used for work or play or thought or innocuous merriment. The attack has a much better chance of success when the man's whole inner world is drab and cold and empty. And it is also to be noted that the Trough sexuality is subtly different in quality from that of the Peak—much less likely to lead to the milk and water phenomenon which the humans call "being in love," much more easily drawn into perversions, much less contaminated by those generous and imaginative and even spiritual concomitants which often render human sexuality so disappointing. It is the same with other desires of the flesh. You are much more likely to make your man a sound drunkard by pressing drink on him as an anodyne when he is dull and weary than by encouraging him to use it as a means of merriment among his friends when he is happy and expansive. Never forget that when we are dealing with any pleasure in its healthy and nomal and satisfying form, we are, in a sense, on the Enemy's ground. I know we have won many a soul through pleasure. All the same, it is His invention, not ours. He made the pleasures; all our research so far has not enabled us to produce one. All we can do is to encourage the humans to take the pleasures which our Enemy has produced, at times, or ways, or in degrees, which He has forbidden. Hence we always try to work away from the natural condition of any pleasure to that in which it is least natural, least redolent of its Maker, and least pleasurable. An ever increasing craving for an ever diminishing pleasure is the formula. It is more certain; and it's better *style*. To get the man's soul and give him *nothing* in return—that is what really gladdens our Father's heart. And the troughs are the time for beginning the process.

But there is an even better way of exploiting the Trough; I mean through the patient's own thoughts about it. As always, the first step is to keep knowledge out of his mind. Do not let him suspect the law of undulation. Let him assume that the first ardours of his conversion might have been expected to last, and ought to have lasted, forever, and that his present dryness is an equally permanent condition. Having once got this misconception well fixed in his head, you may then proceed in various ways. It all depends on whether your man is of the desponding type who can be tempted to despair, or of the wishful-thinking type who can be assured that all is well. The former type is getting rare among the humans. If your patient should happen to belong to it, everything is easy. You have only got to keep him out of the way of experienced Christians (an easy task now-a-days), to direct his attention to the appropriate passages in scripture, and then to set him to work on the desperate design of recovering his old feelings by sheer will-power, and the game is ours. If he is of the more hopeful type, your job is to make him acquiesce in the present low temperature of his spirit and gradually become content with it, persuading himself that it is not so low after all. In a week or two you will be making him doubt whether the first days of his Christianity were not, perhaps, a little excessive. Talk to him about "moderation in all things". If you can once get him to the point of thinking that "religion is all very well up to a point", you can feel quite happy about his soul. A moderated religion is as good for us as no religion at all—and more amusing.

Another possibility is that of direct attack on his faith. When you have caused him to assume that the trough is permanent, can you not persuade him that "his religious phase" is just going to die away like all his previous phases? Of course there is no conceivable way of getting by reason from the proposition "I am losing interest in this" to the proposition "This is false". But, as I said before, it is jargon, not reason, you must rely on. The mere word *phase* will very likely do the trick. I assume that the creature has been through several of them before—they all have—and that he always feels superior and patronising to the ones he has emerged from, not because he has really criticised them but simply because they are in the past. (You keep him well fed on hazy ideas of Progress and Development and the Historical Point of View, I trust, and give him lots of modern Biographies to read? The people in them are always emerging from Phases, aren't they?)

You see the idea? Keep his mind off the plain antithesis between True and False. Nice shadowy expressions—"It was a phase"—"I've been through all that"—and don't forget the blessed word "Adolescent,"

Your affectionate uncle
SCREWTAPE

10.

My Dear Wormwood,

I was delighted to hear from Triptweeze that your patient has made some very desirable new acquaintances and that you seem to have used this event in a really promising manner. I gather that the middle-aged married couple who called at his office are just the sort of people we want him to know—rich, smart, superficially intellectual, and brightly sceptical about everything in the world. I gather they are even vaguely pacifist, not on moral grounds but from an ingrained habit of belittling anything that concerns the great mass of their fellow men and from a dash of purely fashionable and literary communism. This is excellent. And you seem to have made good use of all his social, sexual, and intellectual vanity. Tell me more. Did he commit himself deeply? I don't mean in words. There is a subtle play of looks and tones and laughs by which a mortal can imply that he is of the same party as those to whom he is speaking. That is the kind of betrayal you should specially encourage, because the man does not fully realise it himself; and by the time he does you will have made withdrawal difficult.

No doubt he must very soon realise that his own faith is in direct opposition to the assumptions on which all the conversation of his new friends is based. I don't think that matters much provided that you can persuade him to postpone any open acknowledgment of the fact, and this, with the aid of shame, pride, modesty and vanity, will be easy to do. As long as the postponement lasts he will be in a false position. He will be silent when he ought to speak and laugh when he ought to be silent. He will assume, at first only by his manner, but presently by his words, all

42

sorts of cynical and sceptical attitudes which are not really his. But if you play him well, they may become his. All mortals tend to turn into the thing they are pretending to be. This is elementary. The real question is how to prepare for the Enemy's counter attack.

The first thing is to delay as long as possible the moment at which he realises this new pleasure as a temptation. Since the Enemy's servants have been preaching about "the World" as one of the great standard temptations for two thousand years, this might seem difficult to do. But fortunately they have said very little about it for the last few decades. In modern Christian writings, though I see much (indeed more than I like) about Mammon, I see few of the old warnings about Worldly Vanities, the Choice of Friends, and the Value of Time. All that, your patient would probably classify as "Puritanism"—and may I remark in passing that the value we have given to that word is one of the really solid triumphs of the last hundred years? By it we rescue annually thousands of humans from temperance, chastity, and sobriety of life.

Sooner or later, however, the real nature of his new friends must become clear to him, and then your tactics must depend on the patient's intelligence. If he is a big enough fool you can get him to realise the character of the friends only while they are absent; their presence can be made to sweep away all criticism. If this succeeds, he can be induced to live, as I have known many humans live, for quite long periods, two parallel lives; he will not only appear to be, but actually be, a different man in each of the circles he frequents. Failing this, there is a subtler and more entertaining method. He can be made to take a positive pleasure in the perception that the two sides of his life are inconsistent. This is done by exploiting his vanity. He can be taught to enjoy kneeling beside the grocer on Sunday just because he remembers that the grocer could not possibly understand the urbane and mocking world which he inhabited on Saturday evening; and contrariwise, to enjoy the bawdy and blasphemy over the coffee with these admirable friends all the more because he is aware of a "deeper," "spiritual" world within him which they cannot understand. You see the idea—the worldly friends touch him on one side and the grocer on the other, and he is the complete, balanced, complex man who sees round them all. Thus, while being permanently treacherous to at least two sets of people, he will feel, instead of shame, a continual undercurrent of self-satisfaction. Finally, if all else fails, you can persuade him, in defiance of conscience, to continue the new acquaintance on the ground that he is, in some unspecified way, doing these people "good" by the mere fact of drinking their cocktails and laughing at their jokes, and that to cease to do so would be "priggish," "intolerant," and (of course) "Puritanical."

Meanwhile you will of course take the obvious precaution of seeing that this new development induces him to spend more than he can afford and to neglect his work and his mother. Her jealousy, and alarm, and his increasing evasiveness or rudeness, will be invaluable for the aggravation of the domestic tension,

Your affectionate uncle

SCREWTAPE

I I .

My Dear Wormwood,

Everything is clearly going very well. I am specially glad to hear that the two new friends have now made him acquainted with their whole set. All these, as I find from the record office, are thoroughly reliable people; steady, consistent scoffers and worldlings who without any spectacular crimes are progressing quietly and comfortably towards our Father's house. You speak of their being great laughers. I trust this does not mean that you are under the impression that laughter as such is always in our favour. The point is worth some attention.

I divide the causes of human laughter into Joy, Fun, the Joke Proper, and Flippancy. You will see the first among friends and lovers reunited on the eve of a holiday. Among adults some pretext in the way of Jokes is usually provided, but the facility with which the smallest witticisms produce laughter at such a time shows that they are not the real cause. What that real cause is we do not know. Something like it is expressed in much of that detestable art which the humans call Music, and something like it occurs in Heaven—a meaningless acceleration in the rhythm of celestial experience, quite opaque to us. Laughter of this kind does us no good and should always be discouraged. Besides, the phenomenon is of itself disgusting and a direct insult to the realism, dignity, and austerity of Hell.

Fun is closely related to Joy—a sort of emotional froth arising from the play instinct. It is very little use to us. It can sometimes be used, of course, to divert humans from something else which the Enemy would like them to be feeling or doing: but in itself

it has wholly undesirable tendencies; it promotes charity, courage, contentment, and many other evils.

The Joke Proper, which turns on sudden perception of incongruity, is a much more promising field. I am not thinking primarily of indecent or bawdy humour, which, though much relied
upon by second-rate tempters, is often disappointing in its results.
The truth is that humans are pretty clearly divided on this matter into two classes. There are some to whom "no passion is as
serious as lust" and for whom an indecent story ceases to produce
lasciviousness precisely in so far as it becomes funny: there are
others in whom laughter and lust are excited at the same moment
and by the same thing. The first sort joke about sex because it
gives rise to many incongruities: the second cultivate incongruities because they afford a pretext for talking about sex. If your
man is of the first type, bawdy humour will not help you—I shall
never forget the hours which I wasted (hours to me of unbearable tedium) with one of my early patients in bars and smoking-
rooms before I learned this rule. Find out which group the patient belongs to—and see that he does *not* find out.

The real use of Jokes or Humour is in quite a different direction, and it is specially promising among the English who take
their "sense of humour" so seriously that a deficiency in this
sense is almost the only deficiency at which they feel shame. Humour is for them the all-consoling and (mark this) the all-excusing, grace of life. Hence it is invaluable as a means of destroying
shame. If a man simply lets others pay for him, he is "mean"; if
he boasts of it in a jocular manner and twits his fellows with having been scored off, he is no longer "mean" but a comical fellow.
Mere cowardice is shameful; cowardice boasted of with humorous exaggerations and grotesque gestures can be passed off as
funny. Cruelty is shameful—unless the cruel man can represent
it as a practical joke. A thousand bawdy, or even blasphemous,
jokes do not help towards a man's damnation so much as his discovery that almost anything he wants to do can be done, not only
without the disapproval but with the admiration of his fellows,
if only it can get itself treated as a Joke. And this temptation
can be almost entirely hidden from your patient by that English
seriousness about Humour. Any suggestion that there might

be too much of it can be represented to him as "Puritanical" or as betraying a "lack of humour".

But flippancy is the best of all. In the first place it is very economical. Only a clever human can make a real Joke about virtue, or indeed about anything else; any of them can be trained to talk *as if* virtue were funny. Among flippant people the Joke is always assumed to have been made. No one actually makes it; but every serious subject is discussed in a manner which implies that they have already found a ridiculous side to it. If prolonged, the habit of Flippancy builds up around a man the finest armour-plating against the Enemy that I know, and it is quite free from the dangers inherent in the other sources of laughter. It is a thousand miles away from joy: it deadens, instead of sharpening, the intellect; and it excites no affection between those who practice it,

Your affectionate uncle

SCREWTAPE

12.

My Dear Wormwood,

Obviously you are making excellent progress. My only fear is lest in attempting to hurry the patient you awaken him to a sense of his real position. For you and I, who see that position as it really is, must never forget how totally different it ought to appear to him. We know that we have introduced a change of direction in his course which is already carrying him out of his orbit around the Enemy; but he must be made to imagine that all the choices which have effected this change of course are trivial and revocable. He must not be allowed to suspect that he is now, however slowly, heading right away from the sun on a line which will carry him into the cold and dark of utmost space.

For this reason I am almost glad to hear that he is still a church-goer and a communicant. I know there are dangers in this; but anything is better than that he should realise the break he has made with the first months of his Christian life. As long as he retains externally the habits of a Christian he can still be made to think of himself as one who has adopted a few new friends and amusements but whose spiritual state is much the same as it was six weeks ago. And while he thinks that, we do not have to contend with the explicit repentance of a definite, fully recognised, sin, but only with his vague, though uneasy, feeling that he hasn't been doing very well lately.

This dim uneasiness needs careful handling. If it gets too strong it may awake him up and spoil the whole game. On the other hand, if you suppress it entirely—which, by the by, the Enemy will probably not allow you to do—we lose an element in the situation which can be turned to good account. If such a feeling is allowed to live, but not allowed to become irresistible and flower into real repentance, it has one invaluable tendency. It increases the patient's reluctance to think about the Enemy. All humans at nearly all times have some such reluctance to think about the Enemy. All humans at nearly all times have some such reluctance; but when thinking of Him involves facing and intensifying a whole vague cloud of half-conscious guilt, this relucance is increased tenfold. They hate every idea that suggests Him, just as men in financial embarrassment hate the very sight of a pass-book. In this state your patient will not omit, but he will increasingly dislike, his religious duties. He will think about them as little as he feels he decently can beforehand, and forget them as soon as possible when they are over. A few weeks ago you had to *tempt* him to unreality and inattention in his prayers: but now you will find him opening his arms to you and almost begging you to distract his purpose and benumb his heart. He will *want* his prayers to be unreal, for he will dread nothing so much as effective contact with the Enemy. His aim will be to let sleeping worms lie.

As this condition becomes more fully established, you will be gradually freed from the tiresome business of providing Pleasures as temptations. As the uneasiness and his reluctance to face it cut him off more and more from all real happiness, and as habit renders the pleasures of vanity and excitement and flippancy at once less pleasant and harder to forgo (for that is what habit fortunately does to a pleasure) you will find that anything or nothing is sufficient to attract his wandering attention. You no longer need a good book, which he really likes, to keep him from his prayers or his work or his sleep; a column of advertisements in yesterday's paper will do. You can make him waste his time not only in conversation he enjoys with people whom he likes, but in conversations with those he cares nothing about on subjects that bore him. You can make him do nothing at all for long periods. You can keep him up late at night, not roistering, but staring at a dead fire in a cold room. All the healthy and outgoing activities which we want him to avoid can be inhibited and *nothing* given in return, so that at last he may say, as one of my own patients said on his arrival down here, "I now see that

I spent most of my life in doing *neither* what I ought *nor* what I liked." The Christians describe the Enemy as one "without whom Nothing is strong." And Nothing is very strong: strong enough to steal away a man's best years not in sweet sins but in a dreary flickering of the mind over it knows not what and knows not why, in the gratification of curiosities so feeble that the man is only half aware of them, in drumming of fingers and kicking of heels, in whistling tunes that he does not like, or in the long, dim, labyrinth of reveries that have not even lust or ambition to give them a relish, but which, once chance association has started them, the creature is too weak and fuddled to shake off.

You will say that these are very small sins; and doubtless, like all young tempters, you are anxious to be able to report spectacular wickedness. But do remember, the only thing that matters is the extent to which you separate the man from the Enemy. It does not matter how small the sins are provided that their cumulative effect is to edge the man away from the Light and out into the Nothing. Murder is no better than cards if cards can do the trick. Indeed the safest road to Hell is the gradual one— the gentle slope, soft underfoot, without sudden turnings, without milestones, without signposts,

Your affectionate uncle
SCREWTAPE

13.

My dear Wormwood,

It seems to me that you take a great many pages to tell a very simple story. The long and the short of it is that you have let the man slip through your fingers. The situation is very grave, and I really see no reason why I should try to shield you from the consequences of your inefficiency. A repentance and renewal of what the other side call "grace" on the scale which you describe is a defeat of the first order. It amounts to a second conversion—and probably on a deeper level than the first.

As you ought to have known, the asphyxiating cloud which prevented your attacking the patient on his walk back from the old mill, is a well-known phenomenon. It is the Enemy's most barbarous weapon, and generally appears when He is directly present to the patient under certain modes not yet fully classified. Some humans are permanently surrounded by it and therefore inaccessible to us.

And now for your blunders. On your own showing you first of all allowed the patient to read a book he really enjoyed, because he enjoyed it and not in order to make clever remarks about it to his new friends. In the second place, you allowed him to walk down to the old mill and have tea there—a walk through country he really likes, and taken alone. In other words you allowed him two real positive Pleasures. Were you so ignorant as not to see the danger of this? The characteristic of Pains and Pleasures is that they are unmistakably real, and therefore, as far as they go, give the man who feels them a touchstone of reality. Thus if you had been trying to damn your man by the Romantic method—by making him a kind of Childe Harold or Werther submerged in self-pity for imaginary distresses—you would try to protect him at all costs from any real pain; because, of course, five minutes' genuine toothache would reveal the romantic sorrows for the nonsense they were and unmask your whole stratagem. But you were trying to damn your patient by the World, that is by palming off vanity, bustle, irony, and expensive tedium as pleasures. How can you have failed to see that a *real* pleasure was the last thing you ought to have let him meet? Didn't you foresee that it would just kill by contrast all the trumpery which you have been so laboriously teaching him to value? And that the sort of pleasure which the book and the walk gave him was the most dangerous of all? That it would peel off from his sensibility the kind of crust you have been forming on it, and make him feel that he was coming home, recovering himself? As a preliminary to detaching him from the Enemy, you wanted to detach him from himself, and had made some progress in doing so. Now, all that is undone.

Of course I know that the Enemy also wants to detach men from themselves, but in a different way. Remember always, that He really likes the little vermin, and sets an absurd value on the distinctness of every one of them. When He talks of their losing their selves, He only means abandoning the clamour of self-will; once they have done that, He really gives them back all their personality, and boasts (I am afraid, sincerely) that when they are wholly His they will be more themselves than ever. Hence, while He is delighted to see them sacrificing even their innocent wills to His, He hates to see them drifting away from their own nature for any other reason. And we should always encourage them to do so. The deepest likings and impulses of any man are the raw material, the starting-point, with which the Enemy has furnished him. To get him away from those is therefore always a point gained; even in things indifferent it is always desirable to substitute the standards of the World, or convention, or fashion, for a human's own real likings and dislikings. I myself would carry this very far. I would make it a rule to eradicate from my patient any strong personal taste which is not actually a sin, even if it is something quite trivial such as a fondness for county cricket or collecting stamps or drinking co-

coa. Such things, I grant you, have nothing of virtue in them; but there is a sort of innocence and humility and self-forgetfulness about them which I distrust. The man who truly and disinterestedly enjoys any one thing in the world, for its own sake, and without caring twopence what other people say about it, is by that very fact fore-armed against some of our subtlest modes of attack. You should always try to make the patient abandon the people or food or books he really likes in favour of the "best" people, the "right" food, the "important" books. I have known a human defended from strong temptations to social ambition by a still stronger taste for tripe and onions.

It remains to consider how we can retrieve this disaster. The great thing is to prevent his doing anything. As long as he does not convert it into action, it does not matter how much he thinks about this new repentance. Let the little brute wallow in it. Let him, if he has any bent that way, write a book about it; that is often an excellent way of sterilising the seeds which the Nemy plants in a human soul. Let him do anything but act. No amount of piety in his imagination and affections will harm us if we can keep it out of his will. As one of the humans has said, active habits are strengthened by repetition but passive ones are weakened. The more often he feels without acting, the less he will be able ever to act, and, in the long run, the less he will be able to feel,

Your affectionate uncle

SCREWTAPE

I4.

My dear Wormwood,

The most alarming thing in your last account of the patient is that he is making none of those confident resolutions which marked his original conversion. No more lavish promises of perpetual virtue, I gather; not even the expectation of an endowment of "grace" for life, but only a hope for the daily and hourly pittance to meet the daily and hourly temptation! This is very bad.

I see only one thing to do at the moment. Your patient has become humble; have you drawn his attention to the fact? All virtues are less formidable to us once the man is aware that he has them, but this is specially true of humility. Catch him at the moment when he is really poor in spirit and smuggle into his mind the gratifying reflection, "By jove! I'm being humble," and almost immediately pride—pride at his own humility—will appear. If he awakes to the danger and tries to smother this new form of pride, make him proud of his attempt—and so on, through as many stages as you please. But don't try this too long, for fear you awake his sense of humour and proportion, in which case he will merely laugh at you and go to bed.

But there are other profitable ways of fixing his attention on the virtue of Humility. By this virtue, as by all the others, our Enemy wants to turn the man's attention away from self to Him, and to the man's neighbours. All the abjection and self-hatred are designed, in the long run, solely for this end; unless they attain this end they do us little harm; and they may even do us good if they keep the man concerned with himself, and, above all, if self-contempt can be made the starting-point for contempt of other selves, and thus for gloom, cynicism, and cruelty.

You must therefore conceal from the patient the true end of Humility. Let him think of it not as self-forgetfulness but as a certain kind of opinion (namely, a low opinion) of his own talents and character. Some talents, I gather, he really has. Fix in his mind the idea that humility consists in trying to believe those talents to be less valuable than he believes them to be. No doubt they *are* in fact less valuable than he believes, but that is not the point. The great thing is to make him value an opinion for some quality other than truth, thus introducing an element of dishonesty and make-believe into the heart of what otherwise threatens to become a virtue. By this method thousands of humans have been brought to think that humility means pretty women trying to believe they are ugly and clever men trying to believe they are fools. And since what they are trying to believe may, in some cases, be manifest nonsense, they cannot succeed in believing it and we have the chance of keeping their minds endlessly revolving on themselves in an effort to achieve the impossible. To anticipate the Enemy's strategy, we must consider His aims. The Enemy wants to bring the man to a state of mind in which he could design the best cathedral in the world, and know it to be the best, and rejoice in the fact, without being any more or less) or otherwise glad at having done it than he would be if it had been done by another. The Enemy wants him, in the end, to be so free from any bias in his own favour that he can rejoice in his own talents as frankly and gratefully as in his neighbour's talents —or in a sunrise, an elephant, or a waterfall. He wants each man, in the long run, to be able to recognise all creatures (even himself) as glorious and excellent things. He wants to kill their animal self-love as soon as possible; but it is His long-term policy, I fear, to restore to them a new kind of self-love—a charity and gratitude for all selves, including their own; when they have really learned to love their neighbours as themselves, they will be allowed to love themselves as their neighbours. For we must never forget what is the most repellent and inexplicable trait in our Enemy; He *really* loves the hairless bipeds He has created and always gives back to them with His right hand what He has taken away with His left.

His whole effort, therefore, will be to get the man's mind off the subject of his own value altogether. He would rather the man thought himself a great architect or a great poet and then forgot about it, than that he should spend much time and pains trying to think himself a bad one. Your efforts to instil either vainglory or false modesty into the patient will therefore be met from the Enemy's side with the obvious reminder that a man is not usually called upon to have an opinion of his own talents at all, since he can very well go on improving them to the best of his ability without deciding on his own precise niche in the temple of Fame. You must try to exclude this reminder from the patient's consciousness at all costs. The Enemy will also try to render real in the patient's mind a doctrine which they all profess but find it difficult to bring home to their feelings—the doctrine that they did not create themselves, that their talents were given them, and that they might as well be proud of the colour of their hair. But always and by all methods the Enemy's aim will be to get the patient's mind off such questions, and yours will be to fix it on them. Even of his sins the Enemy does not want him to think too much: once they are repented, the sooner the man turns his attention outward, the better the Enemy is pleased,

Your affectionate uncle

SCREWTAPE

15.

My dear Wormwood,

I had noticed, of course, that the humans were having a lull in their European war—what they naïvely call *"The War!"*—and am not surprised that there is a corresponding lull in the patient's anxieties. Do we want to encourage this, or to keep him worried? Tortured fear and stupid confidence are both desirable states of mind. Our choice between them raises important questions.

The humans live in time but our Enemy destines them to eternity. He therefore, I believe, wants them to attend chiefly to two things, to eternity itself, and to that point of time which they call the Present. For the Present is the point at which time touches eternity. Of the present moment, and of it only, humans have an experience analogous to the experience which our Enemy has of reality as a whole; in it alone freedom and actuality are offered them. He would therefore have them continually concerned either with eternity (which means being concerned with Him) or with the Present—either meditating on their eternal union with, or separation from, Himself, or else obeying the present voice of conscience, bearing the present cross, receiving the present grace, giving thanks for the present pleasure.

Our business is to get them away from the eternal and from the Present. With this in view, we sometimes tempt a human (say a widow or a scholar), to live in the Past. But this is of limited value, for they have some real knowledge of the past and it has a determinate nature and, to that extent, resembles eternity. It is far better to make them live in the Future. Biological necessity makes all their passions point in that direction al-

ready, so that thought about the Future inflames hope and fear.
Also, it is unknown to them, so that in making them think about
it we make them think of unrealities. In a word, the Future is, of
all things, the thing *least like* eternity. It is the most completely
temporal part of time—for the Past is frozen and no longer flows,
and the Present is all lit up with eternal rays. Hence the encour-
agement we have given to all those schemes of thought such as
Creative Evolution, Scientific Humanism, or Communism, which
fix men's affections on the Future, on the very core of temporal-
ity. Hence nearly all vices are roted in the future. Gratitude
looks to the past and love to the present; fear, avarice, lust, and
ambition look ahead. Do not think lust an exception. When the
present pleasure arrives, the sin (which alone interests us) is already over. The pleasure is just the part of the process which we
regret and would exclude if we could do so without losing the
sin; it is the part contributed by the Enemy, and therefore experienced in a Present. The sin, which is our contribution, looked forward.

To be sure, the Enemy wants men to think of the Future too—
just so much as is necessary for *now* planning the acts of justice or
charity which will probably be their duty tomorrow. The duty of
planning the morrow's work is *today's* duty; though its material
is borrowed from the future, the duty, like all duties, is in the
Present. This is not straw splitting. He does not want men to give
the Future their hearts, to place their treasure in it. We do.
His ideal is a man who, having worked all day for the good of
posterity (if that is his vocation), washes his mind of the whole
subject, commits the issue to Heaven, and returns at once to the
patience or gratitude demanded by the moment that is passing
over him. But we want a man hag-ridden by the Future—haunted
by visions of an imminent heaven or hell upon earth—ready
to break the Enemy's commands in the present if by so doing we
make him think he can attain the one or avert the other—dependent for his faith on the success or failure of schemes whose end
he will not live to see. We want a whole race perpetually in pursuit of the rainbow's end, never honest, nor kind, nor happy *now,*
but always using as mere fuel wherewith to heap the altar of the
future every real gift which is offered them in the Present.

It follows then, in general, and other things being equal, that it is better for your patient to be filled with anxiety or hope (it doesn't much matter which) about this war than for him to be living in the present. But the phrase "living in the present" is ambiguous. It may describe a process which is really just as much concerned with the Future as anxiety itself. Your man may be untroubled about the Future, not because he is concerned with the Present, but because he has persuaded himself that the Future is going to be agreeable. As long as that is the real course of his tranquillity, his tranquillity will do us good, because it is only piling up more disappointment, and therefore more impatience, for him when his false hopes are dashed. If, on the other hand, he is aware that horrors may be in store for him and is praying for the virtues, wherewith to meet them, and meanwhile concerning himself with the Present because there, and there alone, all duty, all grace, all knowledge, and all pleasure dwell, his state is very undesirable and should be attacked at once. Here again, our Philological Arm has done good work; try the word "complacency" on him. But, of course, it is most likely that he is "living in the Present" for none of these reasons but simply because his health is good and he is enjoying his work. The phenomenon would then be merely natural. All the same, I should break it up if I were you. No natural phenomenon is really in our favour. And anyway, why *should* the creature be happy?

Your affectionate uncle

SCREWTAPE

16.

My dear Wormwood,

You mentioned casually in your last letter that the patient has continued to attend one church, and one only, since he was converted, and that he is not wholly pleased with it. May I ask what you are about? Why have I no report on the causes of his fidelity to the parish church? Do you realise that unless it is due to indifference it is a very bad thing? Surely you know that if a man can't be cured of churchgoing, the next best thing is to send him all over the neighbourhood looking for the church that "suits" him until he becomes a taster or connoisseur of churches.

The reasons are obvious. In the first place the parochial organisation should always be attacked, because, being a unity of place and not of likings, it brings people of different classes and psychology together in the kind of unity the Enemy desires. The congregational principle, on the other hand, makes each church into a kind of club, and finally, if all goes well, into a coterie or faction. In the second place, the search for a "suitable" church makes the man a critic where the Enemy wants him to be a pupil. What He wants of the layman in church is an attitude which may, indeed, be critical in the sense of rejecting what is false or unhelpful, but which is wholly uncritical in the sense that it does not appraise—does not waste time in thinking about what it rejects, but lays itself open in uncommenting, humble receptivity to any nourishment that is going. (You see how grovelling, how unspiritual, how irredeemably vulgar He is!) This attitude, especially during sermons, creates the condition (most hostile to our whole policy) in which platitudes can become really audible to a human soul. There is hardly any sermon, or any book, which

60

may not be dangerous to us if it is received in this temper. So pray bestir yourself and send this fool the round of the neighbouring churches as soon as possible. Your record up to date has not given us much satisfaction.

The two churches nearest to him, I have looked up in the office. Both have certain claims. At the first of these the Vicar is a man who has been so long engaged in watering down the faith to make it easier for a supposedly incredulous and hard-headed congregation that it is now he who shocks his parishioners with his unbelief, not *vice versa*. He has undermined many a soul's Christianity. His conduct of the services is also admirable. In order to spare the laity all "difficulties" he has deserted both the lectionary and the appointed psalms and now, without noticing it, revolves endlessly round the little treadmill of his fifteen favourite psalms and twenty favourite lessons. We are thus safe from the danger that any truth not already familiar to him and to his flock should ever reach them through Scripture. But perhaps your patient is not quite silly enough for this church—or not yet?

At the other church we have Fr. Spike. The humans are often puzzled to understand the range of his opinions—why he is one day almost a Communist and the next not far from some kind of theocratic Fascism—one day a scholastic, and the next prepared to deny human reason altogether—one day immersed in politics, and, the day after, declaring that all states of this world are *equally* "under judgment." We, of course, see the connecting link, which is Hatred. The man cannot bring himself to preach anything which is not calculated to shock, grieve, puzzle, or humiliate his parents and their friends. A sermon which such people could accept would be to him as insipid as a poem which they could scan. There is also a promising streak of dishonesty in him; we are teaching him to say "The teaching of the Church is" when he really means "I'm almost sure I read recently in Maritain or someone of that sort." But I must warn you that he has one fatal defect: he really believes. And this may yet mar all.

But there is one good point which both these churches have in common—they are both party churches. I think I warned you before that if your patient can't be kept out of the Church, he ought at least to be violently attached to some party within it. I don't mean on really doctrinal issues; about those, the more luke-warm he is the better. And it isn't the doctrines on which we chiefly depend for producing malice. The real fun is working up hatred between those who *say* "mass" and those who *say* "holy communion" when neither party could possibly state the differ-ence between, say, Hooker's doctrine and Thomas Aquinas', in any form which would hold water for five minutes. And all the purely indifferent things—candles and clothes and what not —are an admirable ground for our activities. We have quite removed from men's minds what that pestilent fellow Paul used to teach about food and other unessentials—namely, that the hu-man without scruples should always give in to the human with scruples. You would think they could not fail to see the applica-tion. You would expect to find the "low" churchman genuflect-ing and crossing himself lest the weak conscience of his "high" brother should he moved to irreverence, and the "high" one re-fraining from these exercises lest he should betray his "low" brother into idolatry. And so it would have been but for our ceaseless labour. Without that the variety of usage within the Church of England might have become a positive hotbed of char-ity and humility,

Your affectionate uncle

SCREWTAPE

17.

My dear Wormwood,

The contemptuous way in which you spoke of gluttony as a means of catching souls, in your last letter, only shows your ignorance. One of the great achievements of the last hundred years has been to deaden the human conscience on that subject, so that by now you will hardly find a sermon preached or a conscience troubled about it in the whole length and breadth of Europe. This has largely been effected by concentrating all our efforts on gluttony of Delicacy, not gluttony of Excesss. Your patient's mother, as I learn from the dossier and you might have learned from Glubose, is a good example. She would be astonished—one day, I hope, *will* be—to learn that her whole life is enslaved to this kind of sensuality, which is quite concealed from her by the fact that the quantities involved are small. But what do quantities matter, provided we can use a human belly and palate to produce querulousness, impatience, uncharitableness, and self-concern? Glubose has this old woman well in hand. She is a positive terror to hostesses and servants. She is always turning from what has been offered her to say with a demure little sigh and a smile "Oh please, please . . . *all* I want is a cup of tea, weak but not too weak, and the teeniest weeniest bit of really crisp toast." You see? Because what she wants is smaller and less costly than what has been set before her, she never recognises as gluttony her determination to get what she wants, however troublesome it may be to others. At the very moment of indulging her appetite she believes that she is practising temperance. In a crowded restaurant she gives a little scream at the plate which some overworked waitress has set before her and says, "Oh, that's far, far too much! Take it away and bring me about a quarter of it." If challenged, she would say she was doing this to avoid waste; in reality she does it because the particular shade of delicacy to which we have enslaved her is offended by the sight of more food than she happens to want.

The real value of the quiet, unobtrusive work which Glubose has been doing for years on this old woman can be gauged by the way in which her belly now dominates her whole life. The woman is in what may be called the "All-I-want" state of mind. *All* she wants is a cup of tea properly made, or an egg properly boiled, or a slice of bread properly toasted. But she never finds any servant or any friend who can do these simple things "properly" —because her "properly" conceals an insatiable demand for the exact, and almost impossible, palatal pleasures which she im- agines she remembers from the past; a past described by her as "the days when you could get good servants" but known to us as the days when her senses were more easily pleased and she had pleasures of other kinds which made her less dependent on those of the table. Meanwhile, the daily disappointment produces daily ill temper: cooks give notice and friendships are cooled. If ever the Enemy introduces into her mind a faint suspicion that she is too interested in food, Glubose counters it by suggesting to her that she doesn't mind what she eats hersef but "does like to have things nice for her boy." In fact, of course, her greed has been one of the chief sources of his domestic discomfort for many years.

Now your patient is his mother's son. While working your hardest, quite rightly, on other fronts, you must not neglect a little quiet infiltration in respect of gluttony. Being a male, he is not so likely to be caught by the *"All* I want" camouflage. Males are best turned into gluttons with the help of their vanity. They ought to be made to think themselves very knowing about food, to pique themselves on having found the only restaurant in the town where steaks are really "properly" cooked. What begins as vanity can then be gradually turned into habit. But, however you approach it, the great thing is to bring him into the state in which the denial of any one indulgence—it matters not which, champagne or tea, *sole colbert* or cigarettes—"puts him out," for then his charity, justice, and obedience are all at your mercy.

Mere excess in food is much less valuable than delicacy. Its chief use is as a kind of artillery preparation for attacks on chastity. On that, as on every other subject, keep your man in a condition of false spirituality. Never let him notice the medical aspect. Keep him wondering what pride or lack of faith has delivered him into your hands when a simple enquiry into what he has been eating or drinking for the last twenty-four hours would show him whence your ammunition comes and thus enable him by a very little abstinence to imperil your lines of communication. If he *must* think of the medical side of chastity, feed him the grand lie which we have made the English humans believe, that physical exercise in excess and consequent fatigue are specially favourable to this virtue. How they can believe this, in face of the notorious lustfulness of sailors and soldiers, may well be asked. But we used the schoolmasters to put the story about—men who were really interested in chastity as an excuse for games and therefore recommended games as an aid to chastity. But this whole business is too large to deal with at the tail-end of a letter,

Your affectionate uncle

SCREWTAPE

18.

My dear Wormwood,

Even under Slubgob you must have learned at college the routine technique of sexual temptation, and since, for us spirits, this whole subject is one of considerable tedium (though necessary as part of our training) I will pass it over. But on the larger issues involved I think you have a good deal to learn.

The Enemy's demand on humans takes the form of a dilemma; *either* complete abstinence *or* unmitigated monogamy. Ever since our Father's first great victory, we have rendered the former very difficult to them. The latter, for the last few centuries, we have been closing up as a way of escape. We have done this through the poets and novelists by persuading the humans that a curious, and usually short-lived, experience which they call "being in love" is the only respectable ground for marriage; that marriage can, and ought to, render this excitement permanent; and that a marriage which does not do so is no longer binding. This idea is our parody of an idea that came from the Enemy.

The whole philosophy of Hell rests on recognition of the axiom that one thing is not another thing, and, specially, that one self is not another self. My good is my good and your good is yours. What one gains another loses. Even an inanimate object is what it is by excluding all other objects from the space it occupies; if it expands, it does so by thrusting other objects aside or by absorbing them. A self does the same. With beasts the absorption takes the form of eating; for us, it means the sucking of will and freedom out of a weaker self into a stronger. "To be" *means* "to be in competition."

Now the Enemy's philosophy is nothing more nor less than one continued attempt to evade this very obvious truth. He aims at a contradiction. Things are to be many, yet somehow also one. The good of one self is to be the good of another. This impossibility He calls *love,* and this same monotonous panacea can be detected under all He does and even all He is—or claims to be. Thus He is not content, even Himself, to be a sheer arithmetical unity; He claims to be three as well as one, in order that this nonsense about Love may find a foothold in His own nature. At the other end of the scale, He introduces into matter that obscene invention the organism, in which the parts are perverted from their natural destiny of competition and made to co-operate.

His real motive for fixing on sex as the method of reproduction among humans is only too apparent from the use He has made of it. Sex might have been, from our point of view, quite innocent. It might have been merely one more mode in which a stronger self preyed upon a weaker—as it is, indeed, among the spiders where the bride concludes her nuptials by eating her groom. But in the humans the Enemy has gratuitously associated affection between the parties with sexual desire. He has also made the offspring dependent on the parents and given the parents an impulse to support it—thus producing the Family, which is like the organism, only worse; for the members are more distinct, yet also united in a more conscious and responsible way. The whole thing, in fact, turns out to be simply one more device for dragging in Love.

Now comes the joke. The Enemy described a married couple as "one flesh." He did not say "a happily married couple" or "a couple who married because they were in love," but you can make the humans ignore that. You can also make them forget that the man they call Paul did not confine it to *married* couples. Mere copulation, for him, makes "one flesh." You can thus get the humans to accept as rhetorical eulogies of "being in love" what were in fact plain descriptions of the real significance of sexual intercourse. The truth is that wherever a man lies with a woman, there, whether they like it or not, a transcendental relation is set up between them which must be eternally enjoyed or eternally endured. From the true statement that this transcendental relation was intended to produce, and, if obediently entered into, too often *will* produce, affection and the family, humans can be made to infer the false belief that the blend of affection, fear, and desire which they call "being in love" is the only thing that makes marriage either happy or holy. The error is easy to produce because "being in love" does very often, in Western Europe, precede marriages which are made in obedience to the Enemy's designs, that is, with the intention of fidelity, fertility and good will; just as religious emotion very often, but not always, attends conversion. In other words, the humans are to be encouraged to regard as the basis for marriage a highly-coloured and distorted version of something the Enemy really promises as its result. Two advantages follow. In the first place, humans who have not the gift of continence can be deterred from seeking marriage as a solution because they do not find themselves "in love," and, thanks to us, the idea of marrying with any other motive seems to them low and cynical. Yes, they think that. They regard the intention of loyalty to a partnership for mutual help, for the preservation of chastity, and for the transmission of life, as something lower than a storm of emotion. (Don't neglect to make your man think the marraige-service very offensive.) In the second place any sexual infatuation whatever, so long as it intends marriage, will be regarded as "love," and "love" will be held to excuse a man from all the guilt, and to protect him from all the consequences, of marrying a heathen, a fool, or a wanton. But more of this in my next,

Your affectionate uncle
SCREWTAPE

19.

My dear Wormwood,

I have been thinking very hard about the question in your last letter. If, as I have clearly shown, all selves are by their very nature in competition, and therefore the Enemy's Idea of Love is a contradiction in terms, what becomes of my reiterated warning that He really loves the human vermin and really desires their freedom and continued existence? I hope, my dear boy, you have not shown my letters to anyone. Not that it matters of course. Anyone would see that the appearance of heresy into which I have fallen is purely accidental. By the way, I hope you understood, too, that some apparently uncomplimentary references to Slubgob were purely jocular. I really have the highest respect for him. And, of course, some things I said about not shielding you from the authorities were not seriously meant. You can trust me to look after your interests. But do keep everything under lock and key.

The truth is I slipped by mere carelessness into saying that the Enemy really loves the humans. That, of course, is an impossibility. He is one being, they are distinct from Him. Their good cannot be His. All His talk about Love must be a disguise for something else—He must have some *real* motive for creating them and taking so much trouble about them. The reason one comes to talk as if He really had this impossible Love is our utter failure to find out that real motive. What does He stand to make out of them? That is the insoluble question. I do not see that it can do any harm to tell you that this very problem was a chief cause of Our Father's quarrel with the Enemy. When the creation of man was first mooted and when, even at that stage, the Enemy freely

confessed that he foresaw a certain episode about a cross, Our
Father very naturally sought an interview and asked for an explanation. The Enemy gave no reply except to produce the cock-
and-bull story about disinterested love which He has been cir-
culating ever since. This Our Father naturally could not accept.
He implored the Enemy to lay His cards on the table, and gave
Him every opportunity. He admitted that he felt a real anxiety
to know the secret; the Enemy replied "I wish with all my heart
that you did." It was, I imagine, at this stage in the interview that
Our Father's disgust at such an unprovoked lack of confidence
caused him to remove himself an infinite distance from the Presence with a suddenness which has given rise to the ridiculous
enemy story that he was forcibly thrown out of Heaven. Since
then, we have begun to see why our Oppressor was so secretive.
His throne depends on the secret. Members of His faction have
frequently admitted that if ever we came to understand what He
means by Love, the war would be over and we should re-enter
Heaven. And there lies the great task. We know that He cannot
really love: nobody can: it doesn't make sense. If we could only
find out what He is *really* up to! Hypothesis after hypothesis
has been tried, and still we can't find out. Yet we must never lose
hope; more and more complicated theories, fuller and fuller col-
lections of data, richer rewards for researchers who make progress,
more and more terrible punishments for those who fail—all
this, pursued and accelerated to the very end of time, cannot,
surely, fail to succeed.

You complain that my last letter does not make it clear whether
I regard *being in love* as a desirable state for a human or not. But
really, Wormwood, that is the sort of question one expects *them*
to ask! Leave them to discuss whether "Love," or patriotism, or
celibacy, or candles on altars, or teetotalism, or education, are
"good" or "bad." Can't you see there's no answer? Nothing matters at all except the tendency of a given state of mind, in given
circumstances, to move a particular patient at a particular moment nearer to the Enemy or nearer to us. Thus it would be quite
a good thing to make the patient decide that "love" is "good"
or "bad." If he is an arrogant man with a contempt for the body
really based on delicacy but mistaken by him for purity—and

one who takes pleasure in flouting what most of his fellows approve—by all means let him decide against love. Instil into him an overweening asceticism and then, when you have separated his sexuality from all that might humanise it, weigh in on him with it in some much more brutal and cynical form. If, on the other hand, he is an emotional, gullible man, feed him on minor poets and fifth-rate novelists of the old school until you have made him believe that "Love" is both irresistible and somehow intrinsically meritorious. This belief is not much help, I grant you, in producing casual unchastity; but it is an incomparable recipe for prolonged, "noble," romantic, tragic adulteries, ending, if all goes well, in murders and suicides. Failing that, it can be used to steer the patient into a useful marriage. For marriage, though the Enemy's invention, has its uses. There must be several young women in your patient's neighbourhood who would render the Christian life intensely difficult to him if only you could persuade him to marry one of them. Please send me a report on this when you next write. In the meantime, get it quite clear in your own mind that this state of *falling in love* is not, in itself, necessarily favourable either to us or to the other side. It is simply an occasion which we and the Enemy are both trying to exploit. Like most of the other things which humans are excited about, such as health and sickness, age and youth, or war and peace, it is from the point of view of the spiritual life, mainly raw material,

Your affectionate uncle

SCREWTAPE

20.

My dear Wormwood,

I note with great displeasure that the Enemy has, for the time being, put a forcible end to your direct attacks on the patient's chastity. You ought to have known that He always does in the end, and you ought to have stopped before you reached that stage. For as things are, your man has now discovered the dangerous truth that these attacks don't last forever; consequently you cannot use again what is, after all, our best weapon—the belief of ignorant humans, that there is no hope of getting rid of us except by yielding. I suppose you've tried persuading him that chastity is unhealthy?

I haven't yet got a report from you on young women in the neighbourhood. I should like it at once, for if we can't use his sexuality to make him unchaste we must try to use it for the promotion of a desirable marriage. In the meantime I would like to give you some hint about the type of woman—I mean the physical type—which he should be encouraged to fall in love with if "falling in love" is the best we can manage.

In a rough and ready way, of course, this question is decided for us by spirits far deeper down in the Lowerarchy than you and I. It is the business of these great masters to produce in every age a general misdirection of what may be called sexual "taste." This they do by working through the small circle of popular artists, dressmakers, actresses and advertisers who determine the fashionable type. The aim is to guide each sex away from those members of the other with whom spiritually helpful, happy, and fertile marriages are most likely. Thus we have now for many centuries triumphed over nature to the extent of making certain secondary characteristics of the male (such as the beard) disagreeable to nearly all the females—and there is more in that than you might suppose. As regards the male taste we have varied a good deal. At one time we have directed it to the statuesque and aristocratic type of beauty, mixing men's vanity with their desires and encouraging the race to breed chiefly from the most arrogant and prodigal women. At another, we have selected an exaggeratedly feminine type, faint and languishing, so that folly and cowardice, and all the general falseness and littleness of mind which go with them, shall be at a premium. At present we are on the opposite tack. The age of jazz has succeeded the age of the waltz, and we now teach men to like women whose bodies are scarcely distinguishable from those of boys. Since this is a kind of beauty even more transitory than most, we thus aggravate the female's chronic horror of growing old (with many excellent results) and render her less willing and less able to bear children. And that is not all. We have engineered a great increase in the licence which society allows to the representation of the apparent nude (not the real nude) in art, and its exhibition on the stage or the bathing beach. It is all a fake, of course; the figures in the popular art are falsely drawn; the real women in bathing suits or tights are actually pinched in and propped up to make them appear firmer and more slender and more boyish than nature allows a full-grown woman to be. Yet at the same time, the modern world is taught to believe that it is being "frank" and "healthy" and getting back to nature. As a result we are more and more directing the desires of men to something which does not exist—making the rôle of the eye in sexuality more and more important and at the same time making its demands more and more impossible. What follows you can easily forecast!

That is the general strategy of the moment. But inside that framework you will still find it possible to encourage your patient's desires in one of two directions. You will find, if you look carefully into any woman's heart, that he is haunted by at least two imaginary women—a terrestrial and an infernal Venus, and that his desire differs qualitatively according to its object. There is one type for which his desire is such as to be naturally amenable to the Enemy—readily mixed with charity, readily obedient to marriage, coloured all through with that golden light of reverence and naturalness which we detest; there is another type which he desires brutally, and desires to desire brutally, a type best used to draw him away from marriage altogether but which, even within marriage, he would tend to treat as a slave, an idol, or an accomplice. His love for the first might involve what the Enemy calls evil, but only accidentally; the man would wish that she was not someone else's wife and be sorry that he could not love her lawfully. But in the second type, the felt evil is what he wants; it is that "tang" in the flavour which he is after. In the face, it is the visible animality, or sulkiness, or craft, or cruelty which he likes, and in the body, something quite different from what he ordinarily calls Beauty, something he may even, in a sane hour, describe as ugliness, but which, by our art, can be made to play on the raw nerve of his private obsession.

The real use of the infernal Venus is, no doubt, as prostitute or mistress. But if your man is a Christian, and if he has been well trained in nonsense about irresistible and all-excusing "Love," he can often be induced to marry her. And that is very well worth bringing about. You will have failed as regards fornication and solitary vice; but there are other, and more indirect, methods of using a man's sexuality to his undoing. And, by the way, they are not only efficient, but delightful; the unhappiness produced is of a very lasting and exquisite kind,

Your affectionate uncle

SCREWTAPE

21.

My dear Wormwood,

Yes. A period of sexual temptation is an excellent time for working in a subordinate attack on the patient's peevishness. It may even be the main attack, as long as he thinks it the subordinate one. But here, as in everything else, the way must be prepared for your moral assault by darkening his intellect.

Men are not angered by mere misfortune but by misfortune conceived as injury. And the sense of injury depends on the feeling that a legitimate claim has been denied. The more claims on life, therefore, that your patient can be induced to make, the more often he will feel injured and, as a result, ill-tempered. Now you will have noticed that nothing throws him into a passion so easily as to find a tract of time which he reckoned on having at his own disposal unexpectedly taken from him. It is the unexpected visitor (when he looked forward to a quiet evening), or the friend's talkative wife (turning up when he looked forward to a tête-à-tête with the friend), that throw him out of gear. Now he is not yet so uncharitable or slothful that these small demands on his courtesy are *in themselves* too much for it. They anger him because he regards his time as his own and feels that it is being stolen. You must therefore zealously guard in his mind the curious assumption "My time is my own." Let him have the feeling that he starts each day as the lawful possessor of twenty-four hours. Let him feel as a grievous tax that portion of this property which he has to make over to his employers, and as a generous donation that further portion which he allows to religious duties. But what he must never be permitted to doubt is that the total from which these deductions have been made was, in some mysterious sense, his own personal birthright.

You have here a delicate task. The assumption which you want him to go on making is so absurd that, if once it is questioned, even we cannot find a shred of argument in its defence. The man can neither make, nor retain, one moment of time; it all comes to him by pure gift; he might as well regard the sun and moon as his chattels. He is also, in theory, committed to a total service of the Enemy; and if the Enemy appeared to him in bodily form and demanded that total service for even one day, he would not refuse. He would be greatly relieved if that one day involved nothing harder than listening to the conversation of a foolish woman; and he would be relieved almost to the pitch of disappointment if for one half-hour in that day the Enemy said, "Now you may go and amuse yourself." Now if he thinks about his assumption for a moment, even he is bound to realise that he is actually in this situation every day. When I speak of preserving this assumption in his mind, therefore, the last thing I mean you to do is furnish him with arguments in its defence. There aren't any. Your task is purely negative. Don't let his thoughts come anywhere near it. Wrap a darkness about it, and in the centre of that darkness let his sense of ownership-in-Time lie silent, uninspected, and operative.

The sense of ownership in general is always to be encouraged. The humans are always putting up claims to ownership which sound equally funny in Heaven and in Hell and we must keep them doing so. Much of the modern resistance to chastity comes from men's belief that they "own" their bodies—those vast and perilous estates, pulsating with the energy that made the worlds, in which they find themselves without their consent and from which they are ejected at the pleasure of Another! It is as if a royal child whom his father has placed, for love's sake, in titular command of some great province, under the real rule of wise counsellors, should come to fancy he really owns the cities, the forests, and the corn, in the same way as he owns the bricks on the nursery floor.

We produce this sense of ownership not only by pride but by confusion. We teach them not to notice the different senses of the possessive pronoun—the finely graded differences that run from "my boots" through "my dog," "my servant," "my wife," "my father," "my master" and "my country," to "my God." They can be taught to reduce all these senses to that of "my boots," the "my" of ownership. Even in the nursery a child can be taught to mean by "my Teddy-bear" *not* the old imagined recipient of affection to whom it stands in a special relation (for that is what the Enemy will teach them to mean if we are not careful) but "the bear I can pull to pieces if I like." And at the other end of the scale, we have taught men to say "My God" in a sense not really very different from "My boots," meaning "The God on whom I have a claim for my distinguished services and whom I exploit from the pulpit—the God I have done a corner in."

And all the time the joke is that the word "Mine" in its fully possessive sense cannot be uttered by a human being about anything. In the long run either Our Father or the Enemy will say "Mine" of each thing that exists, and specially of each man. They will find out in the end, never fear, to whom their time, their souls, and their bodies really belong—certainly not to *them,* whatever happens. At present the Enemy says "Mine" of everything on the pedantic, legalistic ground that He made it: Our Father hopes in the end to say "Mine" of all things on the more realistic and dynamic ground of conquest,

Your affectionate uncle

SCREWTAPE

22.

My dear Wormwood,

So! Your man is in love—and in the worst kind he could possibly have fallen into—and with a girl who does not even appear in the report you sent me. You may be interested to learn that the little misunderstanding with the Secret Police which you tried to raise about some unguarded expressions in one of my letters has been tided over. If you were reckoning on that to secure my good offices, you will find yourself mistaken. You shall pay for that as well as for your other blunders. Meanwhile I enclose a little booklet just issued, on the new House of Correction for Incompetent Tempters. It is profusely illustrated and you will not find a dull page in it.

I have looked up this girl's dossier and am horrified at what I find. Not only a Christian but such a Christian—a vile, sneaking, simpering, demure, monosyllabic, mouse-like, watery, insignificant, virginal, bread-and-butter miss. The little brute. She makes me vomit. She stinks and scalds through the very pages of the dossier. It drives me mad, the way the world has worsened. We'd have had her to the arena in the old days. That's what her sort is made for. Not that she'd do much good there, either. A two-faced little cheat (I know the sort) who looks as if she'd faint at the sight of blood and then dies with a smile. A cheat every way. Looks as if butter wouldn't melt in her mouth and yet has a satirical wit. The sort of creature who'd find *ME* funny! Filthy insipid little prude—and yet ready to fall into this booby's arms like any other breeding animal. Why doesn't the Enemy blast her for it, if He's so moonstruck by virginity—instead of looking on there, grinning?

78

He's a hedonist at heart. All those fasts and vigils and stakes and crosses are only a façade. Or only like foam on the sea shore. Out at sea, out in His sea, there is pleasure, and more pleasure. He makes no secret of it; at His right hand are "pleasures for evermore." Ugh! I don't think He has the least inkling of that high and austere mystery to which we rise in the Miserific Vision. He's vulgar, Wormwood. He has a bourgeois mind. He has filled His world full of pleasures. There are things for humans to do all day long without His minding in the least—sleeping, washing, eating, drinking, making love, playing, praying, working. Everything has to be *twisted* before it's any use to us. We fight under cruel disadvantages. Nothing is naturally on our side. (Not that that excuses *you*. I'll settle with you presently. You have always hated me and been insolent when you dared.)

Then, of course, he gets to know this woman's family and whole circle. Could you not see that the very house she lives in is one that he ought never to have entered? The whole place reeks of that deadly odour. The very gardener, though he has only been there five years, is beginning to acquire it. Even guests, after a week-end visit, carry some of the smell away with them. The dog and the cat are tainted with it. And a house full of the impenetrable mystery. We are certain (it is a matter of first principles) that each member of the family must in some way be making capital out of the others—but we can't find out how. They guard as jealously as the Enemy Himself the secret of what really lies behind his pretence of disinterested love. The whole house and garden is one vast obscenity. It bears a sickening resemblance to the description one human writer made of Heaven; "the regions where there is only life and therefore all that is not music is silence."

Music and silence—how I detest them both! How thankful we should be that ever since our Father entered Hell—though longer ago than humans, reckoning in light years, could express —no square inch of infernal space and no moment of infernal time has been surrendered to either of those abominable forces, but all has been occupied by Noise—Noise, the grand dynamism, the audible expression of all that is exultant, ruthless, and virile —Noise which alone defends us from silly qualms, despairing scruples, and impossible desires. We will make the whole universe a noise in the end. We have already made great strides in this direction as regards the Earth. The melodies and silences of Heaven will be shouted down in the end. But I admit we are not yet loud enough, or anything like it. Research is in progress. Meanwhile *you,* disgusting little——

[*Here the MS. breaks off and is resumed in a different hand.*]

In the heat of composition I find that I have inadvertently allowed myself to assume the form of a large centipede. I am accordingly dictating the rest to my secretary. Now that the transformation is complete I recognise it as a periodical phenomenon. Some rumour of it has reached the humans and a distorted account of it appears in the poet Milton, with the ridiculous addition that such changes of shape are a "punishment" imposed on us by the Enemy. A more modern writer—someone with a name like Pshaw—has, however, grasped the truth. Transformation proceeds from within and is a glorious manifestation of that Life Force which Our Father would worship if he worshipped anything but himself. In my present form I feel even more anxious to see you, to unite you to myself in an indissoluble embrace,

(Signed) TOADPIPE

For his Abysmal Sublimity Under Secretary
Screwtape, T.E., B.S., etc.

23.

My dear Wormwood,

Through this girl and her disgusting family the patient is now getting to know more Christians every day, and very intelligent Christians too. For a long time it will be quite impossible to *remove* spirituality from his life. Very well then; we must *corrupt* it. No doubt you have often practised transforming yourself into an angel of light as a parade-ground exercise. Now is the time to do it in the face of the Enemy. The World and the Flesh have failed us; a third Power remains. And success of this third kind is the most glorious of all. A spoiled saint, a Pharisee, an inquisitor, or a magician, makes better sport in Hell than a mere common tyrant or debauchee.

Looking round your patient's new friends I find that the best point of attack would be the border-line between theology and politics. Several of his new friends are very much alive to the social implications of their religion. That, in itself, is a bad thing; but good can be made out of it.

You will find that a good many Christian-political writers think that Christianity began going wrong, and departing from the doctrine of its Founder, at a very early stage. Now this idea must be used by us to encourage once again the conception of a "historical Jesus" to be found by clearing away later "accretions and perversions" and then to be contrasted with the whole Christian tradition. In the last generation we promoted the construction of such a "historical Jesus" on liberal and humanitarian lines; we are now putting forward a new "historical Jesus" on Marxian, catastrophic, and revolutionary lines. The advantages of these constructions, which we intend to change every thirty years or so, are manifold. In the first place they all tend to direct men's devotion to something which does not exist, for each "historical Jesus" is unhistorical. The documents say what they say and cannot be added to; each new "historical Jesus" therefore has to be got out of them by suppression at one point and exaggeration at another, and by that sort of guessing (brilliant is the adjective we teach humans to apply to it) on which no one would risk ten shillings in ordinary life, but which is enough to produce a crop of new Napoleons, new Shakespeares, and new Swifts, in every publisher's autumn list. In the second place, all such constructions place the importance of their Historical Jesus in some peculiar theory He is supposed to have promulgated. He has to be a "great man" in the modern sense of the word—one standing at the terminus of some centrifugal and unbalanced line of thought—a crank vending a panacea. We thus distract men's minds from Who He is, and what He did. We first make Him solely a teacher, and then conceal the very substantial agreement between His teachings and those of all other great moral teachers. For humans must not be allowed to notice that all great moralists are sent by the Enemy not to inform men but to remind them, to restate the primeval moral platitudes against our continual concealment of them. We make the Sophists: He raises up a Socrates to answer them. Our third aim is, by these constructions, to destroy the devotional life. For the real presence of the Enemy, otherwise experienced by men in prayer and sacrament, we substitute a merely probable, remote, shadowy, and uncouth figure, one who spoke a strange language and died a long time ago. Such an object cannot in fact be worshipped. Instead of the Creator adored by its creature, you soon have merely a leader acclaimed by a partisan, and finally a distinguished character approved by a judicious historian. And fourthly, besides being unhistorical in the Jesus it depicts, religion of this kind is false to history in another sense. No nation, and few individuals, are really brought into the Enemy's camp by the historical study of the biography of Jesus, simply as biography. Indeed materials for a full biograpy have been withheld from men. The earliest converts were converted by a single historical fact (the Resurrection) and a single theological doctrine (the Redemption) operating on a sense of sin which they already had—and sin, not against some new fancy-dress law produced as a novelty by a "great man," but against the old, platitudinous, universal moral law which they had been taught by their nurses and mothers. The "Gospels" come later and were written not to make Christians but to edify Christians already made.

The "Historical Jesus" then, however dangerous he may seem to be to us at some particular point, is always to be encouraged. About the general connection between Christianity and politics, our position is more delicate. Certainly we do not want men to allow their Christianity to flow over into their political life, for the establishment of anything like a really just society would be a major disaster. On the other hand we do want, and want very much, to make men treat Christianity as a means; preferably, of course, as a means to their own advancement, but, failing that, as a means to anything—even to social justice. The thing to do is to get a man at first to value social justice as a thing which the Enemy demands, and then work him on to the stage at which he values Christianity because it may produce social justice. For the Enemy will not be used as a convenience. Men or nations who think they can revive the Faith in order to make a good society might just as well think they can use the stairs of Heaven as a short cut to the nearest chemist's shop. Fortunately it is quite easy to coax humans round this little corner. Only today I have found a passage in a Christian writer where he recommends his own version of Christianity on the ground that "only such a faith can outlast the death of old cultures and the birth of new civilisations." You see the little rift? "Believe this, not because it is true, but for some other reason." That's the game,

Your affectionate uncle

SCREWTAPE

24.

My dear Wormwood,

I have been in correspondence with Slumtrimpet who is in charge of your patient's young woman, and begin to see the chink in her armour. It is an unobtrusive little vice which she shares with nearly all women who have grown up in an intelligent circle united by a clearly defined belief; and it consists in a quite untroubled assumption that the outsiders who do not share this belief are really too stupid and ridiculous. The males, who habitually meet these outsiders, do not feel that way; their confidence, if they are confident, is of a different kind. Hers, which she supposes to be due to Faith, is in reality largely due to the mere colour she has taken from her surroundings. It is not, in fact, very different from the conviction she would have felt at the age of ten that the kind of fish-knives used in her father's house were the proper or normal or "real" kind, while those of the neighbouring families were "not real fish-knives" at all. Now the element of ignorance and naïvety and in all this is so large, and the element of spiritual pride so small, that it gives us little hope of the girl herself. But have you thought of how it can be made to influence your own patient?

It is always the novice who exaggerates. The man who has risen in society is over-refined, the young scholar is pedantic. In this new circle your patient is a novice. He is there daily meeting Christian life of a quality he never before imagined and seeing it all through an enchanted glass because he is in love. He is anxious (indeed the Enemy commands him) to imitate this quality. Can you get him to imitate this *defect* in his mistress and to

84

exaggerate it until what was venial in her becomes in him the strongest and most beautiful of the vices—Spiritual Pride?

The conditions seem ideally favourable. The new circle in which he finds himself is one of which he is tempted to be proud for many reasons other than its Christianity. It is a better educated, more intelligent, more agreeable society than any he has yet encountered. He is also under some degree of illusion as to his own place in it. Under the influence of "love" he may still think himself unworthy of the girl, but he is rapidly ceasing to think himself unworthy of the others. He has no notion how much in him is forgiven because they are charitable and made the best of because he is now one of the family. He does not dream how much of his conversation, how many of his opinions, are recognised by them all as mere echoes of their own. Still less does he suspect how much of the delight he takes in these people is due to the erotic enchantment which the girl, for him, spreads over all her surroundings. He thinks that he likes their talk and way of life because of some congruity between their spiritual state and his, when in fact they are so far beyond him that if he were not in love he would be merely puzzled and repelled by much which he now accepts. He is like a dog which should imagine it understood fire-arms because its hunting instinct and love for its master enable it to enjoy a day's shooting!

Here is your chance. While the Enemy, by means of sexual love and of some very agreeable people far advanced in His service, is drawing the young barbarian up to levels he could never otherwise have reached, you must make him feel that he is finding his *own* level—that these people are "his sort" and that, coming among them, he has come home. When he turns from them to other society he will find it dull; partly because almost any society within his reach is, in fact, much less entertaining, but still more because he will miss the enchantment of the young woman. You must teach him to mistake this contrast between the circle that delights and the circle that bores him for the contrast between Christians and unbelievers. He must be made to feel (he'd better not put it into words) "how different we Christians are"; and by "we Christians" he must really, but unknowingly, mean "my set"; and by "my set" he must mean not "The people who, in their charity and humility, have accepted me," but "The people with whom I associate by right."

Success here depends on confusing him. If you try to make him explicitly and professedly proud of being a Christian, you will probably fail; the Enemy's warnings are too well known. If, on the other hand, you let the idea of "we Christians" drop out altogether and merely make him complacent about "his set," you will produce not true spiritual pride but mere social vanity which, by comparison, is a trumpery, puny little sin. What you want is to keep a sly self-congratulation mixing with all his thoughts and never allow him to raise the question "What, precisely, am I congratulating myself *about?*" The idea of belonging to an inner ring, of being in a secret, is very sweet to him. Play on that nerve. Teach him, using the influence of this girl when she is silliest, to adopt an air of *amusement* at the things the unbelievers say. Some theories which he may meet in modern Christian circles may here prove helpful; theories, I mean, that place the hope of society in some inner ring of "clerks," some trained minority of theocrats. It is no affair of yours whether those theories are true or false; the great thing is to make Christianity a mystery religion in which he feels himself one of the initiates.

Pray do not fill your letters with rubbish about this European War. Its final issue is, no doubt, important, but that is a matter for the High Command. I am not in the least interested in knowing how many people in England have been killed by bombs. In what state of mind they died, I can learn from the office at this end. That they were going to die sometime, I knew already. Please keep your mind on your work,

Your affectionate uncle
SCREWTAPE

25.

My dear Wormwood,

The real trouble about the set your patient is living in is that it is *merely* Christian. They all have individual interests, of course, but the bond remains mere Christianity. What we want, if men become Christians at all, is to keep them in the state of mind I call "Christianity And." You know—Christianity and the Crisis, Christianity and the New Psychology, Christianity and the New Order, Christianity and Faith Healing, Christianity and Psychical Research, Christianity and Vegetarianism, Christianity and Spelling Reform. If they must be Christians let them at least be Christians with a difference. Substitute for the faith itself some Fashion with a Christian colouring. Work on their horror of the same Old Thing.

The horror of the Same Old Thing is one of the most valuable passions we have produced in the human heart—an endless source of heresies in religion, folly in counsel, infidelity in marriage, and inconstancy in friendship. The humans live in time, and experience reality successively. To experience much of it, therefore, they must experience many different things; in other words, they must experience change. And since they need change, the Enemy (being a hedonist at heart) has made change pleasurable to them, just as He has made eating pleasurable. But since He does not wish them to make change, any more than eating, an end in itself, He has balanced the love of change in them by a love of permanence. He has contrived to gratify both tastes together in the very world He has made, by that union of change and permanence which we call Rhythm. He gives them the seasons, each season different yet every year the same, so that spring is always felt as a novelty yet always as the recurrence of an immemorial theme. He gives them in His Church a spiritual year; they change from a fast to a feast, but it is the same feast as before.

Now just as we pick out and exaggerate the pleasure of eating to produce gluttony, so we pick out this natural pleasantness of change and twist it into a demand for absolute novelty. This demand is entirely our workmanship. If we neglect our duty, men will be not only contented but transported by the mixed novelty and familiarity of snowdrops *this* January, sunrise *this* morning, plum pudding *this* Christmas. Children, until we have taught them better, will be perfectly happy with a seasoned round of games in which conkers succeed hopscotch as regularly as autumn follows summer. Only by our incessant efforts is the demand for infinite, or unrhythmical, change kept up.

This demand is valuable in various ways. In the first place it diminishes pleasure while increasing desire. The pleasure of novelty is by its very nature more subject than any other to the law of diminishing returns. And continued novelty costs money, so that the desire for it spells avarice or unhappiness or both. And again, the more rapacious this desire, the sooner it must eat up all the innocent sources of pleasure and pass on to those the Enemy forbids. Thus by inflaming the horror of the Same Old Thing we have recently made the Arts, for example, less dangerous to us than perhaps, they have ever been, "low-brow" and "high-brow" artists alike being now daily drawn into fresh, and still fresh, excesses of lasciviousness, unreason, cruelty, and pride. Finally, the desire for novelty is indispensable if we are to produce Fashions or Vogues.

The use of Fashions in thought is to distract the attention of men from their real dangers. We direct the fashionable outcry of each generation against those vices of which it is least in danger and fix its approval on the virtue nearest to that vice which we are trying to make endemic. The game is to have them all running about with fire extinguishers whenever there is a flood, and all crowding to that side of the boat which is already nearly gunwale under. Thus we make it fashionable to expose the dangers of enthusiasm at the very moment when they are all really becoming worldly and lukewarm; a century later, when we are really making them all Byronic and drunk with emotion, the fashionable outcry is directed against the dangers of the mere "understanding." Cruel ages are put on their guard against Sentimentality, feckless and idle ones against Respectability, lecherous ones against Puritanism; and whenever all men are really hastening to be slaves or tyrants we make Liberalism the prime bogey.

But the greatest triumph of all is to elevate this horror of the Same Old Thing into a philosophy so that nonsense in the intellect may reinforce corruption in the will. It is here that the general Evolutionary or Historical character of modern European thought (partly our work) comes in so useful. The Enemy loves platitudes. Of a proposed course of action He wants men, so far as I can see, to ask very simple questions: is it righteous? Is it prudent? Is it possible? Now if we can keep men asking "Is it in accordance with the general movement of our time? Is it progressive or reactionary? Is this the way that History is going?" they will neglect the relevant questions. And the questions they *do* ask are, of course, unanswerable; for they do not know the future, and what the future will be depends very largely on just those choices which they now invoke the future to help them to make. As a result, while their minds are buzzing in this vacuum, we have the better chance to slip in and bend them to the action *we* have decided on. And great work has already been done. Once they knew that some changes were for the better, and others for the worse, and others again indifferent. We have largely removed this knowledge. For the descriptive adjective "unchanged" we have substituted the emotional adjective "stagnant." We have trained them to think of the Future as a promised land which favoured heroes attain—not as something which everyone reaches at the rate of sixty minutes an hour, whatever he does, whoever he is,

Your affectionate uncle

SCREWTAPE

26.

My dear Wormwood,

Yes; courtship is the time for sowing those seeds which will grow up ten years later into domestic hatred. The enchantment of unsatisfied desire produces results which the humans can be made to mistake for the results of charity. Avail yourself of the ambiguity in the word "Love": Let them think they have solved by Love problems they have in fact only waived or postponed under the influence of the enchantment. While it lasts you have your chance to foment the problems in secret and render them chronic.

The grand problem is that of "unselfishness." Note once again, the admirable work of our Philological Arm in substituting the negative unselfishness for the Enemy's positive Charity. Thanks to this you can, from the very outset, teach a man to surrender benefits not that others may be happy in having them but that he may be unselfish in forgoing them. That is a great point gained. Another great help, where the parties concerned are male and female, is the divergence of view about Unselfishness which we have built up between the sexes. A woman means by Unselfishness chiefly taking trouble for others; a man means not giving trouble to others. As a result, a woman who is quite far gone in the Enemy's service will make a nuisance of herself on a larger scale than any man except those whom Our Father has dominated completely; and, conversely, a man will live long in the Enemy's camp before he undertakes as much spontaneous work to please others as a quite ordinary woman may do every day. Thus while the woman thinks of doing good offices and the man of respecting other people's rights, each sex, without any obvious unreason, can and does regard the other as radically selfish.

On top of these confusions you can now introduce a few more. The erotic enchantment produces a mutual complaisance in which each is *really* pleased to give in to the wishes of the other. They also know that the Enemy demands of them a degree of charity which, if attained, would result in similar actions. You must make them establish as a Law for their whole married life that degree of mutual self-sacrifice which is at present sprouting naturally out of the enchantment, but which, when the enchantment dies away, they will not have charity enough to enable them to perform. They will not see the trap, since they are under the double blindness of mistaking sexual excitement for charity and of thinking that the excitement will last.

When once a sort of official, legal, or nominal Unselfishness has been established as a rule—a rule for the keeping of which their emotional resources have died away and their spiritual resources have not yet grown—the most delightful results follow. In discussing any joint action, it becomes obligatory that A should argue in favour of B's supposed wishes and against his own, while B does the opposite. It is often impossible to find out either party's real wishes; with luck, they end by doing something that neither wants, while each feels a glow of self-righteousness and harbours a secret claim to preferential treatment for the unselfishness shown and a secret grudge against the other for the ease with which the sacrifice has been accepted. Later on you can venture on what may be called the Generous Conflict Illusion. This game is best played with more than two players, in a family with grown-up children for example. Something quite trivial, like having tea in the garden, is proposed. One member takes care to make it quite clear (though not in so many words) that he would rather not but is, of course, prepared to do so out of "Unselfishness." The others instantly withdraw their proposal, ostensibly through their "Unselfishness," but really because they don't want to be used as a sort of lay figure on which the first speaker practices petty altruisms. But he is not going to be done out of his debauch of Unselfishness either. He insists on doing "what the others want." They insist on doing what he wants. Passions are roused. Soon someone is saying "Very well then, I won't have any tea at all!", and a real quarrel ensues with bitter resentment on both sides. You see how it is done? If each side had been frankly contending for its own real wish, they would all have kept within the bounds of reason and courtesy; but just because the contention is reversed and each side is fighting the other side's battle, all the bitterness which really flows from thwarted self-righteousness and obstinacy and the accumulated grudges of the last ten years is concealed from them by the nominal or official "Unselfishness" of what they are doing or, at least, held to be excused by it. Each side is, indeed, quite alive to the cheap quality of the adversary's Unselfishness and of the false position into which he is trying to force them; but each manages to feel blameless and ill-used itself, with no more dishonesty than comes natural to a human.

A sensible human once said, "If people knew how much ill-feeling Unselfishness occasions, it would not be so often recommended from the pulpit"; and again, "She's the sort of woman who lives for others—you can always tell the others by their hunted expression." All this can be begun even in the period of courtship. A little *real* selfishness on your patient's part is often of less value in the long run, for securing his soul, than the first beginnings of that elaborate and self-conscious unselfishness which may one day blossom into the sort of thing I have described. Some degree of mutual falseness, some surprise that the girl does not always notice just how Unselfish he is being, can be smuggled in already. Cherish these things, and, above all, don't let the young fools notice them. If they notice them they will be on the road to discovering that "love" is not enough, that charity is needed and not yet achieved and that no external law can supply its place. I wish Slumtrimpet could do something about undermining that young woman's sense of the ridiculous,

Your affectionate uncle

SCREWTAPE

27.

My dear Wormwood,

You seem to be doing very little good at present. The use of his "love" to distract his mind from the Enemy is, of course, obvious, but you reveal what poor use you are making of it when you say that the whole question of distraction and the wandering mind has now become one of the chief subjects of his prayers. That means you have largely failed. When this, or any other distraction, crosses his mind you ought to encourage him to thrust it away by sheer will power and to try to continue the normal prayer as if nothing had happened; once he accepts the distraction as his present problem and lays *that* before the Enemy and makes it the main theme of his prayers and his endeavours, then, so far from doing good, you have done harm. Anything, even a sin, which has the total effect of moving him close up to the Enemy, makes against us in the long run.

A promising line is the following. Now that he is in love, a new idea of *earthly* happiness has arisen in his mind: and hence a new urgency in his purely petitionary prayers—about this war and other such matters. Now is the time for raising intellectual difficulties about prayer of that sort. False spirituality is always to be encouraged. On the seemingly pious ground that "praise and communion with God is the true prayer," humans can often be lured into direct disobedience to the Enemy who (in His usual flat, commonplace, uninteresting way) has definitely told them to pray for their daily bread and the recovery of their sick. You will, of course, conceal from him the fact that the prayer for daily bread, interpreted in a "spiritual sense," is really just as crudely petitionary as it is in any other sense.

But since your patient has contracted the terrible habit of obedience, he will probably continue such "crude" prayers whatever you do. But you can worry him with the haunting suspicion that the practice is absurd and can have no objective result. Don't forget to use the "heads I win, tails you lose" argument. If the thing he prays for doesn't happen, then that is one more proof that petitionary prayers don't work; if it does happen, he will, of course, be able to see some of the physical causes which led up to it, and "therefore it would have happened anyway," and thus a granted prayer becomes just as good a proof as a denied one that prayers are ineffective.

You, being a spirit, will find it difficult to understand how he gets into this confusion. But you must remember that he takes Time for an ultimate reality. He supposes that the Enemy, like himself, sees some things as present, remembers others as past, and anticipates others as future; or even if he believes that the Enemy does not see things that way, yet, in his heart of hearts, he regards this as a peculiarity of the Enemy's mode of perception—he doesn't really think (though he would say he did) that things as the Enemy sees them are things as they are! If you tried to explain to him that men's prayers today are one of the innumerable co-ordinates with which the Enemy harmonises the weather of tomorrow, he would reply that then the Enemy always knew men were going to make those prayers and, if so, they did not pray freely but were predestined to do so. And he would add that the weather on a given day can be traced back through its causes to the original creation of matter itself—so that the whole thing, both on the human and on the material side, is given "from the word go." What he ought to say, of course, is obvious to us; that the problem of adapting the particular weather to the particular prayers is merely the appearance, at two points in his temporal mode of perception, of the total problem of adapting the whole spiritual universe to the whole corporeal universe; that creation in its entirety operates at every point of space and time, or rather that their kind of consciousness forces them to encounter the whole, self-consistent creative act as a series of successive events. *Why* that creative act leaves room for their free will is the problem of problems, the secret behind the Enemy's nonsense about "Love." *How* it does so is no problem at all; for the enemy does not *foresee* the humans making their free contributions in a future, but *sees* them doing so in His unbounded Now. And obviously to watch a man doing something is not to make him do it.

It may be replied that some meddlesome human writers, notably Boetnius, have let this secret out. But in the intellectual climate which we have at last succeeded in producing throughout Western Europe, you needn't bother about that. Only the learned read old books and we have now so dealt with the learned that they are of all men the least likely to acquire wisdom by doing so. We have done this by inculcating the Historical Point of View. The Historical Point of View, put briefly, means that when a learned man is presented with any statement in an ancient author, the one question he never asks is whether it is true. He asks who influenced the ancient writer, and how far the statement is consistent with what he said in other books, and what phase in the writer's development, or in the general history of thought, it illustrates, and how it affected later writers, and how often it has been misunderstood (specally by the learned man's own colleagues) and what the general course of criticism on it has been for the last ten years, and what is the "present state of the question." To regard the ancient writer as a possible source of knowledge—to anticipate that what he said could possibly modify your thoughts or your behaviour—this would be rejected as unutterably simple-minded. And since we cannot deceive the whole human race all the time, it is most important thus to cut every generation off from all others; for where learning makes a free commerce between the ages there is always the danger that the characteristic errors of one may be corrected by the characteristic truths of another. But thanks be to our Father and the Historical Point of View, great scholars are now as little nourished by the past as the most ignorant mechanic who holds that "history is bunk,"

Your affectionate uncle

SCREWTAPE

28.

My dear Wormwood,

When I told you not to fill your letters with rubbish about the war, I meant, of course, that I did not want to have your rather infantile rhapsodies about the death of men and the destruction of cities. In so far as the war really concerns the spiritual state of the patient, I naturally want full reports. And on this aspect you seem singularly obtuse. Thus you tell me with glee that there is reason to expect heavy air raids on the town where the creature lives. This is a crying example of something I have complained about already—your readiness to forget the main point in your immediate enjoyment of human suffering. Do you not know that bombs kill men? Or do you not realise that the patient's death, at this moment, is precisely what we want to avoid? He has escaped the worldly friends with whom you tried to entangle him; he has "fallen in love" with a very Christian woman and is temporarily immune from your attacks on his chastity; and the various methods of corrupting his spiritual life which we have been trying are so far unsuccessful. At the present moment, as the full impact of the war draws nearer and his worldly hopes take a proportionately lower place in his mind, full of his defence work, full of the girl, forced to attend to his neighbours more than he has ever done before and liking it more than he expected, "taken out of himself" as the humans say, and daily increasing in conscious dependence on the Enemy he will almost certainly be lost to us if he is killed tonight. This is so obvious that I am ashamed to write it. I sometimes wonder if you young fiends are not kept out on temptation-duty too long at a time—if you are not in some danger of becoming infected by the sentiments and values of the humans among whom you work. They, of course, do tend to regard death as the prime evil and survival as the greatest good. But that is because we have taught them to do so. Do not let us be infected by our own propaganda. I know it seems strange that your chief aim at the moment should be the very same thing for which the patient's lover and his mother are praying—namely his bodily safety. But so it is; you should be guarding him like the apple of your eye. If he dies now, you lose him. If he survives the war, there is always hope. The Enemy has guarded him from you through the first great wave of temptations. But, if only he can be kept alive, you have time itself for your ally. The long, dull monotonous years of middle-aged prosperity or middle-aged adversity are excellent campaigning weather. You see, it is so hard for these creatures to *persevere*. The routine of adversity, the gradual decay of youthful loves and youthful hopes, the quiet despair (hardly felt as pain) of ever overcoming the chronic temptations with which we have again and again defeated them, the drabness which we create in their lives and the inarticulate resentment with which we teach them to respond to it—all this provides admirable opportunities of wearing out a soul by attrition. If, on the other hand, the middle years prove prosperous, our position is even stronger. Prosperity knits a man to the World, He feels that he is "finding his place in it," while really it is finding its place in him. His increasing reputation, his widening circle of acquaintances, his sense of importance, the growing pressure of absorbing and agreeable work, build up in him a sense of being really at home in earth which is just what we want. You will notice that the young are generally less unwilling to die than the middle-aged and the old.

The truth is that the Enemy, having oddly destined these mere animals to life in His own eternal world, has guarded them pretty effectively from the danger of feeling at home anywhere else. That is why we must often wish long life to our patients; seventy years is not a day too much for the difficult task of unravelling their souls from Heaven and building up a firm attachment to the earth. While they are young we find them always shooting off at a tangent. Even if we contrive to keep them ignorant of explicit religion, the incalculable winds of fantasy and music and poetry

—the mere face of a girl, the song of a bird, or the sight of a horizon—are always blowing our whole structure away. They *will* not apply themselves steadily to worldly advancement, prudent connections, and the policy of safety first. So inveterate is their appetite for Heaven that our best method, at this stage, of attaching them to earth is to make them believe that earth can be turned into Heaven at some future date by politics or eugenics or "science" or psychology, or what not. Real worldliness is a work of time—assisted, of course, by pride, for we teach them to describe the creeping death as good sense or Maturity or Experience. *Experience,* in the peculiar sense we teach them to give it, is, by the bye, a most useful word. A great human philosopher nearly let our secret out when he said that where Virtue is concerned "Experience is the mother of illusion"; but thanks to a change in Fashion, and also, of course, to the Historical Point of View, we have largely rendered his book innocuous.

How valuable time is to us may be gauged by the fact that the Enemy allows us so little of it. The majority of the human race dies in infancy; of the survivors, a good many die in youth. It is obvious that to Him human birth is important chiefly as the qualification for human death, and death solely as the gate to that other kind of life. We are allowed to work only on a selected minority of the race, for what humans call a "normal life" is the exception. Apparently He wants some—but only a very few—of the human animals with which He is peopling Heaven to have had the experience of resisting us through an earthly life of sixty or seventy years. Well, there is our opportunity. The smaller it is, the better we must use it. Whatever you do, keep your patient as safe as you possibly can,

Your affectionate uncle
SCREWTAPE

29.

My dear Wormwood,

Now that it is certain the German humans will bombard your patient's town and that his duties will keep him in the thick of the danger, we must consider our policy. Are we to aim at cowardice—or at courage, with consequent pride—or at hatred of the Germans?

Well, I am afraid it is no good trying to make him brave. Our research department has not yet discovered (though success is hourly expected) how to produce *any* virtue. This is a serious handicap. To be greatly and effectively wicked a man needs some virtue. What would Attila have been without his courage, or Shylock without self-denial as regards the flesh? But as we cannot supply these qualities ourselves, we can only use them as supplied by the Enemy—and this means leaving Him a kind of foothold in those men whom, otherwise, we have made most securely our own. A very unsatisfactory arrangement, but, I trust, we shall one day learn to do better.

Hatred we can manage. The tension of human nerves during noise, danger, and fatigue, makes them prone to any violent emotion and it is only a question of guiding this susceptibility into the right channels. If conscience resists, muddle him. Let him say that he feels hatred not on his own behalf but on that of the women and children, and that a Christian is told to forgive his own, not other people's enemies. In other words let him consider himself sufficiently identified with the women and children to feel hatred on their behalf, but *not* sufficiently identified to regard their enemies as his own and therefore proper objects of forgiveness.

But hatred is best combined with Fear. Cowardice, alone of all the vices, is purely painful—horrible to anticipate, horrible to feel, horrible to remember; Hatred has its pleasures. It is therefore often the *compensation* by which a frightened man reimburses himself for the miseries of Fear. The more he fears, the more he will hate. And Hatred is also a great anodyne for shame. To make a deep wound in his charity, you should therefore first defeat his courage.

Now this is a ticklish business. We have made men proud of most vices, but not of cowardice. Whenever we have almost suc-ceeded in doing so, the Enemy permits a war or an earthquake or some other calamity, and at once courage becomes so obvi-ously lovely and important even in human eyes that all our work is undone, and there is still at least one vice of which they feel genuine shame. The danger of inducing cowardice in our pa-tients, therefore, is lest we produce real self-knowledge and self-loathing with consequent repentance and humility. And in fact, in the last war, thousands of humans, by discovering their own cowardice, discovered the whole moral world for the first time. In peace we can make many of them ignore good and evil en-tirely; in danger, the issue is forced upon them in a guise to which even we cannot blind them. There is here a cruel dilemma before us. If we promoted justice and charity among men, we should be playing directly into the Enemy's hands; but if we guide them to the opposite behaviour, this sooner or later pro-duces (for He permits it to produce) a war or a revolution, and the undisguisable issue of cowardice or courage awakes thousands of men from moral stupor.

This, indeed, is probably one of the Enemy's motives for creating a dangerous world—a world in which moral issues really come to the point. He sees as well as you do that courage is not simply *one* of the virtues, but the form of every virtue at the testing point, which means, at the point of highest reality. A chastity or honesty, or mercy, which yields to danger will be chaste or honest or merciful only on conditions. Pilate was mer-ciful till it became risky.

It is therefore possible to lose as much as we gain by making your man a coward; he may learn too much about himself!

There is, of course, always the chance, not of chloroforming the shame, but of aggravating it and producing Despair. This would be a great triumph. It would show that he had believed in, and accepted, the Enemy's forgiveness of his other sins only because he himself did not fully feel their sinfulness—that in respect of the one vice which he really understands in its full depth of dishonour he cannot seek, nor credit, the Mercy. But I fear you have already let him get too far in the Enemy's school, and he knows that Despair is a greater sin than any of the sins which provoke it.

As to the actual technique of temptations to cowardice, not much need be said. The main point is that precautions have a tendency to increase fear. The precautions publicly enjoined on your patient, however, soon become a matter of routine and this effect disappears. What you must do is to keep running in his mind (side by side with the conscious intention of doing his duty) the vague idea of all sorts of things he can do or not do, *inside* the framework of the duty, which seem to make him a little safer. Get his mind off the simple rule ("I've got to stay here and do so-and-so") into a series of imaginary life lines ("If A happened—though I very much hope it won't—I could do B—and if the worst came to the worst, I could always do C"). Superstitions, if not recognised as such, can be awakened. The point is to keep him feeling that he has *something,* other than the Enemy and courage the Enemy supplies, *to fall back on,* so that what was intended to be a total commitment to duty becomes honeycombed all through with little unconscious reservations. By building up a series of imaginary expedients to prevent "the worst coming to the worst" you may produce, at that level of his will which he is not aware of, a determination that the worst *shall not* come to the worst. Then, at the moment of real terror, rush it out into his nerves and muscles and you may get the fatal act done before he knows what you're about. For remember, the *act* of cowardice is all that matters; the emotion of fear is, in itself, no sin and, though we enjoy it, does us no good,

Your affectionate uncle

SCREWTAPE

30.

My dear Wormwood,

I sometimes wonder whether you think you have been sent into the world for your own amusement. I gather, not from your miserably inadequate report but from that of the Infernal Police, that the patient's behaviour during the first raid has been the worst possible. He has been very frightened and thinks himself a great coward and therefore feels no pride; but he has done everything his duty demanded and perhaps a bit more. Against this disaster all you can produce on the credit side is a burst of ill temper with a dog that tripped him up, some excessive cigarette smoking, and the forgetting of a prayer. What is the use of whining to me about your difficulties? If you are proceeding on the Enemy's idea of "justice" and suggesting that your opportunities and intentions should be taken into account, then I am not sure that a charge of heresy does not lie against you. At any rate, you will soon find that the justice of Hell is purely realistic, and concerned only with results. Bring us back food, or be food yourself.

The only constructive passage in your letter is where you say that you still expect good results from the patient's fatigue. That is well enough. But it won't fall into your hands. Fatigue *can* produce extreme gentleness, and quiet of mind, and even something like vision. If you have often seen men led by it into anger, malice and impatience, that is because those men have had efficient tempters. The paradoxical thing is that moderate fatigue is a better soil for peevishness than absolute exhaustion. This depends partly on physical causes, but partly on something else. It is not fatigue simply as such that produces the anger, but unexpected demands on a man already tired. Whatever men expect they soon come to think they have a right to: the sense of disappointment can, with very little skill on our part, be turned into a sense of injury. It is after men have given in to the irremediable, after they have despaired of relief and ceased to think even a half-hour ahead, that the dangers of humbled and gentle weariness begin. To produce the best results from the patient's fatigue, therefore, you must feed him with false hopes. Put into his mind plausible reasons for believing that the air-raid will not be repeated. Keep him comforting himself with the thought of how much he will enjoy his bed next night. Exaggerate the weariness by making him think it will soon be over; for men usually feel that a stain could have been endured no longer at the very moment when it is ending, or when they think it is ending. In this, as in the problem of cowardice, the thing to avoid is the total commitment. Whatever he *says,* let his inner resolution be not to bear whatever comes to him, but to bear it "for a reasonable period" —and let the reasonable period be shorter than the trial is likely to last. It need not be *much* shorter; in attacks on patience, chastity, and fortitude, the fun is to make the man yield just when (had he but known it) relief was almost in sight.

I do not know whether he is likely to meet the girl under conditions of strain or not. If he does, make full use of the fact that up to a certain point, fatigue makes women talk more and men talk less. Much secret resentment, even between lovers, can be raised from this.

Probably the scenes he is now witnessing will not provide material for an *intellectual* attack on his faith—your previous failures have put that out of your power. But there is a sort of attack on the emotions which can still be tried. It turns on making him *feel,* when first he sees human remains plastered on a wall, that this is "what the world is *really* like" and that all his religion has been a fantasy. You will notice that we have got them completely fogged about the meaning of the word "real." They tell each other, of some great spiritual experience, "All that *really* happened was that you heard some music in a lighted building"; here "real" means the bare physical facts, separated from the other elements in the experience they actually had. On the other hand, they will also say "It's all very well discussing that high dive as you sit here in an armchair, but wait till you get up there and see what it's *really* like": here "real" is being used in the opposite sense to mean, not the physical facts (which they know already while discussing the matter in armchairs) but the emotional effect those facts will have on a human consciousness. Either application of the word could be defended; but our business is to keep the two going at once so that the emotional value of the word "real" can be placed now on one side of the account, now on the other, as it happens to suit us. The general rule which we have now pretty well established among them is that in all experiences which can make them happier or better only the physical facts are "real" while the spiritual elements are "subjective"; in all experiences which can discourage or corrupt them the spiritual elements are the main reality and to ignore them is to be an escapist. Thus in birth the blood and pain are "real," the rejoicing a mere subjective point of view; in death, the terror and ugliness reveal what death "really means." The hatefulness of a hated person is "real"—in hatred you see men as they are, you are disillusioned; but the loveliness of a loved person is merely a subjective haze concealing a "real" core of sexual appetite or economic association. Wars and poverty are "really" horrible; peace and plenty are mere physical facts about which men happen to have certain sentiments. The creatures are always accusing one another of wanting "to eat the cake and have it"; but thanks to our labours they are more often in the predicament of paying for the cake and not eating it. Your patient, properly handled, will have no difficulty in regarding his emotion at the sight of human entrails as a revelation of Reality and his emotion at the sight of happy children or fair weather as mere sentiment,

Your affectionate uncle
SCREWTAPE

31.

My dear, my very dear, Wormwood, my poppet, my pigsnie,

How mistakenly now that all is lost you come whimpering to ask me whether the terms of affection in which I address you meant nothing from the beginning. Far from it! Rest assured, my love for you and your love for me are as like as two peas. I have always desired you, as you (pitiful fool) desired me. The difference is that I am the stronger. I think they will give you to me now; or a bit of you. Love you? Why, yes. As dainty a morsel as ever I grew fat on.

You have let a soul slip through your fingers. The howl of sharpened famine for that loss re-echoes at this moment through all the levels of the Kingdom of Noise down to the very Throne itself. It makes me mad to think of it. How well I know what happened at the instant when they snatched him from you! There was a sudden clearing of his eyes (was there not?) as he saw you for the first time, and recognised the part you had had in him and knew that you had it no longer. Just think (and let it be the beginning of your agony) what he felt at that moment; as if a scab had fallen from an old sore, as if he were emerging from a hideous, shell-like tetter, as if he shuffled off for good and all a defiled, wet, clinging garment. By Hell, it is misery enough to see them in their mortal days taking off dirtied and uncomfortable clothes and splashing in hot water and giving little grunts of pleasure—stretching their eased limbs. What, then, of this final stripping, this complete cleansing?

The more one thinks about it, the worse it becomes. He got through so easily! No gradual misgivings, no doctor's sentence, no nursing home, no operating theatre, no false hopes of life; sheer, instantaneous liberation. One moment it seemed to be all our world; the scream of bombs, the fall of houses, the stink and taste of high explosive on the lips and in the lungs, the feet burning with weariness, the heart cold with horrors, the brain reeling, the legs aching; next moment all this was gone, gone like a bad dream, never again to be of any account. Defeated, out-manœuvred fool! Did you mark how naturally—as if he'd been born for it—the earth-born vermin entered the new life? How all his doubts became, in the twinkling of an eye, ridiculous? I know what the creature was saying to itself! "Yes. Of course. It always was like this. All horrors have followed the same course, getting worse and worse and forcing you into a kind of bottle-neck till, at the very moment when you thought you must be crushed, behold! you were out of the narrows and all was suddenly well. The extraction hurt more and more and then the tooth was out. The dream became a nightmare and then you woke. You die and die and then you are beyond death. How could I ever have doubted it?"

As he saw you, he also saw Them. I know how it was. You reeled back dizzy and blinded, more hurt by them than he had ever been by bombs. The degradation of it!—that this thing of earth and slime could stand upright and converse with spirits before whom you, a spirit, could only cower. Perhaps you had hoped that the awe and strangeness of it would dash his joy. But that is the cursed thing; the gods are strange to mortal eyes, and yet they are not strange. He had no faintest conception till that very hour of how they would look, and even doubted their existence. But when he saw them he knew that he had always known them and realised what part each of them had played at many an hour in his life when he had supposed himself alone, so that now he could say to them, one by one, not "Who *are* you?" but "So it was *you* all the time." All that they were and said at this meeting woke memories. The dim consciousness of friends about him which had haunted his solitudes from infancy was now at last explained; that central music in every pure experience which had always just evaded memory was now at last recovered. Recognition made him free of their company almost before the limbs of his corpse became quiet. Only you were left outside.

He saw not only Them; he saw Him. This animal, this thing begotten in a bed, could look on Him. What is blinding, suffocating fire to you, is now cool light to him, is clarity itself, and wears the form of a Man. You would like, if you could, to interpret the patient's prostration in the Presence, his self-abhorrence and utter knowledge of his sins (yes, Wormwood, a clearer knowledge even than yours) on the analogy of your own choking and paralyzing sensations when you encounter the deadly air that breathes from the heart of Heaven. But it's all nonsense. Pains he may still have to encounter, but they *embrace* those pains. They would not barter them for any earthly pleasure. All the delights of sense, or heart, or intellect, with which you could once have tempted him, even the delights of virtue itself, now seem to him in comparison but as the half nauseous attractions of a raddled harlot would seem to a man who hears that his true beloved whom he has loved all his life and whom he had believed to be dead is alive and even now at his door. He is caught up into that world where pain and pleasure take on transfinite values and all our arithmetic is dismayed. Once more, the inexplicable meets us. Next to the curse of useless tempters like yourself the greatest curse upon us is the failure of our Intelligence Department. If only we could find out what He is really up to! Alas, alas, that knowledge, in itself so hateful and mawkish a thing, should yet be necessary for Power! Sometimes I am almost in despair. All that sustains me is the conviction that our Realism, our rejection (in the face of all temptations) of all silly nonsense and claptrap, *must* win in the end. Meanwhile, I have you to settle with. Most truly do I sign myself

> Your increasingly and ravenously
> affectionate uncle
> SCREWTAPE

THE GREAT DIVORCE

by

C. S. Lewis

FELLOW OF MAGDALEN COLLEGE, OXFORD

THE MACMILLAN COMPANY, NEW YORK

Preface

Blake wrote the Marriage of Heaven and Hell. If I have written of their Divorce, this is not because I think myself a fit antagonist for so great a genius, nor even because I feel at all sure that I know what he meant. But in some sense or other the attempt to make that marriage is perennial. The attempt is based on the belief that reality never presents us with an absolutely unavoidable "either-or"; that, granted skill and patience and (above all) time enough, some way of embracing both alternatives can always be found; that mere development or adjustment or refinement will somehow turn evil into good without our being called on for a final and total rejection of anything we should like to retain. This belief I take to be a disastrous error. You cannot take all luggage with you on all journeys; on one journey even your right hand and your right eye may be among the things you have to leave behind. We are not living in a world where all roads are radii of a circle and where all, if followed long enough, will therefore draw gradually nearer and finally meet at the centre: rather in a world where every road, after a few miles, forks into two, and each of those into two again, and at each fork you must make a decision. Even on the biological level life is not like a pool but like a tree. It does not move towards unity but away from it and the creatures grow further apart as they increase in perfection. Good, as it ripens, becomes continually more different not only from evil but from other good.

I do not think that all who choose wrong roads perish; but their rescue consists in being put back on the right road. A wrong sum can be put right: but only by going back till you find the error and working it afresh from that point, never by simply *going on*. Evil can be undone, but it cannot "develop" into good. Time does not heal it. The spell must be unwound, bit by bit, "with backward mutters of dissevering power"—or else not. It is still "either-or." If we insist on keeping Hell (or even earth) we shall not see Heaven: if we accept Heaven we shall not be able to retain even the smallest and most intimate souvenirs of Hell. I believe, to be sure, that any man who reaches Heaven will find that what he abandoned (even in plucking out his right eye) was precisely nothing: that the kernel of what he was really seeking even in his most depraved wishes will be there, beyond expectation, waiting for him in "the High Countries." In that sense it will be true for those who have completed the journey (and for no others) to say that good is everything and Heaven everywhere. But we, at this end of the road, must not try to anticipate that retrospective vision. If we do, we are likely to embrace the false and disastrous converse and fancy that everything is good and everywhere is Heaven.

But what, you ask, of earth? Earth, I think, will not be found by anyone to be in the end a very distinct place. I think earth, if chosen instead of Heaven, will turn out to have been, all along, only a region in Hell: and earth, if put second to Heaven, to have been from the beginning a part of Heaven itself.

There are only two things more to be said about this small book. Firstly, I must acknowledge my debt to a writer whose name I have forgotten and whom I read several years ago in a highly coloured American magazine of what they call "Scientifiction." The unbendable and unbreakable quality of my heavenly matter was suggested to me by him, though he used the fancy for a different and most ingenious purpose. His hero travelled into the *past:* and there, very properly, found raindrops that would pierce him like bullets and sandwiches that no strength could bite—because, of course, nothing in the past can be altered. I, with less originality but (I hope) equal propriety have transferred this to the eternal. If the writer of that story ever reads these lines I hope he will accept my grateful acknowledgment. The second thing is this. I beg readers to remember that this is a fantasy. It has of course—or I intended it to have—a moral. But the transmortal conditions are solely an imaginative supposal: they are not even a guess or a speculation at what may actually await us. The last thing I wish is to arouse factual curiosity about the details of the after-world.

C. S. Lewis
April, 1945.

I.

I seemed to be standing in a bus queue by the side of a long, mean street. Evening was just closing in and it was raining. I had been wandering for hours in similar mean streets, always in the rain and always in evening twilight. Time seemed to have paused on that dismal moment when only a few shops have lit up and it is not yet dark enough for their windows to look cheering. And just as the evening never advanced to night, so my walking had never brought me to the better parts of the town. However far I went I found only dingy lodging houses, small tobacconists, hoardings from which posters hung in rags, windowless warehouses, goods stations without trains, and bookshops of the sort that sell *The Works of Aristotle*. I never met anyone. But for the little crowd at the bus stop, the whole town seemed to be empty. I think that was why I attached myself to the queue.

I had a stroke of luck right away, for just as I took my stand a little waspish woman who would have been ahead of me snapped out at a man who seemed to be with her, "Very well, then. I won't go at all. So there," and left the queue. "Pray don't imagine," said the man, in a very dignified voice, "that I care about going in the least. I have only been trying to please *you*, for peace sake. My own feelings are of course a matter of no importance. I quite understand *that*"—and suiting the action to the word he also walked away. "Come," thought I, "that's two places gained." I was now next to a very short man with a scowl who glanced at me with an expression of extreme disfavour and observed, rather unnecessarily loudly, to the man beyond him, "This sort of thing really makes one think twice about going at all." "What sort of thing?" growled the other, a big beefy person. "Well," said the

Short Man, "this is hardly the sort of society I'm used to as a matter of fact." "Huh!" said the Big Man: and then added with a glance at me, "Don't you stand any sauce from *him,* Mister. You're not *afraid* of him, are you?" Then, seeing I made no move, he rounded suddenly on the Short Man and said, "Not good enough for you, aren't we? Like your lip." Next moment he had fetched the Short Man one on the side of the face that sent him sprawling into the gutter. "Let him lay, let him lay," said the Big Man to no-one in particular. "I'm a plain man that's what I am and I got to have my rights same as anyone else, see?" As the Short Man showed no disposition to rejoin the queue and soon began limping away, I closed up, rather cautiously, behind the Big Man and congratulated myself on having gained yet another step. A moment later two young people in front of him also left us arm in arm. They were both so trousered, slender, giggly and falsetto that I could be sure of the sex of neither, but it was clear that each for the moment preferred the other to the chance of a place in the bus. "We shall never all get in," said a female voice with a whine in it from some four places ahead of me. "Change places with you for five bob, lady," said someone else. I heard the clink of money and then a scream in the female voice mixed with roars of laughter from the rest of the crowd. The cheated woman leaped out of her place to fly at the man who had bilked her, but the others immediately closed up and flung her out. . . . So what with one thing and another the queue had reduced itself to manageable proportions long before the bus appeared.

It was a wonderful vehicle, blazing with golden light, heraldically coloured. The Driver himself seemed full of light and he used only one hand to drive with. The other he waved before his face as if to fan away the greasy steam of the rain. A growl went up from the queue as he came in sight. "Looks as if *he* had a good time of it, eh? . . . Bloody pleased with himself, I bet. . . . My dear, why can't he behave *naturally?*—Thinks himself too good to look at us. . . . Who does he imagine he is? . . . All that gilding and purple, I call it a wicked waste. Why don't they spend some of the money on their house property down here? —God! I'd like to give him one in the ear-'ole." I could see noth-

ing in the countenance of the Driver to justify all this, unless
it were that he had a look of authority and seemed intent on
carrying out his job.

My fellow passengers fought like hens to get on board the bus
though there was plenty of room for us all. I was the last to get
in. The bus was only half full and I selected a seat at the back,
well away from the others. But a tousle-headed youth at once
came and sat down beside me. As he did so we moved off.

"I thought you wouldn't mind my tacking on to you," he said,
"for I've noticed that you feel just as I do about the present company. Why on earth they insist on coming I can't imagine. They
won't like it at all when we get there, and they'd really be much
more comfortable at home. It's different for you and me."

"Do they *like* this place?" I asked.

"As much as they'd like anything," he answered. "They've got
cinemas and fish and chip shops and advertisements and all sorts
of things they want. The appalling lack of any intellectual life
doesn't worry *them*. I realised as soon as I got here that there'd
been some mistake. I ought to have taken the first bus but I've
fooled about trying to wake people up here. I found a few fellows I'd known before and tried to form a little circle, but they
all seem to have sunk to the level of their surroundings. Even before we came here I'd had some doubts about a man like Cyril
Bellow. I always thought he was working in a false idiom. But
he was at least intelligent: one could get some criticism worth
hearing from him, even if he was a failure on the creative side.
But now he seems to have nothing left but his self-conceit. The
last time I tried to read him some of my own stuff . . . but wait
a minute, I'd just like you to look at it."

Realising with a shudder that what he was producing from his
pocket was a thick wad of typewritten paper, I muttered something about not having any spectacles and exclaimed, "Hullo!
We've left the ground."

It was true. Several hundred feet below us, already half hidden
in the rain and mist, the wet roofs of the town appeared, spreading without a break as far as the eye could reach.

2.

I was not left very long at the mercy of the Tousle-Headed Poet, because another passenger interrupted our conversation: but before that happened I had learned a good deal about him. He appeared to be a singularly ill-used man. His parents had never appreciated him and none of the five schools at which he had been educated seemed to have made any provision for a talent and temperament such as his. To make matters worse he had been exactly the sort of boy in whose case the examination system works out with the maximum unfairness and absurdity. It was not until he reached the university that he began to recognise that all these injustices did not come by chance but were the inevitable results of our economic system. Capitalism did not merely enslave the workers, it also vitiated taste and vulgarised intellect: hence our educational system and hence the lack of "Recognition" for new genius. This discovery had made him a Communist. But when the war came along and he saw Russia in alliance with the capitalist governments, he had found himself once more isolated and had to become a conscientious objector. The indignities he suffered at this stage of his career had, he confessed, embittered him. He decided he could serve the cause best by going to America: but then America came into the war too. It was at this point that he suddenly saw Sweden as the home of a really new and radical art, but the various oppressors had given him no facilities for going to Sweden. There were money troubles. His father, who had never progressed beyond the most atrocious mental complacency and smugness of the Victorian epoch, was giving him a ludicrously inadequate allowance. And he had been very badly treated by a girl too. He had thought her a really civilised and adult personality, and then she had unexpectedly revealed that she was a mass of bourgeois prejudices and monogamic instincts. Jealousy, possessiveness, was a quality he particularly disliked. She had even shown herself, at the end, to be mean about money. That was the last straw. He had jumped under a train. . . .

I gave a start, but he took no notice.

Even then, he continued, ill luck had continued to dog him. He'd been sent to the grey town. But of course it was a mistake. I would find, he assured me, that all the other passengers would be with me on the return journey. But he would not. He was going to stay "there." He felt quite certain that he was going where at *last,* his finely critical spirit would no longer be outraged by an uncongenial environment—where he would find "Recognition" and "Appreciation." Meanwhile, since I hadn't got my glasses, he would read me the passage about which Cyril Blellow had been so insensitive. . . .

It was just then that we were interrupted. One of the quarrels which were perpetually simmering in the bus had boiled over and for a moment there was a stampede. Knives were drawn: pistols were fired; but it all seemed strangely innocuous and when it was over I found myself unharmed, though in a different seat and with a new companion. He was an intelligent-looking man with a rather bulbous nose and a bowler hat. I looked out of the windows. We were now so high that all below us had become featureless. But fields, rivers, or mountains I did not see, and I got the impression that the grey town still filled the whole field of vision.

"It seems the deuce of a town," I volunteered, "and that's what I can't understand. The parts of it that I saw were so empty. Was there once a much larger population?"

"Not at all," said my neighbour. "The trouble is that they're so quarrelsome. As soon as anyone arrives he settles in some street. Before he's been there twenty-four hours he quarrels with his neighbour. Before the week is over he's quarrelled so badly that he decides to move. Very likely he finds the next street empty because all the people there have quarrelled with *their* neighbours—and moved. So he settles in. If by any chance the street is full, he goes further. But even if he stays, it makes no odds. He's sure to have another quarrel pretty soon and then he'll move on again. Finally he'll move right out to the edge of the town and build a new house. You see, it's easy here. You've only got to *think* a house and there it is. That's how the town keeps on growing."

"Leaving more and more empty streets?"

"That's right. And time's sort of odd here. That place where we caught the bus is thousands of miles from the Civic Centre where all the newcomers arrive from earth. All the people you've met were living near the bus stop: but they'd taken centuries—of our time—to get there, by gradual removals."

"And what about the earlier arrivals? I mean—there must be people who came from earth to your town even longer ago."

"That's right. There are. They've been moving on and on. Getting further apart. They're so far off by now that they could never think of coming to the bus stop at all. Astronomical distances. There's a bit of rising ground near where I live and a chap has a telescope. You can see the lights of the inhabited houses, where those old ones live, millions of miles away. Millions of miles from us and from one another. Every now and then they move further still. That's one of the disappointments. I thought you'd meet interesting historical characters. But you don't: they're too far away."

"Would they get to the bus stop in time, if they ever set out?"

"Well—theoretically. But it'd be a distance of light-years. And they wouldn't want to by now: not those old chaps like Tamberlaine and Genghiz Khan, or Julius Caesar, or Henry the Fifth."

"Wouldn't want to?"

"That's right. The nearest of those old ones is Napoleon. We know that because two chaps made the journey to see him. They'd started long before I came, of course, but I was there when they came back. About fifteen thousand years of our time it took them. We've picked out the house by now. Just a little pin prick of light and nothing else near it for millions of miles."

"But they got there?"

"That's right. He'd built himself a huge house all in the Empire style—rows of windows flaming with light, though it only shows as a pin prick from where I live."

"Did they see Napoleon?"

"That's right. They went up and looked through one of the windows. Napoleon was there all right."

"What was he doing?"

"Walking up and down—up and down all the time—left-right, left-right—never stopping for a moment. The two chaps watched him for about a year and he never rested. And muttering to himself all the time. 'It was Soult's fault. It was Ney's fault. It was Josephine's fault. It was the fault of the Russians. It was the fault of the English.' Like that all the time. Never stopped for a moment. A little, fat man and he looked kind of tired. But he didn't seem able to stop it."

From the vibrations I gathered that the bus was still moving, but there was now nothing to be seen from the windows which confirmed this—nothing but grey void above and below.

"Then the town will go on spreading indefinitely?" I said.

"That's right," said the Intelligent Man. "Unless someone can do something about it."

"How do you mean?"

"Well, as a matter of fact, between you and me and the wall, that's my job at the moment. What's the trouble about this place? Not that people are quarrelsome—that's only human nature and was always the same even on earth. The trouble is they have no Needs. You get everything you want (not very good quality, of course) by just imagining it. That's why it never costs any trouble to move to another street or build another house. In other words, there's no proper economic basis for any community life. If they needed real shops, chaps would have to stay near where the real shops were. If they needed real houses they'd have to stay near where builders were. It's scarcity that enables a society to exist. Well, that's where I come in. I'm not going this trip for my health. As far as that goes I don't think it would suit me up there. But if I can come back with some *real* commodities—anything at all that you could really bite or drink or sit on—why, at once you'd get a demand down in our town. I'd start a little business. I'd have something to sell. You'd soon get people coming to live near

—centralisation. Two fully-inhabited streets would accommodate the people that are now spread over a million square miles of empty streets. I'd make a nice little profit and be a public benefactor as well."

"You mean, if they *had* to live together they'd gradually learn to quarrel less?"

"Well, I don't know about that. I daresay they could be kept a bit quieter. You'd have a chance to build up a police force. Knock some kind of discipline into them. Anyway" (here he dropped his voice) "it'd be *better,* you know. Everyone admits that. Safety in numbers."

"Safety from what?" I began, but my companion nudged me to be silent. I changed my question.

"But look here," said I, "if they can get everything just by imagining it, why would they want any *real* things, as you call them?"

"Eh? Oh well, they'd like houses that really kept out the rain."

"Their present houses don't?"

"Well of course not. How could they?"

"What the devil is the use of building them, then?" The Intelligent Man put his head closer to mine. "Safety again," he muttered. "At least, the feeling of safety. It's all right *now*: but later on . . . you understand."

"What?" said I, almost involuntarily sinking my own voice to a whisper.

He articulated noiselessly as if expecting that I understood lip-reading. I put my ear close to his mouth. "Speak up," I said. "It will be dark presently," he mouthed.

"You mean the evening *is* really going to turn into a night in the end?"

He nodded.

"What's that got to do with it?" said I.

"Well . . . no one wants to be out of doors when that happens."

"Why?"

His reply was so furtive that I had to ask him several times to repeat it. When he had done so, being a little annoyed (as one so often is with whisperers) I replied without remembering to lower my voice.

"Who are 'They'?" I asked. "And what are you afraid they'll do to you? And why should they come out when it's dark? And what protection could an imaginary house give if there was any danger?"

"Here!" shouted the Big Man. "Who's talking all that stuff? You stop your whispering you two if you don't want a hiding, see? Spreading rumours, that's what I call it. You shut your face, Ikey, see?"

"Quite right. Scandalous. Ought to be prosecuted. How did they get into the bus?" growled the passengers.

A fat clean-shaven man who sat on the seat in front of me leaned back and addressed me in a cultured voice.

"Excuse me," he said, "but I couldn't help overhearing parts of your conversation. It is astonishing how these primitive superstitions linger on. I beg your pardon? Oh, God bless my soul, that's all it is. There is not a shred of evidence that this twilight is ever going to turn into a night. There has been a revolution of opinion on that in educated circles. I am surprised that you haven't heard of it. All the nightmare fantasies of our ancestors are being swept away. What we now see in this subdued and delicate half-light is the promise of the dawn: the slow turning of a whole nation towards the light. Slow and imperceptible, of course. 'And not through Eastern windows only, When daylight comes, comes in the light.' And that passion for 'real' commodities which our friend speaks of is only materialism, you know. It's retrogressive. Earth-bound! A hankering for matter. But *we* look on this spiritual city—for with all its faults it *is* spiritual—as a nursery in which the creative functions of man, now freed from the clogs of matter, begin to try their wings. A sublime thought."

Hours later there came a change. It began to grow light in the bus. The greyness outside the windows turned from mud-color to mother of pearl, then to faintest blue, then to a bright blueness that stung the eyes. We seemed to be floating in a pure vacancy. There were no lands, no sun, no stars in sight: only the radiant abyss. I let down the window beside me. Delicious freshness came in for a second, and then—

"What the hell are you doing?" shouted the Intelligent Man, leaning roughly across me and pulling the window sharply up. "Want us all to catch our death of cold?"

"Hit him a biff," said the Big Man.

I glanced round the bus. Though the windows were closed, and soon muffed, the bus was full of light. It was cruel light. I shrank from the faces and forms by which I was surrounded. They were all fixed faces, full not of possibilities but of impossibilities, some gaunt, some bloated, some glaring with idiotic ferocity, some drowned beyond recovery in dreams; but all, in one way or another, distorted and faded. One had a feeling that they might fall to pieces at any moment if the light grew much stronger. Then—there was a mirror on the end wall of the bus— I caught sight of my own.

And still the light grew.

3.

A cliff loomed up ahead. It sank vertically beneath us so far that I could not see the bottom, and it was dark and smooth. We were mounting all the time. At last the top of the cliff became visible like a thin line of emerald green stretched tight as a fiddle-string. Presently we glided over that top: we were flying above a level, grassy country through which there ran a wide river. We were losing height now: some of the tallest tree tops were only twenty feet below us. Then, suddenly we were at rest. Everyone had jumped up. Curses, taunts, blows, a filth of vituperation, came to my ears as my fellow-passengers struggled to get out. A moment later, and they had all succeeded. I was alone in the bus, and through the open door there came to me in the fresh stillness the singing of a lark.

I got out. The light and coolness that drenched me were like those of summer morning, early morning a minute or two before the sunrise, only that there was a certain difference. I had the sense of being in a larger space, perhaps even a larger *sort* of space, than I had ever known before: as if the sky were further off and the extent of the green plain wider than they could be on this little ball of earth. I had got "out" in some sense which made the Solar System itself seem an indoor affair. It gave me a feeling of freedom, but also of exposure, possibly of danger, which continued to accompany me through all that followed. It is the impossibility of communicating that feeling, or even of inducing you to remember it as I proceed, which makes me despair of conveying the real quality of what I saw and heard.

At first, or course, my attention was caught by my fellow-passengers, who were still grouped about in the neighbourhood of the omnibus, though beginning, some of them, to walk forward into the landscape with hesitating steps. I gasped when I saw them. Now that they were in the light, they were transparent —fully transparent when they stood between me and it, smudgy and imperfectly opaque when they stood in the shadow of some tree. They were in fact ghosts: man-shaped stains on the brightness of that air. One could attend to them or ignore them at will as you do with the dirt on a window pane. I noticed that the grass did not bend under their feet: even the dew drops were not disturbed.

Then some re-adjustment of the mind or some focussing of my eyes took place, and I saw the whole phenomenon the other way round. The men were as they always had been; as all the men I had known had been perhaps. It was the light, the grass, the trees that were different; made of some different substance, so much soldier than things in our country that men were ghosts by comparison. Moved by a sudden thought, I bent down and tried to pluck a daisy which was growing at my feet. The stalk wouldn't break. I tried to twist it, but it wouldn't twist. I tugged till the sweat stood out on my forehead and I had lost most of the skin off my hands. The little flower was hard, not like wood or even like iron, but like diamond. There was a leaf—a young tender beech-leaf, lying on the grass beside it. I tried to pick the leaf up: my heart almost cracked with the effort, and I believe I did just raise it. But I had to let it go at once; it was heavier than a sack of coal. As I stood, recovering my breath with great gasps and looking down at the daisy, I noticed that I could see the grass not only between my feet but *through* them. I also was a phantom. Who will give me words to express the terror of that discovery? "Golly!" thought I. "I'm in for it this time."

"I don't like it! I don't like it," screamed a voice, "It gives me the pip!" One of the ghosts had darted past me, back into the bus. She never came out of it again as far as I know.

The others remained, uncertain.

"Hi, Mister," said the Big Man, addressing the Driver, "when have we got to be back?"

"You need never come back unless you want to," he replied. "Stay as long as you please." There was an awkward pause.

"This is simply ridiculous," said a voice in my ear. One of the quieter and more respectable ghosts had sidled up to me. "There must be some mismanagement," he continued. "What's the sense of allowing all that riff-raff to float about here all day? Look at them. They're not enjoying it. They'd be far happier at home. They don't even know what to do."

"I don't know very well myself," said I. "What does one do?"

"Oh me? I shall be met in a moment or two. I'm expected. I'm not bothering about that. But it's rather unpleasant on one's first day to have the whole place crowded out with trippers. Damn it, one's chief object in coming here at all was to avoid them!"

He drifted away from me. And I began to look about. In spite of his reference to a "crowd," the solitude was so vast that I could hardly notice the knot of phantoms in the foreground. Greenness and light had almost swallowed them up. But very far away I could see what might be either a great bank of cloud or a range of mountains. Sometimes I could make out in it steep forests, far-withdrawing valleys, and even mountain cities perched on inaccessible summits. At other times it became indistinct. The height was so enormous that my waking sight could not have taken in such an object at all. Light brooded on the top of it: slanting down thence it made long shadows behind every tree on the plain. There was no change and no progression as the hours passed. The promise—or the threat—of sunrise rested immovably up there.

Long after that I saw people coming to meet us. Because they were bright I saw them while they were still very distant, and at first I did not know that they were people at all. Mile after mile they drew nearer. The earth shook under their tread as their strong feet sank into the wet turf. A tiny haze and a sweet smell went up where they had crushed the grass and scattered the dew. Some were naked, some robed. But the naked ones did not seem less adorned, and the robes did not disguise in those who wore them the massive grandeur of muscle and the radiant smoothness of flesh. Some were bearded but no one in that company struck me as being of any particular age. One gets glimpses, even in our country, of that which is ageless—heavy thought in the face of an infant, and frolic childhood in that of a very old man. Here it was all like that. They came on steadily. I did not entirely like it. Two of the ghosts screamed and ran for the bus. The rest of us huddled closer to one another.

4.

As the solid people came nearer still I noticed that they were moving with order and determination as though each of them had marked his man in our shadowy company. "There are going to be affecting scenes," I said to myself. "Perhaps it would not be right to look on." With that, I sidled away on some vague pretext of doing a little exploring. A grove of huge cedars to my right seemed attractive and I entered it. Walking proved difficult. The grass, hard as diamonds to my unsubstantial feet, made me feel as if I were walking on wrinkled rock, and I suffered pains like those of the mermaid in Hans Andersen. A bird ran across in front of me and I envied it. It belonged to that country and was as real as the grass. It could bend the stalks and spatter itself with the dew.

Almost at once I was followed by what I have called the Big Man—to speak more accurately, the Big Ghost. He in his turn was followed by one of the bright people. "Don't you know me?" he shouted to the Ghost: and I found it impossible not to turn and attend. The face of the solid spirit—he was one of those that wore a robe—made me want to dance, it was so jocund, so established in its youthfulness.

"Well, I'm damned," said the Ghost. "I wouldn't have believed it. It's a fair knock-out. It isn't right, Len, you know. What about poor Jack, eh? You look pretty pleased with yourself, but what I say is, What about poor Jack?"

"He is here," said the other. "You will meet him soon, if you stay."

"But you murdered him."

"Of course I did. It is all right now."

"All right, is it? All right for you, you mean. But what about the poor chap himself, laying cold and dead?"

"But he isn't. I have told you, you will meet him soon. He sent you his love."

"What I'd like to understand," said the Ghost, "is what you're here for, as pleased as Punch, you, a bloody murderer, while I've been walking the streets down there and living in a place like a pigstye all these years."

"That is a little hard to understand at first. But it is all over now. You will be pleased about it presently. Till then there is no need to bother about it."

"No need to bother about it? Aren't you ashamed of yourself?"

"No. Not as you mean. I do not look at myself. I have given up myself. I had to, you know, after the murder. That was what it did for me. And that was how everything began."

"Personally," said the Big Ghost with an emphasis which contradicted the ordinary meaning of the word, "personally, I'd have thought you and I ought to be the other way round. That's my personal opinion."

"Very likely we soon shall be," said the other. "If you'll stop thinking about it."

"Look at me, now," said the Ghost, slapping its chest (but the slap made no noise). "I gone straight all my life. I don't say I was a religious man and I don't say I had no faults, far from it. But I done my best all my life, see? I done my best by everyone, that's the sort of chap I was. I never asked for anything that wasn't mine by rights. If I wanted a drink I paid for it and if I took my wages I done my job, see? That's the sort I was and I don't care who knows it."

"It would be much better not to go on about that now."

"Who's going on? I'm not arguing. I'm just telling you the sort of chap I was, see? I'm asking for nothing but my rights. You may think you can put me down because you're dressed up like that (which you weren't when you worked under me) and I'm only a poor man. But I got to have my rights same as you, see?"

"Oh no. It's not so bad as that. I haven't got my rights, or I should not be here. You will not get yours either. You'll get something far better. Never fear."

"That's just what I say. I haven't got my rights. I always done my best and I never done nothing wrong. And what I don't see is why I should be put below a bloody murderer like you."

"Who knows whether you will be? Only be happy and come with me."

"What do you keep on arguing for? I'm only telling you the sort of chap I am. I only want my rights. I'm not asking for anybody's bleeding charity."

"Then do. At once. Ask for the Bleeding Charity. Everything is here for the asking and nothing can be bought."

"That may be very well for you, I daresay. If they choose to let in a bloody murderer all because he makes a poor mouth at the last moment, that's their look out. But I don't see myself going in the same boat with you, see? Why should I? I don't want charity. I'm a decent man and if I had my rights I'd have been here long ago and you can tell them I said so."

The other shook his head. "You can never do it like that," he said. "Your feet will never grow hard enough to walk on our grass that way. You'd be tired out before we got to the mountains. And it isn't exactly true, you know." Mirth danced in his eyes as he said it.

"What isn't true?" asked the Ghost sulkily.

"You weren't a decent man and you didn't do your best. We none of us were and we none of us did. Lord bless you, it doesn't matter. There is no need to go into it all now."

"You!" gasped the Ghost. "*You* have the face to tell *me* I wasn't a decent chap?"

"Of course. Must I go into all that? I will tell you one thing to begin with. Murdering old Jack wasn't the worst thing I did. That was the work of a moment and I was half mad when I did it. But I murdered you in my heart, deliberately, for years. I used to lie awake at nights thinking what I'd do to you if ever I got the chance. That is why I have been sent to you now: to ask your forgiveness and to be your servant as long as you need one, and longer if it pleases you. I was the worst. But all the men who worked under you felt the same. You made it hard for us, you know. And you made it hard for your wife too and for your children."

"You mind your own business, young man," said the Ghost. "None of your lip, see? Because I'm not taking any impudence from you about my private affairs."

"There are no private affairs," said the other.

"And I'll tell you another thing," said the Ghost. "You can clear off, see? You're not wanted. I may be only a poor man but I'm not making pals with a murderer, let alone taking lessons from him. Made it hard for you and your like, did I? If I had you back there I'd show you what work is."

"Come and show me now," said the other with laughter in his voice. "It will be joy going to the mountains, but there will be plenty of work."

"You don't suppose I'd go with you?"

"Don't refuse. You will never get there alone. And I am the one who was sent to you."

"So that's the trick, is it?" shouted the Ghost, outwardly bitter, and yet I thought there was a kind of triumph in its voice. It had been entreated: it could make a refusal: and this seemed to it a kind of advantage. "I thought there'd be some damned nonsense. It's all a clique, all a bloody clique. To tell them I'm not coming, see? I'd rather be damned than go along with you. I came here to get my rights, see? Not to go snivelling along on charity tied onto your apron-strings. If they're too fine to have me without you, I'll go home." It was almost happy now that it could, in a sense, threaten. "That's what I'll do," it repeated, "I'll go home. I didn't come here to be treated like a dog. I'll go home. That's what I'll do. Damn and blast the whole pack of you . . ." In the end, still grumbling, but whimpering also a little as it picked its way over the sharp grasses, it made off.

5·

For a moment there was silence under the cedar trees and then
—*pad, pad, pad*—it was broken. Two velvet-footed lions came
bouncing into the open space, their eyes fixed upon each other,
and started playing some solemn romp. Their manes looked as if
they had been just dipped in the river whose noise I could hear
close at hand, though the trees hid it. Not greatly liking my company, I moved away to find that river, and after passing some thick
flowering bushes, I succeeded. The bushes came almost down to
the brink. It was as smooth as Thames but flowed swiftly like a
mountain stream: pale green where trees overhung it but so clear
that I could count the pebbles at the bottom. Close beside me I
saw another of the Bright People in conversation with a ghost. It
was that fat ghost with the cultured voice who had addressed me
in the bus, and it seemed to be wearing gaiters.

"My dear boy, I'm delighted to see you," it was saying to the
Spirit, who was naked and almost blindingly white. "I was talking to your poor father the other day and wondering where you
were."

"You didn't bring him?" said the other.

"Well, no. He lives a long way from the bus, and, to be quite
frank, he's been getting a little eccentric lately. A little difficult.
Losing his grip. He never was prepared to make any great efforts,
you know. If you remember, he used to go to sleep when you and
I got talking seriously! Ah, Dick, I shall never forget some of our
talks. I expect you've changed your views a bit since then. You
became rather narrow-minded towards the end of your life:
but no doubt you've broadened out again."

"How do you mean?"

"Well, it's obvious by now, isn't it, that you weren't quite right. Why, my dear boy, you were coming to believe in a literal Heaven and Hell!"

"But wasn't I right?"

"Oh, in a spiritual sense, to be sure. I still believe in them in that way. I am still, my dear boy, looking for the Kingdom. But nothing superstitious or mythological. . . ."

"Excuse me. Where do you imagine you've been?"

"Ah, I see. You mean that the grey town with its continual hope of morning (we must all live by hope, must we not?), with its field for indefinite progress, is, in a sense, Heaven, if only we have eyes to see it? That is a beautiful idea."

"I didn't mean that at all. Is it possible you don't know where you've been?"

"Now that you mention it, I don't think we ever do give it a name. What do you call it?"

"We call it Hell."

"There is no need to be profane, my dear boy. I may not be very orthodox, in your sense of that word, but I do feel that these matters ought to be discussed simply, and seriously, and reverently."

"Discuss Hell *reverently*? I meant what I said. You have been in Hell: though if you don't go back you may call it Purgatory."

"Go on, my dear boy, go on. That is *so* like you. No doubt you'll tell me why, on your view, I was sent there. I'm not angry."

"But don't you know? You went there because you are an apostate."

"Are you serious, Dick?"

"Perfectly."

"This is worse than I expected. Do you really think people are penalised for their honest opinions? Even assuming, for the sake of argument, that those opinions were mistaken."

"Do you really think there are no sins of intellect?"

"There are indeed, Dick. There is hide-bound prejudice, and intellectual dishonesty, and timidity, and stagnation. But honest opinions fearlessly followed—they are not sins."

"I know we used to talk that way. I did it too until the end of my life when I became what you call narrow. It all turns on what are honest opinions."

"Mine certainly were. They were not only honest but heroic. I asserted them fearlessly. When the doctrine of the Resurrection ceased to commend itself to the critical faculties which God had given me, I openly rejected it. I preached my famous sermon. I defied the whole chapter. I took every risk."

"What risk? What was at all likely to come of it except what actually came—popularity, sales for your books, invitations, and finally a bishopric?"

"Dick, this is unworthy of you. What are you suggesting?"

"Friend, I am not suggesting at all. You see, I *know* now. Let us be frank. Our opinions were not honestly come by. We simply found ourselves in contact with a certain current of ideas and plunged into it because it seemed modern and successful. At College, you know, we just started automatically writing the kind of essays that got good marks and saying the kind of things that won applause. When, in our whole lives, did we honestly face, in solitude, the one question on which all turned: whether after all the Supernatural might not in fact occur? When did we put up one moment's real resistance to the loss of our faith?"

"If this is meant to be a sketch of the genesis of liberal theology in general, I reply that it is a mere libel. Do you suggest that men like . . ."

"I have nothing to do with any generality. Nor with any man but me and you. Oh, as you love your own soul, remember. You know that you and I were playing with loaded dice. We didn't *want* the other to be true. We were afraid of crude salvationism, afraid of a breach with the spirit of the age, afraid of ridicule, afraid (above all) of real spiritual fears and hopes."

"I'm far from denying that young men may make mistakes. They may well be influenced by current fashions of thought. But it's not a question of how the opinions are formed. The point is that they were my honest opinions, sincerely expressed."

"Of course. Having allowed oneself to drift, unresisting, unpraying, accepting every half-conscious solicitation from our desires, we reached a point where we no longer believed the Faith.

Just in the same way, a jealous man, drifting and unresisting, reaches a point at which he believes lies about his best friend: a drunkard reaches a point at which (for the moment) he actually believes that another glass will do him no harm. The beliefs are sincere in the sense that they do occur as psychological events in the man's mind. If that's what you mean by sincerity they are sincere, and so were ours. But errors which are sincere in that sense are not innocent."

"You'll be justifying the Inquisition in a moment!"

"Why? Because the Middle Ages erred in one direction, does it follow that there is no error in the opposite direction?"

"Well, this is extremely interesting," said the Episcopal Ghost. "It's a point of view. Certainly, it's a point of view. In the meantime . . ."

"There is no meantime," replied the other. "All that is over. We are not playing now. I have been talking of the past (your past and mine) only in order that you may turn from it forever. One wrench and the tooth will be out. You can begin as if nothing had ever gone wrong. White as snow. It's all true, you know. He is in me, for you, with that power. And—I have come a long journey to meet you. You have seen Hell: you are in sight of Heaven. Will you, even now, repent and believe?"

"I'm not sure that I've got the exact point you are trying to make," said the ghost.

"I am not trying to make any point," said the Spirit. "I am telling you to repent and believe."

"But my dear boy, I believe already. We may not be perfectly agreed, but you have completely misjudged me if you do not realise that my religion is a very real and a very precious thing to me."

"Very well," said the other, as if changing his plan. "Will you believe in *me?*"

"In what sense?"

"Will you come with me to the mountains? It will hurt at first, until your feet are hardened. Reality is harsh to the feet of shadows. But will you come?"

"Well, that is a plan. I am perfectly ready to consider it. Of course I should require some assurances . . . I should want a guarantee that you are taking me to a place where I shall find a wider sphere of usefulness—and scope for the talents that God has given me—and an atmosphere of free inquiry—in short, all that one means by civilisation and—er—the spiritual life."

"No," said the other. "I can promise you none of these things. No sphere of usefulness: you are not needed there at all. No scope for your talents: only forgiveness for having perverted them. No atmosphere of inquiry, for I will bring you to the land not of questions but of answers, and you shall see the face of God."

"Ah, but we must all interpret those beautiful words in our own way! For me there is no such thing as a final answer. The free wind of inquiry must *always* continue to blow through the mind, must it not? 'Prove all things' . . . to travel hopefully is better than to arrive."

"If that were true, and known to be true, how could anyone travel hopefully? There would be nothing to hope for."

"But you must feel yourself that there is something stifling about the idea of finality? Stagnation, my dear boy, what is more soul-destroying than stagnation?"

"You think that, because hitherto you have experienced truth only with the abstract intellect. I will bring you where you can taste it like honey and be embraced by it as by a bridegroom. Your thirst shall be quenched."

"Well, really, you know, I am not aware of a thirst for some ready-made truth which puts an end to intellectual activity in the way you seem to be describing. Will it leave me the free play of Mind, Dick? I must insist on that, you know."

"Free, as a man is free to drink while he is drinking. He is not free still to be dry." The Ghost seemed to think for a moment. "I can make nothing of that idea," it said.

"Listen!" said the White Spirit. "Once you were a child. Once you knew what inquiry was for. There was a time when you asked questions because you wanted answers, and were glad when you had found them. Become that child again: even now."

"Ah, but when I became a man I put away childish things."

"You have gone far wrong. Thirst was made for water; inquiry for truth. What you now call the free play of inquiry has neither more nor less to do with the ends for which intelligence was given you than masturbation has to do with marriage."

"If we cannot be reverent, there is at least no need to be obscene. The suggestion that I should return at my age to the mere factual inquisitiveness of boyhood strikes me as preposterous. In any case, that question-and-answer conception of thought only applies to matters of fact. Religious and speculative questions are surely on a different level."

"We know nothing of religion here: we think only of Christ. We know nothing of speculation. Come and see. I will bring you to Eternal Fact, the Father of all other facthood."

"I should object very strongly to describing God as a 'fact.' The Supreme Value would surely be a less inadequate description. It is hardly . . ."

"Do you not even believe that He exists?"

"Exists? What does Existence mean? You *will* keep on implying some sort of static, ready-made reality which is, so to speak, 'there,' and to which our minds have simply to conform. These great mysteries cannot be approached in that way. If there were such a thing (there is no need to interrupt, my dear boy) quite frankly, I should not be interested in it. It would be of no *religious* significance. God, for me, is something purely spiritual. The spirit of sweetness and light and tolerance—and, er, service, Dick, service. We mustn't forget that, you know."

"If the thirst of the Reason is really dead . . . ," said the Spirit, and then stopped as though pondering. Then suddenly he said, "Can you, at least, still desire happiness?"

"Happiness, my dear Dick," said the Ghost placidly, "happiness, as you will come to see when you are older, lies in the path of duty. Which reminds me. . . . Bless my soul, I'd nearly forgotten. Of course I can't come with you. I have to be back next Friday to read a paper. We have a little Theological Society down there. Oh yes! there is plenty of intellectual life. Not of a very high quality, perhaps. One notices a certain lack of grip—a certain confusion of mind. That is where I can be of some use to them. There are even regrettable jealousies. . . . I don't know why, but tempers seem less controlled than they used to be. Still, one mustn't expect too much of human nature. I feel I can do a great work among them. But you've never asked me what my paper is about! I'm taking the text about growing up to the measure of the stature of Christ and working out an idea which I feel sure you'll be interested in. I'm going to point out how people always forget that Jesus (here the Ghost bowed) was a comparatively young man when he died. He would have outgrown some of his earlier views, you know, if he'd lived. As he might have done, with a little more tact and patience. I am going to ask my audience to consider what his mature views would have been. A profoundly interesting question. What a different Christianity we might have had if only the Founder had reached his full stature! I shall end up by pointing out how this deepens the significance of the Crucifixion. One feels for the first time what a disaster it was: what a tragic waste . . . so much promise cut short. Oh, must you be going? Well, so must I. Goodbye, my dear boy. It has been a great pleasure. Most stimulating and provocative. Goodbye, goodbye, goodbye."

The Ghost nodded its head and beamed on the Spirit with a bright clerical smile—or with the best approach to it which such unsubstantial lips could manage—and then turned away humming softly to itself "City of God, how broad and far."

But I did not watch him long, for a new idea had just occurred to me. If the grass were hard as rock, I thought, would not the water be hard enough to walk on? I tried it with one foot, and my foot did not go in. Next moment I stepped boldly out on the surface. I fell on my face at once and got some nasty bruises. I had forgotten that though it was, to me, solid, it was not the less in rapid motion. When I had picked myself up I was about thirty yards further down-stream than the point where I had left the bank. But this did not prevent me from walking up-stream: it only meant that by walking very fast indeed I made very little progress.

6.

The cool smooth skin of the bright water was delicious to my feet and I walked on it for about an hour, making perhaps a couple of hundred yards. Then the going became different. The current grew swifter. Great flakes or islands of foam came swirling down towards me, bruising my shins like stones if I did not get out of their way. The surface became uneven, rounded itself into lovely hollows and elbows of water which distorted the appearance of the pebbles on the bottom and threw me off my balance, so that I had to scramble to shore. But as the banks hereabouts consisted of great flat stones, I continued my journey without much hurt to my feet. An immense yet lovely noise vibrated through the forest. Hours later I rounded a bend and saw the explanation.

Before me green slopes made a wide amphitheatre, enclosing a frothy and pulsating lake into which, over many-coloured rocks, a waterfall was pouring. Here once again I realised that something had happened to my senses so that they were now receiving impressions which would normally exceed their capacity. On earth, such a waterfall could not have been perceived at all as a whole; it was too big. Its sound would have been a terror in the woods for twenty miles. Here, after the first shock, my sensibility "took" both, as a well-built ship takes a huge wave. I exulted. The noise, though gigantic, was like giant's laughter: like the revelry of a whole college of giants together laughing, dancing, singing, roaring at their high works.

Near the place where the fall plunged into the lake there grew a tree. Wet with the spray, half-veiled in foam-bows, flashing with the bright, innumerable birds that flew among its branches, it rose in many shapes of billowy foliage, huge as a fen-land cloud. From every point apples of gold gleamed through the leaves.

Suddenly my attention was diverted by a curious appearance in the foreground. A hawthorn bush not twenty yeards away seemed to be behaving oddly. Then I saw that it was not the bush but something standing close to the bush and on this side of it. Finally I realised that it was one of the Ghosts. It was crouching as if to conceal itself from something beyond the bush, and it was looking back at me and making signals. It kept on signing to me to duck down. As I could not see what the danger was, I stood fast.

Presently the Ghost, after peering around in every direction, ventured beyond the hawthorn bush. It could not get on very fast because of the torturing grasses beneath its feet, but it was obvi-ously going as fast as it possibly could straight for another tree. There it stopped again, standing straight upright against the trunk as though it were taking cover. Because the shadow of the branches now covered it, I could see it better: it was my bowler-hatted companion, the one whom the Big ghost had called Ikey. After it had stood panting at the tree for about ten minutes and carefully reconnoitred the ground ahead, it made a dash for an-other tree—such a dash as was possible to it. In this way, with in-finite labour and caution, it had reached the great Tree in about an hour. That is, it had come within ten yards of it.

Here it was checked. Round the Tree grew a belt of lilies: to the Ghost an insurperable obstacle. It might as well have tried to tread down an anti-tank trap as to walk on them. It lay down and tried to crawl between them but they grew too close and they would not bend. And all the time it was apparently haunted by the terror of discovery. At every whisper of the wind it stopped and cowered: once, at the cry of a bird, it struggled back to its last place of cover: but then desire hounded it out again and it crawled once more to the Tree. I saw it clasp its hands and writhe in the agony of its frustration.

The wind seemed to be rising. I saw the Ghost wring its hands and put its thumb into its mouth—cruelly pinched, I doubt not, between two stems of the lilies when the breeze swayed them.

Then came a real gust. The branches of the Tree began to toss. A moment later and half a dozen apples had fallen round the Ghost and on it. He gave a sharp cry, but suddenly checked it. I thought the weight of the golden fruit where it had fallen on him would have disabled him: and certainly, for a few minutes, he was unable to rise. He lay whimpering, nursing his wounds. But soon he was at work again. I could see him feverishly trying to fill his pockets with the apples. Of course it was useless. One could see how his ambitions were gradually forced down. He gave up the idea of a pocketful: two would have to do. He gave up the idea of two, he would take one, the largest. He gave up that hope. He was not looking for the smallest one. He was trying to find if there was one small enough to carry.

The amazing thing was that he succeeded. When I remembered what the leaf had felt like when I tried to lift it, I could hardly help admiring this unhappy creature when I saw him rise staggering to his feet actually holding the smallest of the apples in his hands. He was lame from his hurts, and the weight bent him double. Yet even so, inch by inch, still availing himself of every scrap of cover, he set out on his *via dolorosa* to the bus, carrying his torture.

"Fool. Put it down," said a great voice suddenly. It was quite unlike any other voice I had heard so far. It was a thunderous yet liquid voice. With an appalling certainty I knew that the waterfall itself was speaking: and I saw now (though it did not cease to look like a waterfall) that it was also a bright angel who stood, like one crucified, against the rocks and poured himself perpetually down towards the forest with loud joy.

"Fool," he said, "put it down. You cannot take it back. There is not room for it in Hell. Stay here and learn to eat such apples. The very leaves and the blades of grass in the wood will delight to teach you."

Whether the Ghost heard or not, I don't know. At any rate, after pausing for a few minutes, it braced itself anew for its agonies and continued with even greater caution till I lost sight of it.

7.

Although I watched the misfortunes of the Ghost in the Bowler with some complacency, I found, when we were left alone, that I could not bear the presence of the Water-Giant. It did not appear to take any notice of me, but I became self-conscious; and I rather think there was some assumed nonchalance in my movements as I walked away over the flat rocks, down-stream again. I was beginning to be tired. Looking at the silver fish which darted over the river-bed, I wished greatly that to me also that water were permeable. I should have liked a dip.

"Thinking of going back?" said a voice close at hand. I turned and saw a tall ghost standing with its back against a tree, chewing a ghostly cheroot. It was that of a lean hard-bitten man with grey hair and a gruff, but not uneducated voice: the kind of man I have always instinctively felt to be reliable.

"I don't know," said I. "Are you?"

"Yes," it replied. "I guess I've seen about all there is to see."

"You don't think of staying?"

"That's all propaganda," it said. "Of course there never was any question of our staying. You can't eat the fruit and you can't drink the water and it takes you all your time to walk on the grass. A human being couldn't live here. All that idea of staying is only an advertisement stunt."

"Then why did you come?"

"Oh, I don't know. Just to have a look round. I'm the sort of chap who likes to see things for himself. Wherever I've been I've always had a look at anything that was being cracked up. When I was out East, I went to see Pekin. When . . ."

"What was Pekin like?"

143

"Nothing to it. Just one darn wall inside another. Just a trap for tourists. I've been pretty well everywhere. Niagara Falls, the Pyramids, Salt Lake City, the Taj Mahal. . . ."

"What was *it* like?"

"Not worth looking at. They're all advertisement stunts. All run by the same people. There's a combine, you know, a World Combine, that just takes an Atlas and decides where they'll have a Sight. Doesn't matter what they choose: anything'll do as long as the publicity's properly managed."

"And you've lived—er—*down there*—in the Town—for some time?"

"In what they call Hell? Yes. It's a flop too. They lead you to expect red fire and devils and all sorts of interesting people sizzling on grids—Henry VIII and all that—but when you get there it's just like any other town."

"I prefer it up here," said I.

"Well, I don't see what all the talk is about," said the Hard-Bitten Ghost. "It's as good as any other park to look at, and darned uncomfortable."

"There seems to be some idea that if one stays here one would get—well, solider—grow acclimatised."

"I know all about that," said the Ghost. "Same old lie. People have been telling me that sort of thing all my life. They told me in the nursery that if I were good I'd be happy. And they told me at school that Latin would get easier as I went on. After I'd been married a month some fool was telling me that there were always difficulties at first, but with Tact and Patience I'd soon 'settle down' and like it! And all through two wars what didn't they say about the good time coming if only I'd be a brave boy and go on being shot at? Of course they'll play the old game here if anyone's fool enough to listen."

"But who are They? This might be run by someone different?"

"Entirely new management, eh? Don't you believe it! It's never a new management. You'll always find the same old Ring. I know all about dear, kind Mummie coming up to your bedroom and getting all she wants to know out of you: but you always found she and Father were the same firm really. Didn't we find that both sides in all the wars were run by the same Armament Firms?

or the same Firm, which is behind the Jews and the Vatican and the Dictators and the Democracies and all the rest of it. All this stuff up here is run by the same people as the Town. They're just laughing at us."

"I thought they were at war?"

"Of course you did. That's the official version. But who's ever seen any signs of it? Oh, I know that's how they *talk*. But if there's a real war why don't they do anything? Don't you see that if the official version were true these chaps up here would attack and sweep the Town out of existence? They've got the strength. If they wanted to rescue *us* they could do it. But obviously the last thing they want is to end their so-called 'war.' The whole game depends on keeping it going."

This account of the matter struck me as uncomfortably plausible. I said nothing.

"Anyway," said the Ghost, "who wants to be rescued? What the hell would there be to *do* here?"

"Or there?" said I.

"Quite," said the Ghost. "They've got you either way."

"What would you like to do if you had your choice?" I asked.

"There you go!" said the Ghost with a certain triumph. "Asking *me* to make a plan. It's up to the Management to find something that doesn't bore us, isn't it? It's their job. Why should we do it for them? That's just where all the parsons and moralists have got the thing upside down. They keep on asking *us* to alter ourselves. But if the people who run the show are so clever and so powerful, why don't they find something to suit their public? All this poppycock about growing harder so that the grass doesn't hurt our feet, now! There's an example. What would you say if you went to a hotel where the eggs were all bad; and when you complained to the Boss, instead of apologising and changing his dairyman, he just told you that if you tried you'd get to like bad eggs in time?"

"Well, I'll be getting along," said the Ghost after a short silence. "You coming my way?"

"There doesn't seem to be much point in going anywhere on your showing," I replied. A great depression had come over me. "And at least it's not raining here."

"Not at the moment," said the Hard-Bitten Ghost. "But I never saw one of these bright mornings that didn't turn to rain later on. And, by gum, when it does rain here! Ah, you hadn't thought of that? It hadn't occurred to you that with the sort of water they have here every raindrop will make a hole in you, like a machine-gun bullet. That's their little joke, you see. First of all tantalise you with ground you can't walk on and water you can't drink and then drill you full of holes. But they won't catch *me* that way."

A few minutes later he moved off.

8.

I sat still on a stone by the river's side feeling as miserable as I ever felt in my life. Hitherto it had not occurred to me to doubt the intentions of the Solid People, nor to question the essential goodness of their country even if it were a country which I could not long inhabit. It had indeed once crossed my mind that if these Solid People were as benevolent as I had heard one or two of them claim to be, they might have done something to help the inhabitants of the Town—something more than meeting them on the plain. Now a terrible explanation came into my mind. How if they had never meant to do us good at all? How if this whole trip were allowed the Ghosts merely to mock them? Horrible myths and doctrines stirred in my memory. I thought how the Gods had punished Tantalus. I thought of the place in the Book of Revelation where it says that the smoke of Hell goes up forever in the sight of the blessed spirits. I remembered how poor Cowper, dreaming that he was not after all doomed to perdition, at once knew the dream to be false and said, "These are the sharpest arrows in His quiver." And what the Hard-Bitten Ghost had said about the rain was clearly true. Even a shower of dew-drops from a branch might tear me in pieces. I had not thought of this before. And how easily I might have ventured into the spray of the waterfall!

The sense of danger, which had never been entirely absent since I left the bus, awoke with sharp urgency. I gazed around on the trees, the flowers, and the talking cataract: they had begun to look unbearably sinister. Bright insects darted to and fro. If one of those were to fly into my face, would it not go right through me? If it settled on my head, would it crush me to earth? Terror

147

whispered, "This is no place for you." I remembered also the lions.

With no very clear plan in my mind, I rose and began walking away from the river in the direction where the trees grew closest together. I had not fully made up my mind to go back to the bus, but I wanted to avoid open places. If only I could find a trace of evidence that it was really possible for a Ghost to stay—that the choice were not only a cruel comedy—I would not go back. In the meantime I went on, gingerly, and keeping a sharp look-out. In about half an hour I came to a little clearing with some bushes in the centre. As I stopped, wondering if I dared cross it, I realised that I was not alone.

A Ghost hobbled across the clearing—as quickly as it could on that uneasy soil—looking over its shoulder as if it were pursued. I saw that it had been a woman: a well-dressed woman, I thought, but its shadows of finery looked ghastly in the morning light. It was making for the bushes. It could not really get in among them—the twigs and leaves were too hard—but it pressed as close up against them as it could. It seemed to believe it was hiding.

A moment later I heard the sound of feet, and one of the Bright People came in sight: one always noticed that sound there, for we Ghosts made no noise when we walked.

"Go away!" squealed the Ghost. "Go away! Can't you see I want to be alone?"

"But you need help," said the Solid One.

"If you have the least trace of decent feeling left," said the Ghost, "you'll keep away. I don't want help. I want to be left alone. Do go away. You know I can't walk fast enough on these horrible spikes to get away from you. It's abominable of you to take advantage."

"Oh, that!" said the Spirit. "That'll soon come right. But you're going in the wrong direction. It's back there—to the mountains—you need to go. You can lean on me all the way. I can't absolutely *carry* you, but you need have almost no weight on your own feet: and it will hurt less at every step."

"I'm not afraid of being hurt. You know that."

"Then what is the matter?"

"Can't you understand *anything*? Do you really suppose I'm going out there among all those people, like *this*?"

"But why not?"

"I'd never have come at all if I'd known you were all going to be dressed like that."

"Friend, you see I'm not dressed at all."

"I didn't mean that. Do go away."

"But can't you even tell me?"

"If you can't understand, there'd be no good trying to explain it. How *can* I go out like this among a lot of people with real solid bodies? It's far worse than going out with nothing on would have been on earth. Have everyone staring *through* me."

"Oh, I see. But we were all a bit ghostly when we first arrived, you know. That'll wear off. Just come out and try."

"But they'll *see* me."

"What does it matter if they do?"

"I'd rather die."

"But you've died already. There's no good trying to go back to that."

The Ghost made a sound something between a sob and a snarl. "I wish I'd never been born," it said. "What *are* we born for?"

"For infinite happiness," said the Spirit. "You can step out into it at any moment. . . ."

"But, I tell you, they'll *see* me."

"An hour hence and you will not care. A day hence and you will laugh at it. Don't you remember on earth—there were things too hot to touch with your finger but you could drink them all right? Shame is like that. If you will accept it—if you will drink the cup to the bottom—you will find it very nourishing: but try to do anything else with it and it scalds."

"You really mean? . . ." said the Ghost, and then paused. My suspense was strained up to the height. I felt that my own destiny hung on her reply. I could have fallen at her feet and begged her to yield.

"Yes," said the Spirit. "Come and try."

Almost, I thought the Ghost had obeyed. Certainly it had moved: but suddenly it cried out: "No, I can't. I tell you I can't. For a moment, while you were talking, I almost thought . . .

but when it comes to the point. . . . You've no right to ask me to do a thing like that. It's disgusting. I should never forgive myself if I did. Never, never. And it's not fair. They ought to have warned us. I'd never have come. And now—please, please go away!"

"Friend," said the Spirit. "Could you, only for a moment, fix your mind on something not yourself?"

"I've already given you my answer," said the Ghost, coldly but still tearful.

"Then only one expedient remains," said the Spirit, and to my great surprise he set a horn to his lips and blew. I put my hands over my ears. The earth seemed to shake: the whole wood trembled and dindled at the sound. I suppose there must have been a pause after that (though there seemed to be none) before I heard the thudding of hoofs—far off at first, but already nearer before I had well identified it, and soon so near that I began to look about for some place of safety. Before I had found one the danger was all about us. A herd of unicorns came thundering through the glades: twenty-seven hands high the smallest of them and white as swans but for the red gleam in eyes and nostrils and the flashing indigo of their horns. I can still remember the squelching noise of the soft wet turf under their hoofs, the breaking of the undergrowth, the snorting and the whinnyings; how their hind legs went up and their horned heads down in mimic battle. Even then I wondered for what real battle it might be the rehearsal. I heard the Ghost scream, and I think it made a bolt away from the bushes . . . perhaps toards the Spirit, but I don't know. For my own nerve failed and I fled, not heeding, for the moment, the horrible going underfoot, and not once daring to pause. So I never saw the end of that interview.

9.

"Where are ye going?" said a voice with a strong Scotch accent. I stopped and looked. The sound of the unicorns had long since died away and my flight had brought me to open country. I saw the mountains where the unchanging sunrise lay, and in the foreground two or three pines on a little knoll, with some large smooth rocks, and heather. On one of the rocks sat a very tall man, almost a giant, with a flowing beard. I had not yet looked one of the Solid People in the face. Now, when I did so, I discovered that one sees them with a kind of double vision. Here was an enthroned and shining god, whose ageless spirit weighed upon mine like a burden of solid gold: and yet, at the very same moment, here was an old weather-beaten man, one who might have been a shepherd—such a man as tourists think simple because he is honest and neighbours think "deep" for the same reason. His eyes had the far-seeing look of one who has lived long in open, solitary places; and somehow I divined the network of wrinkles which must have surrounded them before re-birth had washed him in immortality.

"I—I don't quite know," said I.

"Ye can sit and talk to me, then," he said, making room for me on the stone.

"I don't know you, Sir," said I, taking my seat beside him.

"My name is George," he answered. "George Macdonald."

"Oh!" I cried. "Then you can tell me! You at least will not deceive me." Then, supposing that these expressions of confidence needed some explanation, I tried, trembling, to tell this man all that his writings had done for me. I tried to tell how a certain frosty afternoon at Leatherhead Station when I first bought a copy of *Phantastes* (being then about sixteen years old) had been to me what the first sight of Beatrice had been to Dante: *Here begins the New Life*. I started to confess how long that Life had delayed in the region of imagination merely: how slowly and reluctantly I had come to admit that his Christendom had more than an accidental connexion with it, how hard I had tried not to see that the true name of the quality which first met me in his books is Holiness. He laid his hand on mine and stopped me.

"Son," he said, "your love—all love—is of inexpressible value to me. But it may save precious time" (here he suddenly looked very Scotch) "if I inform ye that I am already well acquainted with these biographical details. In fact, I have noticed that your memory misleads you in one or two particulars."

"Oh!" said I, and became still.

"Ye had started," said my Teacher, "to talk of something more profitable."

"Sir," said I, "I had almost forgotten it, and I have no anxiety about the answer now, though I have still a curiosity. It is about these Ghosts. *Do* any of them stay? *Can* they stay? Is any real choice offered to them? How do they come to be here?"

"Did ye never hear of the *Refrigerium?* A man with your advantages might have read of it in Prudentius, not to mention Jeremy Taylor."

"The name is familiar, Sir, but I'm afraid I've forgotten what it means."

"It means that the damned have holidays—excursions, ye understand."

"Excursions to *this* country?"

"For those that will take them. Of course most of the silly creatures don't. They prefer taking trips back to Earth. They go and play tricks on the poor daft women ye call mediums. They go and try to assert their ownership of some house that once belonged to them: and then ye get what's called a Haunting. Or they go to spy on their children. Or literary ghosts hang about public libraries to see if anyone's still reading their books."

"But if they come here they can really stay?"

"Aye. Ye'll have heard that the emperor Trajan did."

"But I don't understand. Is judgment not final? Is there really a way out of Hell into Heaven?"

"It depends on the way ye're using the words. If they leave that grey town behind it will not have been Hell. To any that leaves it, it is Purgatory. And perhaps ye had better not call this country Heaven. Not *Deep Heaven,* ye understand." (Here he smiled at me.) "Ye can call it the Valley of the Shadow of Life. And yet to those who stay here it will have been Heaven from the first. And ye can call those sad streets in the town yonder the Valley of the Shadow of Death: but to those who remain there they will have been Hell even from the beginning."

I suppose he saw that I looked puzzled, for presently he spoke again.

"Son," he said, "ye cannot in your present state understand eternity: when Anodos looked through the door of the Timeless he brought no message back. But ye can get some likeness of it if ye say that both good and evil, when they are full grown, become retrospective. Not only this valley but all this earthly past will have been Heaven to those who are saved. Not only the twilight in that town, but all their life on earth too, will then be seen by the damned to have been Hell. That is what mortals misunderstand. They say of some temporal suffering, 'No future bliss can make up for it,' not knowing that Heaven, once attained, will work backwards and turn even that agony into a glory. And of some sinful pleasure they say 'Let me but have *this* and I'll take the consequences': little dreaming how damnation will spread back and back into their past and contaminate the pleasure of the sin. Both processes begin even before death. The good man's past begins to change so that his forgiven sins and remembered sorrows take on the quality of Heaven: the bad man's past already conforms to his badness and is filled only with dreariness. And that is why, at the end of all things, when the sun rises here and the twilight turns to blackness down there, the Blessed will say, 'We have never lived anywhere except in Heaven,' and the Lost, 'We were always in Hell.' And both will speak truly."

"Is not that very hard, Sir?"

"I mean, that is the real sense of what they will say. In the actual language of the Lost, the words will be different, no doubt. One will say he has always served his country right or wrong; and another that he has sacrificed everything to his Art; and some that they've never been taken in, and some that, thank God, they've always looked after Number One, and nearly all, that, at least they've been true to themselves."

"And the Saved?"

"Ah, the Saved . . . what happens to them is best described as the opposite of a mirage. What seemed, when they entered it, to be the vale of misery turns out, when they look back, to have been a well; and where present experience saw only salt deserts memory truthfully records that the pools were full of water."

"Then those people are right who say that Heaven and Hell are only states of mind?"

"Hush," said he sternly. "Do not blaspheme. Hell is a state of mind—ye never said a truer word. And every state of mind, left to itself, every shutting up of the creature within the dungeon of its own mind—is, in the end, Hell. But Heaven is not a state of mind. Heaven is reality itself. All that is fully real is Heavenly. For all that can be shaken will be shaken and only the unshakable remains."

"But there is a real choice after death? My Roman Catholic friends would be surprised, for to them souls in Purgatory are already saved. And my Protestant friends would like it no better, for they'd say that the tree lies as it falls."

"They're both right, maybe. Do not fash yourself with such questions. Ye cannot fully understand the relations of choice and Time till you are beyond both. And ye were not brought here to study such curiosities. What concerns you is the nature of the choice itself: and that ye can watch them making."

"Well, Sir," I said, "that also needs explaining. What do they choose, these souls who go back (I have yet seen no others)? And how *can* they choose it?"

"Milton was right," said my Teacher. "The choice of every lost soul can be expressed in the words 'Better to reign in Hell than serve in Heaven.' There is always something they insist on keeping, even at the price of misery. There is always something they prefer to joy—that is, to reality. Ye see it easily enough in a spoiled child that would sooner miss its play and its supper than say it was sorry and be friends. Ye call it the Sulks. But in adult life it has a hundred fine names—Achilles' wrath and Coriolanus' grandeur, Revenge and Injured Merit and Self-Respect and Tragic Greatness and Proper Pride."

"Then is no one lost through the undignified vices, Sir? Through mere sensuality?"

"Some are no doubt. The sensualist, I'll allow ye, begins by pursuing a real pleasure, though a small one. His sin is the less. But the time comes on when, though the pleasure becomes less and less and the craving fiercer and fiercer, and though he knows that joy can never come that way, yet he prefers to joy the mere fondling of unappeasable lust and would not have it taken from him. He'd fight to the death to keep it. He'd like well to be able to scratch: but even when he can scratch no more he'd rather itch than not."

He was silent for a few minutes, and then began again.

"Ye'll understand, there are innumerable forms of this choice. Sometimes forms that one hardly thought of at all on earth. There was a creature came here not long ago and went back—Sir Archibald they called him. In his earthly life he'd been interested in nothing but Survival. He'd written a whole shel-full of books about it. He began by being philosophical, but in the end he took up Psychical Research. It grew to be his only occupation—experimenting, lecturing, running a magazine. And travelling too: digging out queer stories among Thibetan lamas and being initiated into brotherhoods in Central Africa. Proofs—and more proofs—and then more proofs again—were what he wanted. It drove him mad if ever he saw anyone taking an interest in anything else. He got into trouble during one of your wars for running up and down the country telling them not to fight because it wasted a lot of money that ought to be spent on Research. Well, in good time, the poor creature died and came here: and there was no power in the universe would have prevented him staying and going on to the mountains. But do ye think that did him any good? This country was no use to him at all. Everyone here had 'survived' already. Nobody took the least interest in the question. There was nothing more to prove. His occupation was clean gone. Of course if he would only have admitted that he'd mistaken the means for the end and had a good laugh at himself he could have begun all over again like a little child and entered into joy. But he would not do that. He cared nothing about joy. In the end he went away."

"How fantastic!" said I.

"Do ye think so?" said the Teacher with a piercing glance. "It is nearer to such as you than ye think. There have been men before now who got so interested in proving the existence of God that they came to care nothing for God Himself . . . as if the good Lord had nothing to do but *exist!* There have been some who were so occupied in spreading Christianity that they never gave a thought to Christ. Man! Ye see it in smaller matters. Did ye never know a lover of books that with all his first editions and signed copies had lost the power to read them? Or an organiser of charities that had lost all love for the poor? It is the subtlest of all the snares."

Moved by a desire to change the subject, I asked why the Solid People, since they were full of love, did not go down into Hell to rescue the Ghosts. Why were they content simply to meet them on the plain? One would have expected a more militant charity.

"Ye will understand that better, perhaps, before ye go," said he. "In the meantime, I must tell ye they have come further for the sake of the Ghosts than ye can understand. Every one of us lives only to journey further and further into the mountains. Every one of us has interrupted that journey and retraced immeasurable distances to come down today on the mere chance of saving some Ghosts. Of course it is also joy to do so, but ye cannot blame us for that! And it would be no use to come further even if it were possible. The sane would do no good if they made themselves mad to help madmen."

"But what of the poor Ghosts who never get into the omnibus at all?"

"Everyone who wishes it does. Never fear. There are only two kinds of people in the end: those who say to God, 'Thy will be done,' and those to whom God says, in the end, '*Thy* will be done.' All that are in Hell, choose it. Without that self-choice there could be no Hell. No soul that seriously and constantly desires joy will ever miss it. Those who seek find. To those who knock it is opened."

At this moment we were suddenly interrupted by the thin voice of a Ghost talking at an enormous speed. Looking behind us we saw the creature. It was addressing one of the Solid People and was doing so too busily to notice us. Every now and then the Solid Spirit tried to get in a word but without success. The Ghost's talk was like this:

"Oh, my dear, I've had such a dreadful time, I don't know how I ever got here at all, I was coming with Elinor Stone and we'd arranged the whole thing and we were to meet at the corner of Sink Street; I made it perfectly plain because I knew what she was like and if I told her once I told her a hundred times I would *not* meet her outside that dreadful Marjoribanks woman's house, not after the way she'd treated me . . . that was one of the most dreadful things that happened to me; I've been dying to tell you because I felt sure you'd tell me I acted rightly; no, wait a moment, dear, till I've told you—I tried living with her when I first came and it was all fixed up, she was to do the cooking and I was to look after the house and I *did* think I was going to be comfortable after all I'd been through but she turned out to be *so* changed, absolutely selfish, and not a particle of sympathy for anyone but herself—and as I once said to her 'I *do* think I'm entitled to a little consideration because you at least lived out your time, but I oughtn't to have been here for years and years yet'—but of course I'm forgetting you don't know—I was murdered, simply murdered, dear, that man should never have operated, I ought to be alive to-day and they simply *starved* me in that dreadful nursing home and no one ever came near me and . . ."

The shrill monotonous whine died away as the speaker, still accompanied by the bright patience at her side, moved out of hearing.

"What troubles ye, son?" asked my Teacher.

"I am troubled, Sir," said I, "because that unhappy creature doesn't seem to me to be the sort of soul that ought to be even in danger of damnation. She isn't wicked: she's only a silly, garrulous old woman who has got into a habit of grumbling, and one feels that a little kindness, and rest, and change would put her all right."

"That is what she once was. That is maybe what she still is. If so, she certainly will be cured. But the whole question is whether she *is* now a grumbler."

"I should have thought there was no doubt about that!"

"Aye, but ye misunderstand me. The question is whether she is a grumbler, or only a grumble. If there is a real woman—even the least trace of one—still there inside the grumbling, it can be brought to life again. If there's one wee spark under all those ashes, we'll blow it till the whole pile is red and clear. But if there's nothing but ashes we'll not go on blowing them in our own eyes forever. They must be swept up."

"But how can there be a grumble without a grumbler?"

"The whole difficulty of understanding Hell is that the thing to be understood is so nearly Nothing. But ye'll have had experiences . . . it begins with a grumbling mood, and yourself still distinct from it: perhaps criticising it. And yourself, in a dark hour, may will that mood, embrace it. Ye can repent and come out of it again. But there may come a day when you can do that no longer. Then there will be no *you* left to criticise the mood, nor even to enjoy it, but just the grumble itself going on forever like a machine. But come! Ye are here to watch and listen. Lean on my arm and we will go for a little walk."

I obeyed. To lean on the arm of someone older than myself was an experience that carried me back to childhood, and with this support I found the going tolerable: so much so, indeed, that I flattered myself my feet were already growing more solid, until a glance at the poor transparent shapes convinced me that I owed all this ease to the strong arm of the Teacher. Perhaps it was because of his presence that my other senses also appeared to be quickened. I noticed scents in the air which had hitherto escaped me, and the country put on new beauties. There was water everywhere the tiny flowers quivering in the early breeze. Far off in the woods we saw the deer glancing past, and, once, a sleek panther came purring to my companion's side. We also saw many of the Ghosts.

I think the most pitiable was a female Ghost. Her trouble was the very opposite of that which afflicted the other, the lady frightened by the Unicorns. This one seemed quite unaware of her phantasmal appearance. More than one of the Solid People tried to talk to her, and at first I was quite at a loss to understand her behaviour to them. She appeared to be contorting her all but invisible face and writhing her smokelike body in a quite meaningless fashion. At last I came to the conclusion—incredible as it seemed—that she supposed herself still capable of attracting them and was trying to do so. She was a thing that had become incapable of conceiving conversation save as a means to that end. If a corpse already liquid with decay had arisen from the coffin, smeared its gums with lipstick, and attempted a flirtation, the result could not have been more appalling. In the end she muttered "Stupid creatures," and turned back to the bus.

This put me in mind to ask my Teacher what he thought of the affair with the Unicorns. "It will maybe have succeeded," he said. "Ye will have divined that he meant to frighten her; not that fear itself could make her less a Ghost, but if it took her mind a moment off herself, there might, in that moment, be a chance. I have seen them saved so."

We met several Ghosts that had come so near to Heaven only in order to tell the Celestials about Hell. Indeed this is one of the commonest types. Others, who had perhaps been (like myself) teachers of some kind actually wanted to give lectures about it: they brought fat notebooks full of statistics, and maps, and (one of them) a magic lantern. Some wanted to tell anecdotes of the notorious sinners of all ages whom they had met below. But the most part seemed to think that the mere fact of having contrived for themselves so much misery gave them a kind of superiority. "You have led a sheltered life!" they bawled. "You don't know the seamy side. We'll tell you. We'll give you some hard facts"—as if to tinge Heaven with infernal images and colours had been the only purpose for which they came. All alike, so far as I could judge from my own exploration of the lower world, were wholly unreliable, and all equally incurious about the country in which they had arrived. They repelled every attempt to teach them, and when they found that nobody listened to them they went back, one by one, to the bus.

This curious wish to describe Hell turned out, however, to be only the mildest form of a desire very common among the Ghosts—the desire to *extend* Hell, to bring it bodily, if they could, into Heaven. There were tub-thumping Ghosts who in thin, batlike voices urged the blessed spirits to shake off their fetters, to escape from their imprisonment in happiness, to tear down the mountains with their hands, to seize Heaven "for their own": Hell offered her co-operation. There were planning Ghosts who implored them to dam the river, cut down the trees, kill the animals, build a mountain railway, smooth out the horrible grass and moss and heather with asphalt. There were materialistic Ghosts who informed the immortals that they were deluded: there was no life after death, and this whole country was a hallucination. There were Ghosts, plain and simple: mere bogies, fully conscious of their own decay, who had accepted the traditional rôle of the spectre, and seemed to hope they could frighten someone. I had had no idea that this desire was possible. But my Teacher reminded me that the pleasure of frightening is by no means unknown on earth, and also of Tacitus' saying: "They terrify lest they should fear." When the *débris* of a decayed human soul finds itself crumbled into ghosthood and realises "I myself am now that which all humanity has feared, I am just that cold churchyard shadow, that horrible thing which cannot be, yet somehow is," then to terrify others appears to it an escape from the doom of being a Ghost yet still fearing Ghosts—fearing even the Ghost it is. For to be afraid of oneself is the last horror.

But, beyond all these, I saw other grotesque phantoms in which hardly a trace of the human form remained; monsters who had faced the journey to the bus stop—perhaps for them it was thousands of miles—and come up to the country of the Shadow of Life and limped far into it over the torturing grass, only to spit and gibber out in one ecstasy of hatred their envy and (what is harder to understand) their contempt, of joy. The voyage seemed to them a small price to pay if once, only once, within sight of that eternal dawn, they could tell the prigs, the toffs, the sanctimonious humbugs, the snobs, the "haves," what they thought of them.

"How do they come to be here at all?" I asked my Teacher.

"I have seen that kind converted," said he, "when those ye would think less deeply damned have gone back. Those that hate goodness are sometimes nearer than those that know nothing at all about it and think they have it already."

"Whisht, now!" said my Teacher suddenly. We were standing close to some bushes and beyond them I saw one of the Solid People and a Ghost who had apparently just that moment met. The outlines of the Ghost looked vaguely familiar, but I soon realized that what I had seen on earth was not the man himself but photographs of him in the papers. He had been a famous artist.

"God!" said the Ghost, glancing round the landscape.

"God what?" asked the Spirit.

"What do you mean, 'God what'?" asked the Ghost.

"In our grammar *God* is a noun."

"Oh—I see. I only meant 'by Gum' or something of the sort. I meant . . . well, all *this*. It's . . . it's . . . I should like to paint this."

"I shouldn't bother about that just at present if I were you."

"Look here; isn't one going to be allowed to go on painting?"

"Looking comes first."

"But I've had my look. I've seen just what I want to do. God! —I wish I'd thought of bringing my things with me!"

The Spirit shook his head, scattering light from his hair as he did so. "That sort of thing's no good here," he said.

"What do you mean?" said the Ghost.

"When you painted on earth—at least in your earlier days— it was because you caught glimpses of Heaven in the earthly landscape. The success of your painting was that it enabled others to see the glimpses too. But here you are having the thing itself. It is from here that the messages came. There is no good *telling* us about this country, for we see it already. In fact we see it better than you do."

"Then there's never going to be any point in painting here?"

"I don't say that. When you've grown into a Person (it's all right, we all had to do it) there'll be some things which you'll see better than anyone else. One of the things you'll want to do will be to tell us about them. But not yet. At present your business is to see. Come and see. He is endless. Come and freed."

There was a little pause. "That will be delightful," said the Ghost presently in a rather dull voice.

"Come, then," said the Spirit, offering it his arm.

"How soon do you think I *could* begin painting?" it asked.

The Spirit broke into laughter. "Don't you see you'll never paint at all if that's what you're thinking about?" he said.

"What do you mean?" asked the Ghost.

"Why, if you are interested in the country only for the sake of painting it, you'll never learn to see the country."

"But that's just how a real artist *is* interested in the country."

"No. You're forgetting," said the Spirit. "That was not how you began. Light itself was your first love: you loved paint only as a means of telling about light."

"Oh, that's ages ago," said the Ghost. "One grows out of that. Of course, you haven't seen my later works. One becomes more and more interested in paint for its own sake."

"One does, indeed. I also have had to recover from that. It was all a snare. Ink and catgut and paint were necessary down there, but they are also dangerous stimulants. Every poet and musician and artist, but for Grace, is drawn away from love of the thing he tells, to love of the telling till, down in Deep Hell, they cannot be interested in God at all but only in what they say about Him. For it doesn't stop at being interested in paint, you know. They sink lower—become interested in their own personalities and then in nothing but their own reputations."

"I don't think I'm much troubled in *that* way," said the Ghost stiffly.

"That's excellent," said the Spirit. "Not many of us had quite got over it when we first arrived. But if there is any of that inflammation left it will be cured when you come to the fountain."

"What fountain's that?"

"It is up there in the mountains," said the Spirit. "Very cold and clear, between two green hills. A little like Lethe. When you have drunk of it you forget forever all proprietorship in your own works. You enjoy them just as if they were someone else's: without pride and without modesty."

"That'll be grand," said the Ghost without enthusiasm.

"Well, come," said the Spirit: and for a few paces he supported the hobbling shadow forward to the East.

"Of course," said the Ghost, as if speaking to itself, "there'll always be interesting people to meet. . . ."

"Everyone will be interesting."

"Oh—ah—yes, to be sure. I was thinking of people in our own line. Shall I meet Claude? Or Cezanne? Or——."

"Sooner or later—if they're here."

"But don't you know?"

"Well, of course not. I've only been here a few years. All the chances are against my having run across them . . . there are a good many of us, you know."

"But surely in the case of distinguished people, you'd hear?"

"But they aren't distinguished—no more than anyone else. Don't you understand? The Glory flows into everyone, and back from everyone: like light and mirrors. But the light's the thing."

"Do you mean there are no famous men?"

"They are all famous. They are all known, remembered, recognised by the only Mind that can give a perfect judgement."

"Oh, of course, in *that* sense . . ." said the Ghost.

"Don't stop," said the Spirit, making to lead him still forward.

"One must be content with one's reputation among posterity, then," said the Ghost.

"My friend," said the Spirit. "Don't you know?"

"Know what?"

"That you and I are already completely forgotten on the Earth?"

"Eh? What's that?" exclaimed the Ghost, disengaging its arm. "Do you mean those damned Neo-Regionalists have won after all?"

"Lord love you, yes!" said the Spirit, once more shaking and shining with laughter. "You couldn't get five pounds for any picture of mine or even of yours in Europe or America to-day. We're dead out of fashion."

"I must be off at once," said the Ghost. "Let me go! Damn it all, one has one's duty to the future of Art. I must go back to my friends. I must write an article. There must be a manifesto. We must start a periodical. We must have publicity. Let me go. This is beyond a joke!"

And without listening to the Spirit's reply, the spectre vanished.

10.

This conversation also we overheard.

"That is quite, *quite* out of the question," said a female Ghost to one of the bright Women, "I should not dream of staying if I'm expected to meet Robert. I am ready to forgive him, of course. But anything more is quite impossible. How he comes to be here . . . but that is your affair."

"But if you have forgiven him," said the other, "surely——."

"I forgive him as a Christian," said the Ghost. "But there are some things one can never forget."

"But I don't understand . . ." began the She-Spirit.

"Exactly," said the Ghost with a little laugh. "You never did. You always thought Robert could do no wrong. *I* know. Please don't interrupt for *one* moment. You haven't the faintest conception of what I went through with your dear Robert. The ingratitude! It was I who made a man of him! Sacrificed my whole life to him! And what was my reward? Absolute, utter selfishness. No, but listen. He was pottering along on about six hundred a year when I married him. And mark my words, Hilda, he'd have been in that position to the day of his death if it hadn't been for me. It was I who had to drive him every step of the way. He hadn't a spark of ambition. It was like trying to lift a sack of coal. I had to positively nag him to take on the extra work in the other department, though it was really the beginning of everything for him. The laziness of men! He said, if you please, he couldn't work more than thirteen hours a day! As if I weren't working far longer. For *my* day's work wasn't over when his was. I had to keep him going all evening, if you understand what I mean. If he'd had his way he'd have just sat in an armchair and sulked

165

when dinner was over. It was I who had to draw him out of himself and brighten him up and make conversation. With no help from him, of course. Sometimes he didn't even listen. As I said to him, I should have thought good manners, if nothing else . . . he seemed to have forgotten that I was a lady even if I *had* married him, and all the time I was working my fingers to the bone for him: and without the slightest appreciation. I used to spend simply *hours* arranging flowers to make that poky little house nice, and instead of thanking me, what do you think he said? Said he wished I wouldn't fill up the writing desk with them when he wanted to use it: and there was a perfectly frightful fuss one evening because I'd spilled one of the vases over some papers of his. It was all nonsense really, because they weren't anything to do with his work. He had some silly idea of writing a book in those days . . . as if he could. I cured him of that in the end.

"No, Hilda, you *must* listen to me. The trouble I went to, entertaining! Robert's idea was that he'd just slink off by himself every now and then to see what he called his old friends . . . and leave me to amuse myself! But I knew from the first that those friends were doing him no good. 'No, Robert,' said I, 'your friends are now mine. It is my duty to have them *here,* however tired I am and however little we can afford it.' You'd have thought that would have been enough. But they did come for a bit. That is where I had to use a certain amount of tact. A woman who has her wits about her can always drop in a word here and there. I wanted Robert to see them against a different background. They weren't quite at their ease, somehow, in my drawing-room: nor at their best. I couldn't help laughing sometimes. Of course Robert was uncomfortable while the treatment was going on, but it was all for his own good in the end. None of that set were friends of his any longer by the end of the first year.

"And then, he got the new job. A great step up. But what *do* you think? Instead of realising that we now had a chance to spread out a bit, all he said was 'Well *now,* for God's sake, let's have some peace.' That nearly finished me. I nearly gave him up altogether: but I knew my duty. I have always done my duty. You can't believe the work I had getting him to agree to a bigger house, and then finding a house. I wouldn't have grudged it one scrap if only he'd taken it in the right spirit—if only he'd seen the *fun* of it all. If he'd been a different sort of man it *would* have been fun meeting him on the doorstep as he came back from the office and saying, 'Come along, Bobs, no time for dinner tonight. I've just heard of a house out near Watford and I've got the keys and we can get there and back by one o'clock.' But with *him!* It was perfect misery, Hilda. For by this time your wonderful Robert was turning into the sort of man who cares about nothing but food.

"Well, I got him into the new house at last. Yes, I know. It was a little more than we could really afford at the moment, but all sorts of things were opening out before him. And, of course, I began to entertain properly. No more of his sort of friends, thank you. I was doing it all for his sake. Every useful friend he ever made was due to me. Naturally, I had to dress well. They ought to have been the happiest years of both our lives. If they weren't, he had no one but himself to thank. Oh, he was a maddening man, simply maddening! He just set himself to get old and silent and grumpy. Just sank into himself. He could have looked years younger if he'd taken the trouble. He needn't have walked with a stoop—I'm sure I warned him about that often enough. He was the most miserable host. Whenever we gave a party everything rested on my shoulders: Robert was simply a wet blanket. As I said to him (and if I said it once, I said it a hundred times) he hadn't always been like that. There had been a time when he took an interest in all sorts of things and had been quite ready to make friends. 'What on earth is coming over you?' I used to say. But now he just didn't answer at all. He would sit staring at me with his great big eyes (I came to hate a man with dark eyes) and—I know it now—just hating me. That was my reward. After all I'd done. Sheer wicked, senseless hatred: at the very moment when he was a richer man than he'd ever dreamed of being! As I used to say to him, 'Robert, you're simply letting yourself go to seed.' The younger men who came to the house—it wasn't *my* fault if they liked me better than my old bear of a husband—used to laugh at him.

"I did my duty to the very end. I *forced* him to take exercise—that was really my chief reason for keeping a great Dane. I kept on giving parties. I took him for the most wonderful holidays. I saw that he didn't drink too much. Even, when things became desperate, I encouraged him to take up his writing again. It couldn't do any harm by then. How could I help it if he *did* have a nervous breakdown in the end? My conscience is clear. I've done my duty by him, if ever a woman has. So you see why it would be impossible to . . .

"And yet . . . I don't know. I believe I have changed my mind. I'll make them a fair offer, Hilda. I will *not* meet him, if it means just meeting him and no more. But if I'm given a free hand I'll take charge of him again. I will take up my burden once more. But I must have a free hand. With all the time one would have here, I believe I could make something of him. Somewhere quite to ourselves. Wouldn't that be a good plan? He's not fit to be on his own. Put me in charge of him. He wants firm handling. I know him better than you do. What's that? No, give him to me, do you hear? Don't consult *him:* just give him to me. I'm his wife, aren't I? I was only beginning. There's lots, lots, lots of things I still want to do with him. No, listen, Hilda. Please, please! I'm so miserable. I must have someone to—to do things to. It's simply frightful down there. No one minds about me at all. I can't alter them. It's dreadful to see them all sitting about and not be able to do anything with them. Give him back to me. Why should he have everything his own way? It's not good for him. It isn't right, it's not fair. I want Robert. What right have you to keep him from me? I hate you. How can I pay him out if you won't let me have him?"

The Ghost which had towered up like a dying candleflame snapped suddenly. A sour, dry smell lingered in the air for a moment and then there was no Ghost to be seen.

II.

One of the most painful meetings we witnessed was between a woman's Ghost and a Bright Spirit who had apparently been her brother. They must have met only a moment before we ran across them, for the Ghost was just saying in a tone of unconcealed disappointment, "Oh . . . Reginald! It's *you*, is it?"

"Yes, dear," said the Spirit. "I know you expected someone else. Can you . . . I hope you can be a little glad to see even me; for the present."

"I did think Michael would have come," said the Ghost; and then, almost fiercely, "He *is* here, of course?" "He's there—far up in the mountains."

"Why hasn't he come to meet me? Didn't he know?"

"My dear (don't worry, it will all come right presently) it wouldn't have done. Not yet. He wouldn't be able to see or hear you as you are at present. You'd be totally invisible to Michael. But we'll soon build you up."

"I should have thought if *you* can see me, my own son could!"

"It doesn't always happen like that. You see, I have specialised in this sort of work."

"Oh, it's work, is it?" snapped the Ghost. Then, after a pause, "Well, When *am* I going to be allowed to see him?"

"There's no question of being *allowed*, Pam. As soon as it's possible for him to see you, of course he will. You need to be thickened up a bit."

"How?" said the Ghost. The monosyllable was hard and a little threatening.

"I'm afraid the first step is a hard one," said the Spirit. "But after that you'll go on like a house on fire. You will become solid enough for Michael to perceive you when you learn to want someone else besides Michael. I don't say 'more than Michael,' not as a beginning. That will come later. It's only the little germ of a desire for God that we need to start the process."

"Oh, you mean religion and all that sort of thing? This is hardly the moment . . . and from *you,* of all people. Well, never mind. I'll do whatever's necessary. What do you want me to do? Come on. The sooner I begin it, the sooner they'll let me see my boy. I'm quite ready."

"But, Pam, do think! Don't you see you are not beginning at all as long as you are in that state of mind? You're treating God only as a means to Michael. But the whole thickening treatment consists in learning to want God for His own sake."

"You wouldn't talk like that if you were a Mother."

"You mean, if I were *only* a mother. But there is no such thing as being only a mother. You exist as Michael's mother only because you first exist as God's creature. That relation is older and closer. No, listen, Pam! He also loves. He also has suffered. He also has waited a long time."

"If He loved me He'd let me see my boy. If He loved me why did He take Michael away from me? I wasn't going to say anything about that. But it's pretty hard to forgive, you know."

"But He had to take Michael away. Partly for Michael's sake. . . ."

"I'm sure I did my best to make Michael happy. I gave up my whole life. . . ."

"Human beings can't make one another really happy for long. And secondly, for your sake. He wanted your merely instinctive love for your child (tigresses share *that,* you know!) to turn into something better. He wanted you to love Michael as He understands love. You cannot love a fellow-creature fully till you love God. Sometimes this conversion can be done while the instinctive love is still gratified. But there was, it seems, no chance of that in your case. The instinct was uncontrolled and fierce and monomaniac. (Ask your daughter, or your husband. Ask our own mother. You haven't once thought of *her.*) The only remedy was to take away its object. It was a case for surgery. When that first kind of love was thwarted, then there was just a chance that in the loneliness, in the silence, something else might begin to grow."

"This is all nonsense—cruel and wicked nonsense. What *right* have you to say things like that about Mother-love? It is the highest and holiest feeling in human nature."

"Pam, Pam—no natural feelings are high or low, holy or unholy, in themselves. They are all holy when God's hand is on the rein. They all go bad when they set up on their own and make themselves into false gods."

"My love for Michael would never have gone bad. Not if we'd lived together for millions of years."

"You are mistaken. And you must know. Haven't you met—down there—mothers who have their sons with them, in Hell? Does *their* love make them happy?"

"If you mean people like the Guthrie woman and her dreadful Bobby, of course not. I hope you're not suggesting. . . . If I had Michael I'd be perfectly happy, even in that town. I wouldn't be always talking about him till everyone hated the sound of his name, which is what Winifred Guthrie does about *her* brat. I wouldn't quarrel with people for not taking enough notice of him and then be furiously jealous if they did. I wouldn't go about whining and complaining that he wasn't nice to me. Because, of course, he would be nice. Don't you dare to suggest that Michael could ever become like the Guthrie boy. There are some things I won't stand."

"What you have seen in the Guthries is what natural affection turns to in the end if it will not be converted."

"It's a lie. A wicked, cruel lie. How could anyone love their son more than I did? Haven't I lived only for his memory all these years?"

"That was rather a mistake, Pam. In your heart of hearts you know it was."

"What was a mistake?"

"All that ten years' ritual of grief. Keeping his room exactly as he'd left it: keeping anniversaries: refusing to leave that house though Dick and Muriel were both wretched there."

"Of course they didn't care. I know that. I soon learned to expect no real sympathy from them."

"You're wrong. No man ever felt his son's death more than Dick. Not many girls loved their brothers better than Muriel. It wasn't against Michael they revolted: it was against you—against having their whole life dominated by the tyranny of the past: and not really even Michael's past, but your past."

"You are heartless. Everyone is heartless. The past was all I had."

"It was all you chose to have. It was the wrong way to deal with a sorrow. It was Egyptian—like enbalming a dead body."

"Oh, of course. I'm wrong. Everything I say or do is wrong, according to you."

"But of course!" said the Spirit, shining with love and mirth so that my eyes were dazzled. "That's what we all find when we reach this country. We've all been wrong! That's the great joke. There's no need to go on pretending one was right! After that we begin living."

"How dare you laugh about it? Give me my boy. Do you hear? I don't care about all your rules and regulations. I don't believe in a God who keeps mother and son apart. I believe in a God of Love. No one has a right to come between me and my son. Not even God. Tell Him that to His face. I want my boy, and I mean to have him. He is mine, do you understand? Mine, mine, mine, forever and ever."

"He will be, Pam. Everything will be yours. God Himself will be yours. But not that way. Nothing can be yours by nature."

"What? Not my own son, born out of my own body?"

"And where is your own body now? Didn't you know that Nature draws to an end? Look! The sun is coming, over the mountains there: it will be up any moment now."

"Michael is mine."

"How yours? You didn't make him. Nature made him to grow in your body without your will. Even against your will . . . you sometimes forget that you didn't intend to have a baby then at all. Michael was originally an Accident."

"Who told you that?" said the Ghost: and then, recovering itself, "It's a lie. It's not true. And it's no business of yours. I hate your religion and I hate and despise your God. I believe in a God of Love."

"And yet, Pam, you have no love at this moment for your own mother or for me."

"Oh, I see! *That's* the trouble, is it? *Really*, Reginald! The idea of your being hurt because . . ."

"Lord love you!" said the Spirit with a great laugh. "You needn't bother about that! Don't you know that you *can't* hurt anyone in this country?"

The Ghost was silent and open-mouthed for a moment; more wilted, I thought, by this reassurance than by anything else that had been said.

"Come. We will go a bit further," said my Teacher, laying his hand on my arm.

"Why did you bring me away, Sir?" said I when we had passed out of earshot of this unhappy Ghost.

"It might take a long while, that conversation," said my Teacher. "And ye have heard enough to see what the choice is."

"Is there any hope for her, Sir?"

"Aye, there's some. What she calls her love for her son has turned into a poor, prickly, astringent sort of thing. But there's still a wee spark of something that's not just her self in it. That might be blown into a flame."

"Then some natural feelings are really better than others—I mean, are a better starting-point for the real thing?"

"Better *and* worse. There's something in natural affection which will lead it on to eternal love more easily than natural appetite could be led on. But there's also something in it which makes it easier to stop at the natural level and mistake it for the heavenly. Brass is mistaken for gold more easily than clay is. And if it finally refuses conversion its corruption will be worse than the corruption of what ye call the lower passions. It is a stronger angel, and therefore, when it falls, a fiercer devil."

"I don't know that I dare repeat this on Earth, Sir," said I. "They'd say I was inhuman: they'd say I believed in total depravity: they'd say I was attacking the best and the holiest things. They'd call me . . ."

"It might do you no harm if they did," said he with (I really thought) a twinkle in his eye.

"But could one dare—could one have the face—to go to a bereaved mother, in her misery—when one's not bereaved one-self? . . ."

"No, no, Son, that's no office of yours. You're not a good enough man for that. When your own heart's been broken it will be time for you to think of talking. But someone must say in general what's been unsaid among you this many a year: that love, as mortals understand the word, isn't enough. Every natural love will rise again and live forever in this country: but none will rise again until it has been buried."

"The saying is almost too hard for us."

"Ah, but it's cruel not to say it. They that know have grown afraid to speak. That is why sorrows that used to purify now only fester."

"Keats was wrong, then, when he said he was certain of the holiness of the heart's affections."

"I doubt if he knew clearly what he meant. But you and I must be clear. There is but one good; that is God. Everything else is good when it looks to Him and bad when it turns from Him. And the higher and mightier it is in the natural order, the more demoniac it will be if it rebels. It's not out of bad mice or bad fleas you make demons, but out of bad archangels. The false religion of lust is baser than the false religion of mother-love or patriotism or art: but lust is less likely to be made into a religion. But look!"

I saw coming towards us a Ghost who carried something on his shoulder. Like all the Ghosts, he was unsubstantial, but they differed from one another as smokes differ. Some had been whitish; this one was dark and oily. What sat on his shoulder was a little red lizard, and it was twitching its tail like a whip and whispering things in his ear. As we caught sight of him he turned his head to the reptile with a snarl of impatience. "Shut up, I tell you!" he said. It wagged its tail and continued to whisper to him. He ceased snarling, and presently began to smile. Then he turned and started to limp westward, away from the mountains.

"Off so soon?" said a voice.

The speaker was more or less human in shape but larger than a man, and so bright that I could hardly look at him. His presence smote on my eyes and on my body too (for there was heat coming from him as well as light) like the morning sun at the beginning of a tyrannous summer day.

"Yes. I'm off," said the Ghost. "Thanks for all your hospitality. But it's no good, you see. I told this little chap," (here he indicated the lizard), "that he'd have to be quiet if he came—which he insisted on doing. Of course his stuff won't do here: I realise that. But he won't stop. I shall just have to go home."

"Would you like me to make him quiet?" said the flaming Spirit —an angel, as I now understood.

"Of course I would," said the Ghost.

"Then I will kill him," said the Angel, taking a step forward.

"Oh—ah—look out! You're burning me. Keep away," said the Ghost, retreating.

"Don't you *want* him killed?"

"You didn't say anything about *killing* him at first. I hardly meant to bother you with anything so drastic as that."

"It's the only way," said the Angel, whose burning hands were now very close to the lizard. "Shall I kill it?"

"Well, that's a further question. I'm quite open to consider it, but it's a new point, isn't it? I mean, for the moment I was only thinking about silencing it because up here—well, it's so damned embarrassing."

"May I kill it?"

"Well, there's time to discuss that later."

"There is no time. May I kill it?"

"Please, I never meant to be such a nuisance. Please—really— don't bother. Look! It's gone to sleep of its own accord. I'm sure it'll be all right now. Thanks ever so much."

"May I kill it?"

"Honestly, I don't think there's the slightest necessity for that. I'm sure I shall be able to keep it in order now. I think the gradual process would be far better than killing it."

"The gradual process is of no use at all."

"Don't you think so? Well, I'll think over what you've said very carefully. I honestly will. In fact I'd let you kill it now, but as a matter of fact I'm not feeling frightfully well to-day. It would be silly to do it *now*. I'd need to be in good health for the operation. Some other day, perhaps."

"There is no other day. All days are present now."

"Get back! You're burning me. How can I tell you to kill it? You'd kill *me* if you did."

"It is not so."

"Why, you're hurting me now."

"I never said it wouldn't hurt you. I said it wouldn't kill you."

"Oh, I know. You think I'm a coward. But it isn't that. Really it isn't. I say! Let me run back by tonight's bus and get an opinion from my own doctor. I'll come again the first moment I can."

"This moment contains all moments."

"Why are you torturing me? You are jeering at me. How *can* I let you tear me to pieces? If you wanted to help me, why didn't you kill the damned thing without asking me—before I knew? It would be all over by now if you had."

"I cannot kill it against your will. It is impossible. Have I your permission?"

The Angel's hands were almost closed on the Lizard, but not quite. Then the Lizard began chattering to the Ghost so loud that even I could hear what it was saying.

"Be careful," it said. "He can do what he says. He can kill me. One fatal word from you and he *will!* Then you'll be without me for ever and ever. It's not natural. How could you live? You'd be only a sort of ghost, not a real man as you are now. He doesn't understand. He's only a cold, bloodless abstract thing. It may be natural for him, but it isn't for us. Yes, yes. I know there are no real pleasures now, only dreams. But aren't they better than nothing? And I'll be so good. I admit I've sometimes gone too far in the past, but I promise I won't do it again. I'll give you nothing but really nice dreams—all sweet and fresh and almost innocent. You might say, quite innocent. . . ."

"Have I your permission?" said the Angel to the Ghost.

"I know it will kill me."

"It won't. But supposing it did?"

"You're right. It would be better to be dead than to live with this creature."

"Then I may?"

"Damn and blast you! Go on can't you? Get it over. Do what

you like," bellowed the Ghost: but ended, whimpering, "God help me. God help me."

Next moment the Ghost gave a scream of agony such as I never heard on Earth. The Burning One closed his crimson grip on the reptile: twisted it, while it bit and writhed, and then flung it, broken backed, on the turf.

"Ow! That's done for me," gasped the Ghost, reeling backwards.

For a moment I could make out nothing distinctly. Then I saw, between me and the nearest bush, unmistakably solid but growing every moment solider, the upper arm and shoulder of a man. Then, brighter still and stronger, the legs and hands. The neck and golden head materialised while I watched, and if my attention had not wavered I should have seen the actual completing of a man—an immense man, naked, not much smaller than the Angel. What distracted me was the fact that at the same moment something seemed to be happening to the Lizard. At first I thought the operation had failed. So far from dying, the creature was still struggling and even growing bigger as it struggled. And as it grew it changed. Its hinder parts grew rounder. The tail, still flickering, became a tail of hair that flickered between huge and glossy buttocks. Suddenly I started back, rubbing my eyes. What stood before me was the greatest stallion I have ever seen, silvery white but with mane and tail of gold. It was smooth and shining, rippled with swells of flesh and muscle, whinnying and stamping with its hoofs. At each stamp the land shook and the trees dindled.

The new-made man turned and clapped the new horse's neck. It nosed his bright body. Horse and master breathed each into the other's nostrils. The man turned from it, flung himself at the feet of the Burning One, and embraced them. When he rose I thought his face shone with tears, but it may have been only the liquid love and brightness (one cannot distinguish them in that country) which flowed from him. I had not long to think about it. In joyous haste the young man leaped upon the horse's back. Turning in his seat he waved a farewell, then nudged the stallion with his heels. They were off before I well knew what was happening. There was riding if you like! I came out as quickly as I could from among the bushes to follow them with my eyes; but already they were only like a shooting star far off on the green plain, and soon among the foothills of the mountains. Then, still like a star, I saw them winding up, scaling what seemed impossible steeps, and quicker every moment, till near the dim brow of the landscape, so high that I must strain my neck to see them, they vanished, bright themselves, into the rose-brightness of that everlasting morning.

While I still watched, I noticed that the whole plain and forest were shaking with a sound which in our world would be too large to hear, but there I could take it with joy. I knew it was not the Solid People who were singing. It was the voice of that earth, those woods and those waters. A strange archaic, inorganic noise, that came from all directions at once. The Nature or Arch-nature of that land rejoiced to have been once more ridden, and therefore consummated, in the person of the horse. It sang,

"The Master says to our master, Come up. Share my rest and splendour till all natures that were your enemies become slaves to dance before you and backs for you to ride, and firmness for your feet to rest on.

"From beyond all place and time, out of the very Place, authority will be given you: the strengths that once opposed your will shall be obedient fire in your blood and heavenly thunder in your voice.

"Overcome us that, so overcome, we may be ourselves: we desire the beginning of your reign as we desire dawn and dew, wetness at the birth of light.

"Master, your Master has appointed you for ever: to be our King of Justice and our high Priest."

"Do ye understand all this, my Son?" said the Teacher.

"I don't know about *all*, Sir," said I. "Am I right in thinking the Lizard really turned into the Horse?"

"Aye. But it was killed first. Ye'll not forget that part of the story?"

"I'll try not to, Sir. But does it mean that everything—everything—that is in us can go on to the Mountains?"

"Nothing, not even the best and noblest, can go on as it now is. Nothing, not even what is lowest and most bestial, will not be raised again if it submits to death. It is sown a natural body, it is raised a spiritual body. Flesh and blood cannot come to the Mountains. Not because they are too rank, but because they are too weak. What is a Lizard compared with a stallion? Lust is a poor, weak, whimpering, whispering thing compared with that richness and energy of desire which will arise when lust has been killed."

"But am I to tell them at home that this man's sensuality proved less of an obstacle than that poor woman's love for her son? For that was, at any rate, an excess of *love*."

"Ye'll tell them no such thing," he replied sternly. "Excess of love, did ye say? There was no excess, there was defect. She loved her son too little, not too much. If she had loved him more there'd be no difficulty. I do not know how her affair will end. But it may well be that at this moment she's demanding to have him down with her in Hell. That kind is sometimes perfectly ready to plunge the soul they say they love in endless misery if only they can still in some fashion possess it. No, no. Ye must draw another lesson. Ye must ask, if the risen body even of appetite is as grand a horse as ye saw, what would the risen body of maternal love or friendship be?"

But once more my attention was diverted. "Is there *another* river, Sir?" I asked.

12.

The reason why I asked if there were another river was this. All down one long aisle of the forest the under-sides of the leafy branches had begun to tremble with dancing light; and on earth I knew nothing so likely to produce this appearance as the reflected lights cast upward by moving water. A few moments later I realised my mistake. Some kind of procession was approaching us, and the light came from the persons who composed it.

First came bright Spirits, not the Spirits of men, who danced and scattered flowers—soundlessly falling, lightly drifting flowers, though by the standards of the ghost-world each petal would have weighed a hundred-weight and their fall would have been like the crashing of boulders. Then, on the left and right, at each side of the forest avenue, came youthful shapes, boys upon one hand, and girls upon the other. If I could remember their singing and write down the notes, no man who read that score would ever grow sick or old. Between them went musicians: and after these a lady in whose honour all this was being done.

I cannot now remember whether she was naked or clothed. If she were naked, then it must have been the almost visible penumbra of her courtesy and joy which produces in my memory the illusion of a great and shining train that followed her across the happy grass. If she were clothed, then the illusion of nakedness is doubtless due to the clarity with which her inmost spirit shone through the clothes. For clothes in that country are not a disguise: the spiritual body lives along each thread and turns them into living organs. A robe or a crown is there as much one of the wearer's features as a lip or an eye.

But I have forgotten. And only partly do I remember the unbearable beauty of her face.

"Is it? . . . is it?" I whispered to my guide.

"Not at all," said he. "It's someone ye'll never have heard of. Her name on earth was Sarah Smith and she lived at Golders Green."

"She seems to be . . . well, a person of particular importance?"

"Aye. She is one of the great ones. Ye have heard that fame in this country and fame on Earth are two quite different things."

"And who are these gigantic people . . . look! They're like emeralds . . . who are dancing and throwing flowers before her?"

"Haven't ye read your Milton? *A thousand liveried angels lackey her.*"

"And who are all these young men and women on each side?"

"They are her sons and daughters."

"She must have had a very large family, Sir."

"Every young man or boy that met her became her son—even if it was only the boy that brought the meat to her back door. Every girl that met her was her daughter."

"Isn't that a bit hard on their own parents?"

"No. There *are* those that steal other people's children. But her motherhood was of a different kind. Those on whom it fell went back to their natural parents loving them more. Few men looked on her without becoming, in a certain fashion, her lovers. But it was the kind of love that made them not less true, but truer, to their own wives."

"And how . . . but hullo! What are all these animals? A cat—two cats—dozens of cats. And all those dogs . . . why, I can't count them. And the birds. And the horses."

"They are her beasts."

"Did she keep a sort of zoo? I mean, this is a bit too much."

"Every beast and bird that came near her had its place in her love. In her they became themselves. And now the abundance of life she has in Christ from the Father flows over into them."

I looked at my Teacher in amazement.

"Yes," he said. "It is like when you throw a stone into a pool, and the concentric waves spread out further and further. Who knows where it will end? Redeemed humanity is still young, it has hardly come to its full strength. But already there is joy enough in the little finger of a great saint such as yonder lady to waken all the dead things of the universe into life."

While we spoke the Lady was steadily advancing towards us, but it was not at us she looked. Following the direction of her eyes, I turned and saw an oddly-shaped phantom approaching. Or rather two phantoms: a great tall Ghost, horribly thin and shaky, who seemed to be leading on a chain another Ghost no bigger than an organ-grinder's monkey. The taller Ghost wore a soft black hat, and he reminded me of something that my memory could not quite recover. Then, when he had come within a few feet of the Lady he spread out his lean, shaky hand flat on his chest with the fingers wide apart, and exclaimed in a hollow voice, "At last!" All at once I realised what it was that he had put me in mind of. He was like a seedy actor of the old school.

"Darling! At last!" said the Lady. "Good Heavens!" thought I. "Surely she can't——," and then I noticed two things. In the first place, I noticed that the little Ghost was not being led by the big one. It was the dwarfish figure that held the chain in its hand and the theatrical figure that wore the collar round its neck. In the second place, I noticed that the Lady was looking solely at the dwarf Ghost. She seemed to think it was the Dwarf who had addressed her, or else she was deliberately ignoring the other. On the poor dwarf she turned her eyes. Love shone not from her face only, but from all her limbs, as if it were some liquid in which she had just been bathing. Then, to my dismay, she came nearer. She stooped down and kissed the Dwarf. It made me shudder to see her in such close contact with that cold, damp, shrunken thing. But she did not shudder.

"Frank," she said, "before anything else, forgive me. For all I ever did wrong and for all I did not do right since the first day we met, I ask your pardon."

I looked properly at the Dwarf for the first time now: or perhaps, when he received her kiss he became a little more visible. One could just make out the sort of face he must have had when he was a man: a little, oval freckled face with a weak chin and a tiny wisp of unsuccessful moustache. He gave her a glance, not a full look. He was watching the Tragedian out of the corner of his eyes. Then he gave a jerk to the chain: and it was the Tragedian, not he, who answered the Lady.

"There, there," said the Tragedian. "We'll say no more about it. We all make mistakes." With the words there came over his features a ghastly contortion which, I think, was meant for an indulgently playful smile. "We'll say no more," he continued. "It's not myself I'm thinking about. It is you. That is what has been continually on my mind—all these years. The thought of you—you here alone, breaking your heart about me."

"But now," said the Lady to the Dwarf, "you can set all that aside. Never think like that again. It is all over."

Her beauty brightened so that I could hardly see anything else, and under that sweet compulsion the Dwarf really looked at her for the first time. For a second I thought he was growing more like a man. He opened his mouth. He himelf was going to speak this time. But oh, the disappointment when the words came!

"You missed me?" he croaked in a small, bleating voice.

Yet even then she was not taken aback. Still the love and courtesy flowed from her.

"Dear, you will understand about that very soon," she said. "But to-day——."

What happened next gave me a shock. The Dwarf and the Tragedian spoke in unison, not to her but one another. "You'll notice," they warned one another, "she hasn't answered our question." I realised then that they were one person, or rather that both were remains of what had once been a person. The Dwarf again rattled the chain.

"You missed me?" said the Tragedian to the Lady, throwing a dreadful theatrical tremor into his voice.

"Dear friend," said the Lady, still attending exclusively to the Dwarf, "you may be happy about that and about everything else. Forget all about it for ever."

And really, for a moment, I thought the Dwarf was going to obey: partly because the outlines of his face became a little clearer, and partly because the invitation to all joy, singing out of her whole being like a bird's son on an April evening, seemed to me such that no creature could resist it. Then he hesitated.

And then—once more he and his accomplice spoke in unison.

"Of course it would be rather fine and magnanimous not to press the point," they said to one another. "But can we be sure she'd notice? We've done these sort of things before. There was the time we let her have the last stamp in the house to write to her mother and said nothing although she *had* known we wanted to write a letter ourself. We'd thought she'd remember and see how unselfish we'd been. But she never did. And there was the time . . . oh, lots and lots of times!" So the Dwarf gave a shake to the chain and——.

"I can't forget it," cried the Tragedian. "And I won't forget it, either. I could forgive them all they've done to me. But for your miseries——."

"Oh, don't you understand?" said the Lady. "There *are* no miseries here."

"Do you mean to say," answered the Dwarf, as if this new idea had made him quite forget the Tragedian for a moment, "do you mean to say you've been *happy?*"

"Didn't you want me to be? But no matter. Want it now. Or don't think about it at all."

The Dwarf blinked at her. One could see an unheard-of idea trying to enter his little mind: one could see even that there was for him some sweetness in it. For a second he had almost let the chain go: then, as if it were his life-line, he clutched it once more.

"Look here," said the Tragedian. "We've got to face this." He was using his "manly" bullying tone this time: the one for bringing women to their senses.

"Darling," said the Lady to the Dwarf, "there's nothing to face. You don't want me to have been miserable for misery's sake. You only think I must have been if I loved you. But if you'll only wait you'll see that isn't so."

"Love!" said the Tragedian striking his forehead with his hand: then, a few notes deeper, "Love! Do you know the meaning of the word?"

"How should I not?" said the Lady. "I am in love. *In* love, do you understand? Yes, now I love truly."

"You mean," said the Tragedian, "you mean—you did *not* love me truly in the old days?"

"Only in a poor sort of way," she answered. "I have asked you to forgive me. There was a little real love in it. But what we called love down there was mostly the craving to be loved. In the main I loved you for my own sake: because I needed you."

"And now!" said the Tragedian with a hackneyed gesture of despair. "Now, you need me no more?"

"But of course not!" said the Lady; and her smile made me wonder how both the phantoms could refrain from crying out with joy.

"What needs could I have," she said, "now that I have all? I am full now, not empty. I am in Love Himself, not lonely. Strong, not weak. You shall be the same. Come and see. We shall have no *need* for one another now: we can begin to love truly."

But the Tragedian was still striking attitudes. "She needs me no more—no more. No more," he said in a choking voice to no one in particular. "Would to God," he continued, but he was now pronouncing it *Gud*—"Would to Gud I had seen her lying dead at my feet before I heard those words. Lying dead at my feet. Lying dead at my feet."

I do not know how long the creature intended to go on repeating the phrase, for the Lady put an end to that. "Frank! Frank!" she cried in a voice that made the whole wood ring. "Look at me. *Look* at me. What are you doing with that great, ugly doll? Let go of the chain. Send it away. It is *you* I want. Don't you see what nonsense it's talking?" Merriment danced in her eyes. She was sharing a joke with the Dwarf, right over the head of the Tragedian. Something not at all unlike a smile struggled to appear on the Dwarf's face. For he *was* looking at her now. Her laughter was past his first defences. He was struggling hard to keep it out, but already with imperfect success. Against his will, he was even growing a little bigger. "Oh, you great goose," said she. "What *is* the good of talking like that here? You know as well as I do that you *did* see me lying dead years and years ago. Not 'at your feet,' of course, but on a bed in a nursing home. A very good nursing home it was too. Matron would never have dreamed of leaving bodies lying about the floor! It's ridiculous for that doll to try to be impressive about death *here*. It just won't work."

13.

I do not know that I ever saw anything more terrible than the struggle of that Dwarf Ghost against joy. For he had almost been overcome. Somewhere, incalculable ages ago, there must have been gleams of humour and reason in him. For one moment, while she looked at him in her love and mirth, he saw the absurdity of the Tragedian. For one moment he did not at all misunderstand her laughter: he too must once have known that no people find each other more absurd than lovers. But the light that reached him, reached him against his will. This was not the meeting he had pictured; he would not accept it. Once more he clutched at his death-line, and at once the Tragedian spoke.

"You dare to laugh at it!" it stormed. "To my face? And this is my reward. Very well. It is fortunate that you give yourself no concern about my fate. Otherwise you might be sorry afterwards to think that you had driven me back to Hell. What? Do you think I'd stay *now?* Thank you. I believe I'm fairly quick at recognising where I'm not wanted. 'Not needed' was the exact expression, if I remember rightly."

From this time on the Dwarf never spoke again: but still the Lady addressed it.

"Dear, no one sends you back. Here is all joy. Everything bids you stay." But the Dwarf was growing smaller even while she spoke.

"Yes," said the Tragedian. "On terms you might offer to a dog. I happen to have some self-respect left, and I see that my going will make no difference to you. It is nothing to you that I go back to the cold and the gloom, the lonely, lonely streets——."

"Don't, don't, Frank," said the Lady. "Don't let it talk like

186

that." But the Dwarf was now so small that she had dropped on her knees to speak to it. The Tragedian caught her words greedily as a dog catches a bone.

"Ah, you can't bear to hear it!" he shouted with miserable triumph. "That was always in the way. *You* must be sheltered. Grim realities must be kept out of *your* sight. You who can be happy without me, forgetting me! You don't want even to hear of my sufferings. You say, *don't*. Don't tell you. Don't make you unhappy. Don't break in on your sheltered, self-centered little heaven. And this is the reward——."

She stooped still lower to speak to the Dwarf which was now a figure no bigger than a kitten, hanging on to the end of the chain with his feet off the ground.

"That wasn't why I said, Don't," she answered. "I meant, stop acting. It's no good. He is killing you. Let go of that chain. Even now."

"Acting," screamed the Tragedian. "What do you mean?"

The Dwarf was now so small that I could not distinguish him from the chain to which he was clinging. And now for the first time I could not be certain whether the Lady was addressing him or the Tragedian.

"Quick," she said. "There is still time. Stop it. Stop it at once."

"Stop what?"

"Using pity, other people's pity, in the wrong way. We have all done it a bit on earth, you know. Pity was meant to be a spur that drives joy to help misery. But it can be used the wrong way round. It can be used for a kind of blackmailing. Those who choose misery can hold joy up to ransom, by pity. You see, I know now. Even as a child you did it. Instead of saying you were sorry, you went and sulked in the attic . . . because you knew that sooner or later one of your sisters would say, "I can't bear to think of him sitting up there alone, crying.' You used your pity to blackmail them, and they gave in in the end. And afterwards, when we were married . . . oh, it doesn't matter, if only you will *stop* it."

"And *that*," said the Tragedian, "that is all you have understood of me, after all these years." I don't know what had become of the Dwarf Ghost by now. Perhaps it was climbing up the chain like an insect: perhaps it was somehow absorbed into the chain.

"No, Frank, not *here*," said the Lady. "Listen to reason. Did you think joy was created to live always under that threat? Always defenceless against those who would rather be miserable than have their self-will crossed? For it was real misery. I know that now. You made yourself really wretched. That you can still do. But you can no longer communicate your wretchedness. Everything becomes more and more itself. Here is joy that cannot be shaken. Our light can swallow up your darkness: but your darkness cannot now infect our light. No, no, no. Come to us. We will not go to you. Can you really have thought that love and joy would always be at the mercy of frowns and sighs? Did you not know they were stronger than their opposites?"

"Love? How dare *you* use that sacred word?" said the Tragedian. At the same moment he gathered up the chain which had now for some time been swinging uselessly at his side, and somehow disposed of it. I am not quite sure, but I think he swallowed it. Then for the first time it became clear that the Lady saw and addressed him only.

"Where is Frank?" she said. "And who are you, Sir? I never knew you. Perhaps you had better leave me. Or stay, if you prefer. If it would help you and if it were possible I would go down with you into Hell: but you cannot bring Hell into me."

"You do not love me," said the Tragedian in a thin bat-like voice: and he was now very difficult to see.

"I cannot love a lie," said the Lady. "I cannot love the thing which is not. I am in Love, and out of it I will not go."

There was no answer. The Tragedian had vanished. The Lady was alone in that woodland place, and a brown bird went hopping past her, bending with its light feet the grasses I could not bend.

Presently the Lady got up and began to walk away. The other Bright Spirits came forward to receive her, singing as they came:

"The Happy Trinity is her home: nothing can trouble her joy.
She is the bird that evades every net: the wild deer that leaps
*   every pitfall.*
Like the mother bird to its chickens or a shield to the arm'd

knight: so is the Lord to her mind, in His unchanging
lucidity.

*Bogies will not scare her in the dark: bullets will not frighten
her in the day.*

*Falsehoods tricked out as truths assail her in vain: she sees
through the lie as if it were glass.*

*The invisible germ will not harm her: nor yet the glittering
sun-stroke.*

*A thousand fail to solve the problem, ten thousand choose
the wrong turning: but she passes safely through.*

*He details immortal gods to attend her: upon every road where
she must travel.*

*They take her hand at hard places: she will not stub her toes
in the dark.*

*She may walk among Lions and rattlesnakes: among dinosaurs
and nurseries of lionets.*

*He fills her brim full with immensity of life: he leads her to
see the world's desire."*

"And yet . . . and yet . . . ," said I to my Teacher, when all
the shapes and the singing had passed some distance away into
the forest, "even now I am not quite sure. Is it really tolerable
that she should be untouched by his misery, even his self-made
misery?"

"Would ye rather he still had the power of tormenting her?
He did it many a day and many a year in their earthly life."

"Well, no. I suppose I don't want that."

"What then?"

"I hardly know, Sir. What some people say on earth is that the
final loss of one soul gives the lie to all the joy of those who are
saved."

"Ye see it does not."

"I feel in a way that it ought to."

"That sounds very merciful: but see what lurks behind it."

"What?"

"The demand of the loveless and the self-imprisoned that they
should be allowed to blackmail the universe: that till they consent
to be happy (on their own terms) no one else shall taste joy:

that theirs should be the final power; that Hell should be able to *veto* Heaven."

"I don't know what I want, Sir."

"Son, son, it must be one way or the other. Either the day must come when joy prevails and all the makers of misery are no longer able to infect it: or else for ever and ever the makers of misery can destroy in others the happiness they reject for themselves. I know it has a grand sound to say ye'll accept no salvation which leaves even one creature in the dark outside. But watch that sophistry or ye'll make a Dog in a Manger the tyrant of the universe."

"But dare one say—it is horrible to say—that Pity must ever die?"

"Ye must distinguish. The action of Pity will live for ever: but the passion of Pity will not. The passion of pity, the pity we merely suffer, the ache that draws men to concede what should not be conceded and to flatter when they should speak truth, the pity that has cheated many a woman out of her virginity and many a statesman out of his honesty—that will die. It was used as a weapon by bad men against good ones: their weapon will be broken."

"And what is the other kind—the action?"

"It's a weapon on the other side. It leaps quicker than light from the highest place to the lowest to bring healing and joy, whatever the cost to itself. It changes darkness into light and evil into good. But it will not, at the cunning tears of Hell, impose on good the tyranny of evil. Every disease that submits to a cure shall be cured: but we will not call blue yellow to please those who insist on still having jaundice, nor make a midden of the world's garden for the sake of some who cannot abide the smell of roses."

"You say it will go down to the lowest, Sir. But she didn't go down with him to Hell. She didn't even see him off by the bus."

"Where would ye have had her go?"

"Why, where we all came from by that bus. The big gulf, beyond the edge of the cliff. Over there. You can't see it from here, but you must know the place I mean."

My Teacher gave a curious smile. "Look," he said, and with

the word he went down on his hands and knees. I did the same (how it hurt my knees!) and presently saw that he had plucked a blade of grass. Using its thin end as a pointer, he made me see, after I had looked very closely, a crack in the soil so small that I could not have identified it without this aid.

"I cannot be certain," he said, "that this *is* the crack ye came up through. But through a crack no bigger than that ye certainly came."

"But—but," I gasped with a feeling of bewilderment not unlike terror. "I saw an infinite abyss. And cliffs towering up and up. And then *this* country on top of the cliffs."

"Aye. But the voyage was not mere locomotion. That bus, and all you inside it, were increasing *in size*."

"Do you mean then that Hell—all that infinite empty town— is down in some little crack like this?"

"Yes. All Hell is smaller than one pebble of your earthly world: but it is smaller than one atom of *this* world, the Real World. Look at yon butterfly. If it swallowed all Hell, Hell would not be big enough to do it any harm or to have any taste."

"It seems big enough when you're in it, Sir."

"And yet all loneliness, angers, hatreds, envies and itchings that it contains, if rolled into one single experience and put into the scale against the least moment of the joy that is felt by the least in Heaven, would have no weight that could be registered at all. Bad cannot succeed even in being bad as truly as good is good. If all Hell's miseries together entered the consciousness of yon wee yellow bird on the bough there, they would be swallowed up without trace, as if one drop of ink had been dropped into that Great Ocean to which your terrestrial Pacific itself is only a molecule."

"I see," said I at last. "She couldn't *fit* into Hell."

He nodded. "There's not room for her," he said. "Hell could not open its mouth wide enough."

"And she couldn't make herself smaller?—like Alice, you know."

"Nothing like small enough. For a damned soul is nearly nothing: it is shrunk, shut up in itself. Good beats upon the damned incessantly as sound waves beat on the ears of the deaf, but they cannot receive it. Their fists are clenched, their teeth are clenched, their eyes fast shut. First they will not, in the end they cannot, open their hands for gifts, or their mouths for food, or their eyes to see."

"Then no one can ever reach them?"

"Only the Greatest of all can make Himself small enough to enter Hell. For the higher a thing is, the lower it can descend— a man can sympathise with a horse but a horse cannot sympathise with a rat. Only One has descended into Hell."

"And will He ever do so again?"

"It was not once long ago that He did it. Time does not work that way when once ye have left the Earth. All moments that have been or shall be were, or are, present in the moment of His descending. There is no spirit in prison to Whom He did not preach."

"And some hear him?"

"Aye."

"In your own books, Sir," said I, "you were a Universalist. You talked as if all men would be saved. And St. Paul too."

"Ye can know nothing of the end of all things, or nothing expressible in those terms. It may be, as the Lord said to the Lady Julian, that all will be well, and all will be well, and all manner of thing will be well. But it's ill talking of such questions."

"Because they are too terrible, Sir?"

"No. Because all answers deceive. If ye put the question from within Time and are asking about possibilities, the answer is certain. The choice of ways is before you. Neither is closed. Any man may choose eternal death. Those who choose it will have it. But if ye are trying to leap on into eternity, if ye are trying to see the final state of all things as it *will* be (for so ye must speak) when there are no more possibilities left but only the Real, then ye ask what cannot be answered to mortal ears. Time is the very lens through which ye see—small and clear, as men see through the wrong end of a telescope—something that would otherwise be too big for ye to see at all. That thing is Freedom: the gift whereby ye must resemble your Maker and are yourselves parts of eternal reality. But ye can see it only through the lens of Time, in a little clear picture, through the inverted telescope. It is a picture of moments following one another and yourself in each moment making some choice that might have been otherwise. Neither the temporal succession nor the phantom of what ye might have chosen and didn't is itself Freedom. They are a lens. The picture is a symbol: but it's truer than any philosophical theorem (or, perhaps, than any mystic's vision) that claims to go behind it. For every attempt to see the shape of eternity except through the lens of Time destroys your knowledge of Freedom. Witness the doctrine of Predestination which shows (truly enough) that eternal reality is not waiting for a future in which to be real; but at the price of removing Freedom which is the deeper truth of the two. And wouldn't Universalism do the same? Ye *cannot* know eternal reality by a definition. Time itself, and all acts and events that fill Time, are the definition, and it must be lived. The Lord said we were gods. How long could ye bear to look (without Time's lens) on the greatness of your own soul and the eternal reality of her choice?"

14.

And suddenly all was changed. I saw a great assembly of gigantic forms all motionless, all in deepest silence, standing forever about a little silver table and looking upon it. And on the table there were little figures like chessmen who went to and fro doing this and that. And I knew that each chessman was the *idolum* or puppet representative of some one of the great presences that stood by. And the acts and motions of each chessman were a moving portrait, a mimicry or pantomime, which delineated the inmost nature of his giant master. And these chessmen are men and women as they appear to themselves and to one another in this world. And the silver table is Time. And those who stand and watch are the immortal souls of those same men and women. Then vertigo and terror seized me and, clutching at my Teacher, I said, "Is *that* the truth? Then is all that I have been seeing in this country false? These conversations between the Spirits and the Ghosts—were they only the mimicry of choices that had really been made long ago?"

"Or might ye not as well say, anticipations of a choice to be made at the end of all things? But ye'd do better to say neither. Ye saw the choices a bit more clearly than ye could see them on earth: the lens was clearer. But it was still seen through the lens. Do not ask of a vision in a dream more than a vision in a dream can give."

"A dream? Then—then—am I not really here, Sir?"

"No, Son," said he kindly, taking my hand in his. "It is not so good as that. The bitter drink of death is still before you. Ye are only dreaming. And if ye come to tell of what ye have seen, make it plain that it was but a dream. See ye make it very plain. Give no poor fool the pretext to think ye are claiming knowledge of what no mortal knows. I'll have no Swedenborgs and no Vale Owens among my children."

"God forbid, Sir," said I, trying to look very wise.

"He *has* forbidden it. That's what I'm telling ye." As he said this he looked more Scotch than ever. I was gazing steadfastly on his face. The vision of the chessmen had faded, and once more the quiet woods in the cool light before sunrise were about us. Then, still looking at his face, I saw there something that sent a quiver through my whole body. I stood at that moment with my back to the East and the mountains, and he, facing me, looked towards them. His face flushed with a new light. A fern, thirty yards behind him, turned golden. The eastern side of every tree-trunk grew bright. Shadows deepened. All the time there had been bird noises, trillings, chatterings, and the like; but now suddenly the full chorus was poured from every branch; cocks were crowing, there was music of hounds, and horns; above all this ten thousand tongues of men and woodland angels and the wood itself sang. "It comes! It comes!" they sang. "Sleepers awake! It comes, it comes, it comes." One dreadful glance over my shoulder I essayed—not long enough to see (or did I see?) the rim of the sunrise that shoots Time dead with golden arrows and puts to flight all phantasmal shapes. Screaming, I buried my eyes in the folds of my Teacher's robe. "The morning! The morning!" I cried, "I am caught by the morning and I am a ghost." But it was too late. The light, like solid blocks, intolerable of edge and weight, came thundering upon my head. Next moment the folds of my Teacher's garment were only the folds of the old ink-stained cloth on my study table which I had pulled down with me as I fell from my chair. The blocks of light were only the books which I had pulled off with it, falling about my head. I awoke in a cold room, hunched on the floor beside a black and empty grate, the clock striking three, and the siren howling overhead.

MIRACLES

A Preliminary Study

by

C. S. Lewis

FELLOW OF MAGDALEN COLLEGE, OXFORD

THE MACMILLAN COMPANY, NEW YORK

TO
CECIL AND DAPHNE HARWOOD

Contents

Among the hills a meteorite
Lies huge; and moss has overgrown,
And wind and rain with touches light
Made soft, the contours of the stone.

Thus easily can Earth digest
A cinder of sidereal fire,
And make her translunary guest
The native of an English shire.

Nor is it strange these wanderers
Find in her lap their fitting place,
For every particle that's hers
Came at the first from outer space.

All that is Earth has once been sky;
Down from the sun of old she came,
Or from some star that travelled by
Too close to his entangling flame.

Hence, if belated drops yet fall
From heaven, on these her plastic power
Still works as once it worked on all
The glad rush of the golden shower.

C.S.L.

(Reprinted by permission of *Time and Tide*)

MIRACLES

I.

THE SCOPE OF THIS BOOK

Those who wish to succeed must ask the right preliminary questions.

ARISTOTLE,
Metaphysics, II, (III), i.

In all my life I have met only one person who claims to have seen a ghost. And the interesting thing about the story is that that person disbelieved in the immortal soul before she saw the ghost and still disbelieves after seeing it. She says that what she saw must have been an illusion or a trick of the nerves. And obviously she may be right. Seeing is not believing.

For this reason, the question whether miracles occur can never be answered simply by experience. Every event which might claim to be a miracle is, in the last resort, something presented to our senses, something seen, heard, touched, smelled, or tasted. And our senses are not infallible. If anything extraordinary seems to have happened, we can always say that we have been the victims of an illusion. If we hold a philosophy which excludes the supernatural, this is what we always shall say. What we learn from experience depends on the kind of philosophy we bring to experience. It is therefore useless to appeal to experience before we have settled, as well as we can, the philosophical question.

If immediate experience cannot prove or disprove the miraculous, still less can history do so. Many people think one can decide whether a miracle occurred in the past by examining the evidence "according to the ordinary rules of historical inquiry." But the ordinary rules cannot be worked until we have decided whether miracles are possible, and if so, how probable they are.

For if they are impossible, then no amount of historical evidence will convince us. If they are possible but immensely improbable, then only mathematically demonstrative evidence will convince us: and since history never provides that degree of evidence for any event, history can never convince us that a miracle occurred. If, on the other hand, miracles are not intrinsically improbable, then the existing evidence will be sufficient to convince us that quite a number of miracles have occurred. The result of our historical inquiries thus depends on the philosophical views which we have been holding before we even began to look at the evidence. The philosophical question must therefore come first.

Here is an example of the sort of thing that happens if we omit the preliminary philosophical task, and rush on to the historical. In a popular commentary on the Bible you will find a discussion of the date at which the Fourth Gospel was written. The author says it must have been written after the execution of St. Peter, because, in the Fourth Gospel, Christ is represented as predicting the execution of St. Peter. "A book," thinks the author, "cannot be written *before* events which it refers to." Of course it cannot—unless real predictions ever occur. If they do, then this argument for the date is in ruins. And the author has not discussed at all whether real predictions are possible. He takes it for granted (perhaps unconsciously) that they are not. Perhaps he is right: but if he is, he has not discovered this principle by historical inquiry. He has brought his disbelief in predictions to his historical work, so to speak, ready made. Unless he had done so his historical conclusion about the date of the Fourth Gospel could not have been reached at all. His work is therefore quite useless to a person who wants to know *whether* predictions occur. The author gets to work only after he has already answered that question in the negative, and on grounds which he never communicates to us.

This book is intended as a preliminary to historical inquiry. I am not a trained historian and I shall not examine the historical evidence for the Christian miracles. My effort is to put my readers in a position to do so. It is no use going to the texts until we have some idea about the possibility or probability of the miraculous. Those who assume that miracles cannot happen are merely wasting their time by looking into the texts; we know in advance what results they will find for they have begun by begging the question.

2.

THE NATURALIST AND
THE SUPERNATURALIST

"Gracious!" exclaimed Mrs. Snip, "and is there a place where people venture to live above the ground?" "I never heard of people living *under* ground," replied Tim, "before I came to Giant-Land." "Came to Giant-Land!" cried Mrs. Snip, "why, isn't everywhere Giant-Land?"

ROLAND QUIZ,
Giant-Land, chap. xxxii.

I use the word *Miracle* to mean an interference with Nature by supernatural power.[1] Unless there exists, in addition to Nature, something else which we may call the supernatural, there can be no miracles. Some people believe that nothing exists except Nature; I call these people *Naturalists.* Others think that, besides Nature, there exists something else: I call them *Supernaturalists.* Our first question, therefore, is whether the Naturalists or the Supernaturalists are right. And here comes our first difficulty.

Before the Naturalist and the Supernaturalist can begin to discuss their difference of opinion, they must surely have an agreed definition both of Nature and of Supernature. But unfortunately it is almost impossible to get such a definition. Just because the Naturalist thinks that nothing but Nature exists, the word *Nature* means to him merely "everything" or "the whole show" or "whatever there is." And if that is what we mean by Na-

---

[1] This definition is not that which would be given by many theologians. I am adopting it not because I think it an improvement upon theirs but precisely because, being crude and "popular," it enables me most easily to treat those questions which "the common reader" probably has in mind when he takes up a book on Miracles.

ture, then of course nothing else exists. The real question between him and the Supernaturalist has evaded us. Some philosophers have defined Nature as "What we perceive with our five
senses." But this also is unsatisfactory; for we do not perceive our
own emotions in that way, and yet they are presumably "natural"
events. In order to avoid this deadlock and to discover what the
Naturalist and the Supernaturalist are really differing about,
we must approach our problem in a more roundabout way.

I begin by considering the following sentences. (1) Are those
his natural teeth or a set? (2) The dog in his natural state is covered with fleas. (3) I love to get away from tilled lands and
metalled roads and be alone with Nature. (4) Do be natural.
Why are you so affected? (5) It may have been wrong to kiss her
but it was very natural.

A common thread of meaning in all these usages can easily be
discovered. The natural teeth are those which grow in the mouth;
we do not have to design them, make them, or fit them. The dog's
natural state is the one he will be in if no one takes soap and
water and prevents it. The countryside where Nature reigns
supreme is the one where soil, weather, and vegetation produce their results unhelped and unimpeded by man. Natural
behaviour is the behaviour which people would exhibit if they
were not at the pains to alter it. The natural kiss is the kiss which
will be given if moral or prudential consideration do not inter-
vene. In all the examples Nature means what happens "of itself" or "of its own accord": what you do not need to labour for;
what you will get if you take no measures to stop it. The Greek
word for Nature (Physis) is connected with the Greek verb for
"to grow"; Latin *Natura,* with the verb "to be born." The Natural is what springs up, or comes forth, or arrives, or goes on, *of
its own accord:* the given, what is there already: the spontaneous, the unintended, the unsolicited.

What the Naturalist believes is that the ultimate Fact, the
thing you can't go behind, is a vast process in space and time
which is *going on of its own accord.* Inside that total system every
particular event (such as your sitting reading this book) happens
because some other event has happened; in the long run, because
the Total Event is happening. Each particular thing (such as this

page) is what it is because other things are what they are; and so, eventually, because the whole system is what it is. All the things and events are so completely interlocked that no one of them can claim the slightest independence from "the whole show." None of the exists "on its own" or "goes on of its own accord" except in the sense that it exhibits, at some particular place and time, that general "existence on its own" or "behaviour of its own accord" which belongs to "Nature" (the great total inter-locked event) as a whole. Thus no thoroughgoing Naturalist be-lieves in free will: for free will would mean that human beings have the power of independent action, the power of doing some-thing more or other than what was involved by the total series of events. And any such separate power of originating events is what the Naturalist denies. Spontaneity, originality, action "on its own," is a privilege reserved for "the whole show," which he calls *Nature*.

The Supernaturalist agrees with the Naturalist that there must be something which exists in its own right; some basic Fact whose existence it would be nonsensical to try to explain because this Fact is itself the ground or startingpoint of all explanations. But he does not identify this Fact with "the whole show." He thinks that things fall into two classes. In the first class we find either things or (more probably) One Thing which is basic and original, which exists on its own. In the second we find things which are merely derivative from that One Thing. The one basic Thing has caused all the other things to be. It exists on its own; they exist because it exists. They will cease to exist if it ever ceases to maintain them in existence; they will be altered if it ever alters them.

The difference between the two views might be expressed by saying that Naturalism gives us a democratic, Supernaturalism a monarchical, picture of reality. The Naturalist thinks that the privilege of "being on its own" resides in the total mass of things, just as in a democracy sovereignty resides in the whole mass of the people. The Supernaturalist thinks that this privilege belongs to some things or (more probably) One Thing and not to others— just as, in a real monarchy, the king has sovereignty and the people have not. And just as, in a democracy, all citizens are equal, so for the Naturalist one thing or event is as good as another, in the sense that they are all equally dependent on the total system of things. Indeed each of them is only the way in which the character of that total system exhibits itself at a particular point in space and time. The Supernaturalist, on the other hand, believes that the one original or self-existent thing is on a different level from, and more important than, all other things.

At this point a suspicion may occur that Supernaturalism first arose from reading into the universe the structure of monarchical societies. But then of course it may with equal reason be suspected that Naturalism has arisen from reading into it the structure of modern democracies. The two suspicions thus cancel out and give us no help in deciding which theory is more likely to be true. They do indeed remind us that Supernaturalism is the characteristic philosophy of a monarchical age and Naturalism of a democratic, in the sense that Supernaturalism, even if false, would have been believed by the great mass of unthinking people four hundred years ago, just as Naturalism, even if false, will be believed by the great mass of unthinking people to-day.

Everyone will have seen that the One Self-existent Thing— or the small class of self-existent things—in which Supernaturalists believe, is what we call God or the gods. I propose for the rest of this book to treat only that form of Supernaturalism which believes in one God; partly because polytheism is not likely to be a live issue for most of my readers, and partly because those who believed in many gods very seldom, in fact, regarded their gods as creators of the universe and as self-existent. The gods of Greece were not really supernatural in the strict sense which I am giving to the word. They were products of the total system of things and included within it. This introduces an important distinction.

The difference between Naturalism and Supernaturalism is not exactly the same as the difference between belief in a God and disbelief. Naturalism, without ceasing to be itself, could admit a certain kind of God. The great interlocking event called Nature might be such as to produce at some stage a great cosmic consciousness, an indwelling "God" arising from the whole process as human mind arises (according to the Naturalists) from human organisms. A Naturalist would not object to that sort of

God. The reason is this. Such a God would not stand outside Nature or the total system, would not be existing "on his own." It would still be "the whole show" which was the basic Fact, and such a God would merely be one of the things (even if he were the most interesting) which the basic Fact contained. What Naturalism cannot accept is the idea of a God who stands outside Nature and made it.

We are now in a position to state the difference between the Naturalist and the Supernaturalist despite the fact that they do not mean the same by the word Nature. The Naturalist believes that a great process, or "becoming," exists "on its own" in space and time, and that nothing else exists—what we call particular things and events being only the parts into which we analyse the great process or the shapes which that process takes at given moments and given points in space. This single, total reality he calls Nature. The Supernaturalist believes that one Thing exists on its own and has produced the framework of space and time and the procession of systematically connected events which fill them. This framework, and this filling, he calls Nature. It may, or may not, be the only reality which the one Primary Thing has produced. There might be other systems in addition to the one we call Nature.

In that sense there might be several "Natures." This conception must be kept quite distinct from what is commonly called "plurality of worlds"—i.e. different solar systems or different galaxies, "island universes" existing in widely separated parts of a single space and time. These, however remote, would be parts of the same Nature as our own sun: it and they would be interlocked by being in relations to one another, spatial and temporal relations and casual relations as well. And it is just this reciprocal interlocking within a system which makes it what we call a Nature. Other Natures might not be spatio-temporal at all: or, if any of them were, their space and time would have no spatial or temporal relation to ours. It is just this discontinuity, this failure of interlocking, which would justify us in calling them different Natures. This does not mean that there would be absolutely no relation between them; they would be related by their common derivation from a single Supernatural source. They would, in this respect, be like different novels by a single author; the events in one story have no relation to the events in another *except* that they are invented by the same author. To find the relation between them you must go right back to the author's mind: there is no cutting across from anything Mr. Pickwick says in *Pickwick Papers* to anything Mrs. Gamp hears in *Martin Chuzzlewit*. Similarly there would be no normal cutting across from an event in one Nature to an event in any other. By a "normal" relation I mean one which occurs in virtue of the character of the two systems. We have to put in the qualification "normal" because we do not know in advance that God might not bring two Natures into partial contact at some particular point: that is, He might allow *selected* events in the one to produce results in the other. There would thus be, at certain points, a partial interlocking; but this would not turn the two Natures into one, for the total reciprocity which makes a Nature would still be lacking, and the spasmodic interlocking would arise not from what either system was in itself but from the Divine act which was bringing them together. If this occurred each of the two Natures would be "supernatural" in relation to the other: but the fact of their contact would be supernatural in a more absolute sense—not as being beyond this or that Nature but beyond any and every Nature. It would be one kind of Miracle. The other kind would be Divine "interference" not by the bringing together of two Natures, but simply.

All this is, at present, purely speculative. It by no means follows from Supernaturalism that Miracles of any sort do in fact occur. God (the primary thing) may never in fact interfere with the natural system He has created. If He has created more natural systems than one, He may never cause them to impinge on one another.

But that is a question for further consideration. If we decide that Nature is not the only thing there is, then we cannot say in advance whether she is safe from miracles or not. There are things outside her: we do not yet know whether they can get in. The gates may be barred, or they may not. But if Naturalism is true, then we do know in advance that miracles are impossible; nothing can come into Nature from the outside because there is nothing outside to come in, Nature being everything. No doubt, events which we in our ignorance should mistake for miracles might occur: but they would in reality be (just like the commonest events) an inevitable result of the character of the whole system.

Our first choice, therefore, must be between Naturalism and Supernaturalism.

3.

THE SELF-CONTRADICTION
OF THE NATURALIST

We cannot have it both ways, and no sneers at the limitations
of logic . . . amend the dilemma.

I. A. RICHARDS,
Principles of Literary Criticism, chap. xxv.

If Naturalism is true, every finite thing or event must be (in
principle) explicable in terms of the Total System. I say "explicable *in principle"* because of course we are not going to demand
that naturalists, at any given moment, should have found the detailed explanation of every phenomenon. Obviously many things
will only be explained when the sciences have made further progress. But if Naturalism is to be accepted we have a right to demand that every single thing should be such that we see, in general, how it could be explained in terms of the Total System. If
any one thing exists which is of such a kind that we see in advance the impossibility of ever giving it *that kind* of explanation,
then Naturalism would be in ruins. If necessities of thought
force us to allow to any one thing any degree of independence
from the Total System—if any one thing makes good a claim to
be on its own, to be something more than an expression of the
character of Nature as a whole—then we have abandoned Naturalism. For by Naturalism we mean the doctrine that only
Nature—the whole interlocked system—exists. And if that were
true, every thing and event would, if we knew enough, be explicable without remainder (no *heel-taps*) as a necessary product of
the system. The whole system being what it is, it ought to be a
contradiction in terms if you were not reading this book at the
moment; and, conversely, the only cause why you are reading

it ought to be that the whole system, at such and such a place and hour, was bound to take that course.

One threat against strict Naturalism has recently been launched on which I myself will base no argument, but which it will be well to notice. The older scientists believed that the smallest particles of matter moved according to strict laws: in other words, that the movements of each particle were "interlocked" with the total system of Nature. Some modern scientists seem to think—if I understand them—that this is not so. They seem to think that the individual unit of matter (it would be rash to call it any longer a "particle") moves in an indeterminate or random fashion; moves, in fact, "on its own" or "of its own accord." The regularity which we observe in the movements of the smallest visible bodies is explained by the fact that each of these contains millions of units and that the law of averages therefore levels out the idiosyncrasies of the individual unit's behaviour. The movement of one unit is incalculable, just as the result of tossing a coin once is incalculable: the majority movement of a billion units can however be predicted, just as, if you tossed a coin a billion times, you could predict a nearly equal number of heads and tails. Now it will be noticed that if this theory is true we have really admitted something other than Nature. If the movements of the individual units are events "on their own," events which do not interlock with all other events, then these movements are not part of Nature. It would be, indeed, too great a shock to our habits to describe them as *super*natural. I think we should have to call them *sub*natural. But all our confidence that Nature has no doors, and no reality outside herself for doors to open on, would have disappeared. There is apparently *something* outside her, the Subnatural; it is indeed from this Subnatural that all events and all "bodies" are, as it were, fed into her. And clearly if she thus has a back door opening on the Subnatural, it is quite on the cards that she may also have a front door opening on the Supernatural and events might be fed into her at that door too.

I have mentioned this theory because it puts in a fairly vivid light certain conceptions which we shall have to use later on. But I am not, for my own part, assuming its truth. Those who (like myself) have had a philosophical rather than a scientific education find it almost impossible to believe that the scientists really mean what they seem to be saying. I cannot help thinking they mean no more than that the movements of individual units are permanently incalculable *to us,* not that they are in themselves random and lawless. And even if they mean the latter, a layman can hardly feel any certainty that some new scientific development may not to-morrow abolish this whole idea of a lawless Subnature. For it is the glory of science to progress. I therefore turn willingly to other ground.

It is clear that everything we know, beyond our own immediate sensations, is inferred from those sensations. I do not mean that we begin as children, by regarding our sensations as "evidence" and thence arguing consciously to the existence of space, matter, and other people. I mean that if, after we are old enough to understand the question, our confidence in the existence of anything else (say, the solar system or the Spanish Armada) is challenged, our argument in defence of it will have to take the form of inferences from our immediate sensations. Put in its most general form the inference would run, "Since I am presented with colours, sounds, shapes, pleasures and pains which I cannot perfectly predict or control, and since the more I investigate them the more regular their behaviour appears, therefore there must exist something other than myself and it must be systematic." Inside this very general inference, all sorts of special trains of inference lead us to more detailed conclusions. We infer Evolution from fossils: we infer the existence of our own brains from what we find inside the skulls of other creatures like ourselves in the dissecting room.

All possible knowledge, then, depends on the validity of reasoning. If the feeling of certainty which we express by words like *must be* and *therefore* and *since* is a real perception of how things outside our own minds really "must" be, well and good. But if this certainty is merely a feeling *in* our own minds and not a genuine insight into realities beyond them—if it merely represents the way our minds happen to work—then we can have no knowledge. Unless human reasoning is valid no science can be true.

It follows that no account of the universe can be true unless

that account leaves it possible for our thinking to be a real insight. A theory which explained everything else in the whole
universe but which made it impossible to believe that our thinking was valid, would be utterly out of court. For that theory
would itself have been reached by thinking, and if thinking is not
valid that theory would, of course, be itself demolished. It would
have destroyed its own credentials. It would be an argument
which proved that no argument was sound—a proof that there
are no such things as proofs—which is nonsense.

We must believe in the validity of rational thought, and we
must not believe in anything inconsistent with its validity. But we
can believe in the validity of thought only under certain conditions. Consider the following sentences. (1) "He thinks that dog
dangerous because he has often seen it muzzled and he has noticed that messengers always try to avoid going to that house."
(2) "He thinks that dog dangerous because it is black and ever
since he was bitten by a black dog in childhood he has always
been afraid of black dogs."

Both sentences explain *why* the man thinks as he does. But
the one explanation substantiates the value of his thought, the
other wholly discredits it. Why is it that to discover the cause of a
thought sometimes damages its credit and sometimes reinforces
it? Because the one cause is a good cause and the other a bad
cause? But the man's complex about black dogs is not a bad cause
in the sense of being a weak or inefficient one. If the man is in a
sufficiently pathological condition, it may be quite irresistible
and, in that sense, as good a cause for his belief as the Earth's
revolution is for day and night. The real difference is that in the
first instance the man's belief is caused by something rational
(by argument from observed facts) while in the other it is caused
by something irrational (association of ideas).

We may in fact state it as a rule that *no thought is valid if it
can be fully explained as the result of irrational causes.* Every
reader of this book applies this rule automatically all day long.
When a sober man tells you that the house is full of rats or snakes,
you attend to him: if you know that his belief in the rats and
snakes is due to *delirium tremens* you do not even bother to
look for them. If you even *suspect* an irrational cause, you be-

gin to pay less attention to a man's beliefs; your friend's pessimistic view of the European situation alarms you less when you discover that he is suffering from a bad liver attack. Conversely, when we discover a belief to be false we then first look about for irrational causes ("I was tired"—"I was in a hurry"—"I wanted to believe it"). The whole disruptive power of Marxism and Freudianism against traditional beliefs has lain in their claim to expose irrational causes for them. If any Marxist is reading these lines at this moment, he is murmuring to himself, "All this argument really results from the fact that the author is a bourgeois" —in fact he is applying the rule I have just stated. Because he thinks that my thoughts result from an irrational cause he therefore discounts them. All thoughts which are so caused are valueless. We never, in our ordinary thinking, admit any exceptions to this rule.

Now it would clearly be preposterous to apply this rule to each particular thought as we come to it and yet not to apply it to all thoughts taken collectively, that is, to human reason as a whole. Each particular thought is valueless if it is the result of irrational causes. Obviously, then, the whole process of human thought, what we call Reason, is equally valueless if it is the result of irrational causes. Hence every theory of the universe which makes the human mind a result of irrational causes is inadmissible, for it would be a proof that there are no such things as proofs. Which is nonsense.

But Naturalism, as commonly held, is precisely a theory of this sort. The mind, like every other particular thing or event, is supposed to be simply the product of the Total System. It is supposed to be that and nothing more, to have no power whatever of "going on of its own accord." And the Total System is not supposed to be rational. All thoughts whatever are therefore the results of irrational causes, and nothing more than that. The finest piece of scientific reasoning is caused in just the same irrational way as the thoughts a man has because a bit of bone is pressing on his brain. If we continue to apply our Rule, both are equally valueless. And if we stop applying our Rule we are no better off. For then the Naturalist will have to admit that thoughts produced by lunacy or alcohol or by the mere wish to disbelieve in Naturalism are just as valid as his own thoughts. What is sauce for the goose is sauce for the gander. The Naturalist cannot condemn other people's thoughts because they have irrational causes and continue to believe his own which have (if Naturalism is true) equally irrational causes.

The shortest and simplest form of this argument is that given by Professor J. B. S. Haldane in *Possible Worlds* (p. 209). He writes, "If my mental processes are determined wholly by the motions of atoms in my brain, I have no reason to suppose that my beliefs are true . . . and hence I have no reason for supposing my brain to be composed of atoms." If I have avoided this form of the argument, this is because I do not wish to have on our hands at this stage so difficult a concept as Matter. The trouble about atoms is not that they are material (whatever that may mean) but that they are, presumably, irrational. Or even if they were rational they do not produce my beliefs by honestly arguing with me and proving their point but by compelling me to think in a certain way. I am still subject to brute force: my beliefs have irrational causes.

An attempt to get out of the difficulty might be made along the following lines. Even if thoughts are produced by irrational causes, still it might happen by mere accident that some of them were true—just as the black dog might, after all, have been really dangerous though the man's reason for thinking it so was worthless. Now individuals whose thoughts happened, in this accidental way, to be truer than other people's would have an advantage in the struggle for existence. And if habits of thought can be inherited, natural selection would gradually eliminate or weed out the people who have the less useful types of thought. It might therefore have come about by now that the present type of human mind—the sort of thought that has survived—was tolerably reliable.

But it won't do. In the first place, this argument works only if there are such things as heredity, the struggle for existence, and elimination. But we know about these things—certainly about their existence in the past—only by inference. Unless, therefore, you start by assuming inference to be valid, you cannot know about them. You have to assume that inference is valid before you can even begin your argument for its validity. And a proof which sets out by assuming the thing you have to prove, is rubbish. But waive that point. Let heredity and the rest be granted. Even then you cannot show that our processes of thought yield truth unless you are allowed to argue "Because a thought is useful, therefore it must be (at least partly) true." But this is itself an inference. If you trust it, you are once more assuming that very validity which you set out to prove.

In order to avoid endless waste of time we must recognise once and for all that this will happen to any argument whatever which attempts to prove or disprove the validity of thought. By trusting to argument at all you have assumed the point at issue. All arguments about the validity of thought make a tacit, and illegitimate, exception in favour of the bit of thought you are doing at that moment. It has to be left outside the discussion and simply believed in, in the simple old-fashioned way. Thus the Freudian proves that all thoughts are merely due to complexes except the thoughts which constitute this proof itself. The Marxist proves that all thoughts result from class conditioning—except the thought he is thinking while he says this. It is therefore always impossible to begin with any other data whatever and from them to find out whether thought is valid. You must do exactly the opposite—must begin by admitting the self-evidence of logical thought and then believe all other things only in so far as they agree with that. The validity of thought is central: all other things have to be fitted in round it as best they can.

Some Naturalists whom I have met attempt to escape by saying that there *is* no ground for believing our thoughts to be valid and that this does not worry them in the least. "We find that they work," it is said, "and we admit that we cannot argue from this that they give us a true account of any external reality. But we don't mind. We are not interested in truth. Our habits of thought seem to enable humanity to keep alive and that is all we care about." One is tempted to reply that every free man wants truth as well as life: that a mere life-addict is no more respectable than a cocaine addict. But opinions may differ on that point. The real answer is that unless the Naturalists put forward Naturalism as a true theory, we have of course no dispute with them. You can argue with a man who says, "Rice is unwholesome": but you neither can nor need argue with a man who says, "Rice is unwholesome, but I'm not saying this is true." I feel also that this surrender of the claim to truth has all the air of an expedient adopted at the last moment. If the Naturalists do not claim to know any truths, ought they not to have warned us rather earlier of the fact? For really from all the books they have written, in which the behaviour of the remotest nebula, the shyest photon and the most prehistoric man are described, one would have got the idea that they were claiming to give a true account of real things. The fact surely is that they nearly always are claiming to do so. The claim is surrendered only when the question discussed in this chapter is pressed; and when the crisis is over the claim is tacitly resumed.

4.

NATURE AND SUPERNATURE

Throughout the long tradition of European thought it has been said, not by everyone but by most people, or at any rate by most of those who have proved that they have a right to be heard, that Nature, though it is a thing that really exists, is not a thing that exists in itself or in its own right, but a thing which depends for its existence upon something else.

R. G. COLLINGWOOD,
The Idea of Nature, III, iii.

If our argument has been sound, rational thought or Reason is not interlocked with the great interlocking system of irrational events which we call Nature. I am not maintaining that consciousness as a whole must necessarily be put in the same position. Pleasures, pains, fears, hopes, affections and mental images need not. No absurdity would follow from regarding them as part of Nature. The distinction we have to make is not one between "mind" and "matter," much less between "soul" and "body" (hard words, all four of them) but between Reason and Nature: the frontier coming not where the "outer world" ends and what I should ordinarily call "myself" begins, but between Reason and the whole mass of irrational events whether physical or psychological.

At that frontier we find a great deal of traffic but it is all one-way traffic. It is a matter of daily experience that Rational thoughts induce and enable us to alter the course of Nature—of physical nature when we use mathematics to build bridges, or of psychological nature when we apply arguments to alter our own emotions. We succeed in modifying physical nature more often and more completely than we succeed in modifying psychological nature, but we do at least a little to both. On the other hand, Nature is quite powerless to produce Rational thought: not that she never modifies our thinking but that the moment she does so, it ceases (for that very reason) to be rational. For, as we have seen, a train of thought loses all rational credentials as soon as it can be shown to be wholly the result of irrational causes. When Nature, so to speak, attempts to do things to Rational thoughts she only succeeds in killing them. That is the peculiar state of affairs at the frontier. Nature can only raid Reason to kill; but Reason can invade Nature to take prisoners and even to colonise. Every object you see before you at this moment —the walls, ceiling, and furniture, the book, your own washed hands and cut fingernails, bears witness to the colonisation of Nature by Reason: for none of this matter would have been in these states if Nature had had her way. And if you are attending to my argument as closely as I hope, that attention also results from habits which Reason has imposed on the natural ramblings of consciousness. If, on the other hand, a toothache or an anxiety is at this very moment preventing you from attending, then Nature is indeed interfering with your consciousness: but not to produce some new variety of reasoning, only (as far as in her lies) to suspend Reason altogether.

In other words the relation between Reason and Nature is what some people call an Unsymmetrical Relation. Brotherhood is a symmetrical relation because if A is the brother of B, B is the brother of A. Father-and-Son is an unsymmetrical relation because if A is the father of B, B is *not* the father of A. The relation between Reason and Nature is of this kind. Reason is not related to Nature as Nature is related to Reason.

I am only too well aware how shocking those who have been brought up to Naturalism will find the picture which begins to show itself. It is, frankly, a picture in which Nature (at any rate on the surface of our own planet) is perforated or pock-marked all over by little orifices at each of which something of a different kind from herself—namely a Reason—can do things to her. I can only beg you, before you throw the book away, to consider seriously whether your instinctive repugnance to such a conception is really rational, or whether it is only emotional or aesthetic. I know that the hankering for a universe which is all of a piece, and in which everything is the same sort of thing as everything else—a continuity, a seamless web, a democratic universe—is very deep-seated in the modern heart: in mine, no less than in yours. But have we any real assurance that things are like that? Are we mistaking for an intrinsic probability what is really a human desire for tidiness and harmony? Bacon warned us long ago that "the human understanding is of its own nature prone to suppose the existence of more order and regularity in the world than it finds. And though there be many things which are singular and unmatched, yet it devises for them parallels and conjugates and relatives which do not exist. Hence the fiction that all celestial bodies move in perfect circles" (*Novum Organum*, I. 45) . I think Bacon was right. Science itself has already made reality appear less homogeneous than we expected it to be: Newtonian atomism was much more the sort of thing we expected (and desired) than Quantum physics.

If you can, even for the moment, endure the suggested picture of Nature, let us now consider the other factor—the Reasons, or instances of Reason which attack her. We have seen that rational thought is not part of the system of Nature. Within each man there must be an area (however small) of activity which is outside or independent of her. In relation to Nature, rational thought goes on "of its own accord" or exists "on its own." It does not follow that rational thought exists *absolutely* on its own. It might be independent of Nature by being dependent on something else. For it is not dependence simply but dependence on the irrational which undermines the credentials of thought. One step in an argument depends on the previous step, and is all the better for doing so. One man's reason has been led to see things by the aid of another man's reason, and is none the worse for that. It is thus still an open question whether each man's reason exists absolutely on its own or whether it is the result of some (rational) cause—in fact, of some other Reason. That other Reason might conceivably be found to depend on a third, and so on; it would not matter how far this process was carried provided you found Reason coming from Reason at each stage. It is only when you are asked to believe in Reason coming from non-reason that you must cry Halt, for, if you don't, all thought is discredited. It is therefore obvious that sooner or later you must admit a Reason which exists absolutely on its own. The problem is whether you or I can be such a self-existent Reason.

This question almost answers itself the moment we remember what existence "on one's own" means. It means that kind of existence which Naturalists attribute to "the whole show" and Supernaturalists attribute to God. For instance, what exists on its own must have existed from all eternity; for if anything else could make it begin to exist then it would not exist on its own but because of something else. It must also exist incessantly: that is, it cannot cease to exist and then begin again. For having once ceased to be, it obviously could not recall itself to existence, and if anything else recalled it it would then be a dependent being. Now it is clear that my Reason has grown up gradually since my birth and is interrupted for several hours each night. I therefore cannot be that eternal self-existent Reason which neither slumbers nor sleeps. Yet if any thought is valid, such a Reason must exist and must be the source of my own imperfect and intermittent rationality. Human minds, then, are not the only supernatural entities that exist. They do not come from nowhere. Each has come into Nature from Supernature: each has its tap-root in an eternal, self-existent, rational Being, whom we call God. Each is an offshoot, or spearhead, or incursion of that Supernatural reality into Nature.

Some people may here raise the following question. If Reason is sometimes present in my mind and sometimes not, then, instead of saying that "I" am a product of eternal Reason, would it not be wiser to say simply that eternal Reason itself occasionally works through my organism, leaving me a merely natural being? A wire does not become something other than a wire because an electric current has passed through it. But to talk thus is, in my opinion, to forget what reasoning is like. It is not an object which knocks against us, nor even a sensation which we feel. Reasoning doesn't "happen to" us: we *do* it. Every train of thought is accompanied by what Kant called "the *I think*." The traditional doctrine that I am a creature to whom God has given reason but who is distinct from God seems to me much more philosophical than the theory that what appears to be my thinking is only God's thinking through me. On the latter view it is very diffi-cult to explain what happens when I think correctly but reach a false conclusion because I have been misinformed about facts. Why God—who presumably knows the real facts—should be at the pains to think one of His perfectly rational thoughts through a mind in which it is bound to produce error, I do not understand. Nor indeed do I understand why, if all "my" valid thinking is really God's, He should either Himself mistake it for mine or cause me to mistake it for mine. It seems much more likely that human thought is not God's but God-kindled.

I must hasten, however, to add that this is a book about Mir-acles, not about everything. I am attempting no full doctrine of Man[1]: and I am not in the least trying to smuggle in an argu-ment for the "immortality of the soul." The earliest Christian documents give a casual and unemphatic assent to the belief that the supernatural part of a man survives the death of the natural organism. But they are very little interested in the matter. What they are intensely interested in is the restoration or "resurrec-tion" of the whole composite creature by a miraculous divine act: and until we have come to some conclusion about miracles in general we shall certainly not discuss that. At this stage the su-pernatural element in Man concerns us solely as evidence that something beyond Nature exists. The dignity and destiny of man have, at present, nothing to do with the argument. We are inter-ested in Man only because his rationality is the little telltale rift in Nature which shows that there is something beyond or behind her.

In a pond whose surface was completely covered with scum and floating vegetation, there might be a few waterlilies. And you might of course be interested in them for their beauty. But you might also be interested in them because from their structure you could deduce that they had stalks underneath which went down to roots in the bottom. The Naturalist thinks that the pond (Nature—the great event in space and time) is of an infinite depth—that there is nothing but water however far you go down. My claim is that some of the things on the surface (i.e. in our ex-perience) show the contrary. These things (rational minds) re-

[1] See Appendix A.

veal, on inspection, that they at least are not floating but attached by stalks to the bottom. Therefore the pond has a bottom. It is not pond, pond forever. Go deep enough and you will come to something that is not pond—to mud and earth and then to rock and finally the whole bulk of Earth and the subterranean fire.

At this point it is tempting to try whether Naturalism cannot still be saved. I pointed out in Chapter 2 that one could remain a Naturalist and yet believe in a certain kind of God—a cosmic consciousness to which "the whole show" somehow gave rise: what we might call an *Emergent* God. Would not an Emergent God give us all we need? Is it really necessary to bring in a *super*natural God, distinct from and outside the whole interlocked system? (Notice, Modern Reader, how your spirits rise—how much more at home you would feel with an emergent, than with a transcendent, God—how much less primitive, repugnant, and naif the emergent conception seems to you. For by that, as you will see later, there hangs a tale.)

But I am afraid it will not do. It is, of course, possible to suppose that when all the atoms of the universe got into a certain relation (which they were bound to get into sooner or later) they would give rise to a universal consciousness. And it might have thoughts. And it might cause those thoughts to pass through our minds. But unfortunately its own thoughts, on this supposition, would be the product of irrational causes and therefore, by the rule which we use daily, they would have no validity. This cosmic mind would be, just as much as our own minds, the product of mindless Nature. We have not escaped from the difficulty, we have only put it a stage further back. The cosmic mind will help us only if we put it at the beginning, if we suppose it to be, not the product of the total system, but the basic, original, self-existent Fact which exists in its own right. But to admit *that* sort of cosmic mind is to admit a God outside Nature, a transcendent and supernatural God. This route, which looked like offering an escape, really leads us round again to the place we started from.

There is, then, a God who is not a part of Nature. But nothing has yet been said to show that He must have created her. Might God and Nature be both self-existent and totally independent of each other? If you thought they were you would be a Dualist and would hold a view which I consider manlier and more reasonable than any form of Naturalism. You might be many worse things than a Dualist, but I do not think Dualism is true. There is an enormous difficulty in conceiving two things which simply co-exist and have no other relation. If this difficulty sometimes escapes our notice, that is because we are the victims of picture-thinking. We really imagine them side by side in some kind of space. But of course if they were both in a common space, or a common time, or in any kind of common medium whatever, they would both be parts of a system, in fact of a "Nature." Even if we succeed in eliminating such pictures, the mere fact of our trying to think of them together slurs over the real difficulty because, for that moment anyway, our own mind is the common medium. If there can be such a thing as sheer "otherness," if things can co-exist and no more, it is at any rate a conception which my mind cannot form. And in the present instance it seems specially gratuitous to try to form it, for we already know that God and Nature have come into a certain relation. They have, at the very least, a relation—almost, in one sense, a common frontier—in every human mind.

The relations which arise at that frontier are indeed of a most complicated and intimate sort. That spearhead of the Supernatural which I call my reason links up with all my natural contents —my sensations, emotions, and the like—so completely that I call the mixture by the single word "me." Again, there is what I have called the unsymmetrical character of the frontier relations. When the physical state of the brain dominates my thinking, it produces only disorder. But my brain does not become any less a brain when it is dominated by Reason: nor do my emotions and sensations become any the less emotions and sensations. Reason saves and strengthens my whole system, psychological and physical, whereas that whole system, by rebelling against Reason, destroys both Reason and itself. The military metaphor of a spearhead was apparently ill-chosen. The supernatural Reason enters my natural being not like a weapon—more like a beam of light which illuminates or a principle of organisation which unifies and develops. Our whole picture of Nature being "invaded" (as if by a foreign enemy) was wrong. When we actually examine one of these invasions it looks much more like the arrival of a king among his own subjects or a mahout visiting his own elephant. The elephant may run amuck, Nature may be rebellious. But from observing what happens when Nature obeys it is almost impossible not to conclude that it is her very "nature" to be a subject. All happens *as if* she had been designed for that very role.

To believe that Nature produced God, or even the human mind is, as we have seen, absurd. To believe that the two are both independently self-existent is impossible: at least the attempt to do so leaves me unable to say that I am thinking of anything at all. It is true that Dualism has a certain theological attraction; it seems to make the problem of evil easier. But if we cannot, in fact, think Dualism out to the end, this attractive promise can never be kept, and I think there are better solutions of the problem of evil. There remains, then, the belief that God created Nature. This at once supplies a relation between them and gets rid of the difficulty of sheer "otherness." This also fits in with the observed frontier situation, in which everything looks as if Nature were not resisting an alien invader but rebelling against a lawful sovereign. This, and perhaps this alone, fits in with the fact that Nature, though not apparently intelligent, is intelligible—that events in the remotest parts of space appear to obey the laws of rational thought. Even the act of creation itself presents none of the intolerable difficulties which seem to meet us on every other hypothesis. There is in our own human minds something that bears a faint resemblance to it. We can imagine: that is, we can cause to exist the mental pictures of material objects, and even human characters, and events. We fall short of creation in two ways. In the first place we can only recombine elements borrowed from the real universe: no one can imagine a new primary colour or a sixth sense. In the second place, what we imagine exists only for our own consciousness—though we can, by words, induce other people to build for themselves pictures in their own minds which may be roughly similar to it. We should have to attribute to God the power both of producing the basic elements, of inventing not only colours but colour itself, the senses themselves, space time and matter themselves, and also of imposing what He has invented on created minds. This seems to me no intolerable assumption. It is certainly easier than the idea of God and Nature as wholly unrelated entities, and far easier than the idea of Nature producing valid thought.

I do not maintain that God's creation of Nature can be proved as rigorously as God's existence, but it seems to me overwhelmingly probable, so probable that no one who approached the question with an open mind would very seriously entertain any other hypothesis. In fact one seldom meets people who have grasped the existence of a supernatural God and yet deny that He is the creator. All the evidence we have points in that direction, and difficulties spring up on every side if we try to believe otherwise. No philosophical theory which I have yet come across is a radical improvement on the words of *Genesis,* that "In the beginning God made Heaven and Earth." I say "radical" improvement, because the story in *Genesis*—as St. Jerome said long ago—is told in the manner "of a popular poet," or as we should say, in the form of folk tale. But if you compare it with the creation legends of other peoples—with all these delightful absurdities in which giants to be cut up and floods to be dried up are made to exist *before* Creation—the depth and originality of this Hebrew folk tale will soon be apparent. The idea of *creation* in the rigorous sense of the word is there fully grasped.

5.

A FURTHER DIFFICULTY
IN NATURALISM

Even as rigorous a determinist as Karl Marx, who at times described the social behaviour of the bourgeoisie in terms which suggested a problem in social physics, could subject it at other times to a withering scorn which only the presupposition of moral responsibility could justify.

R. NIEBUHR,
An Interpretation of Christian Ethics, chap. iii.

Some people regard logical thinking as the deadest and driest of our activities and may therefore be repelled by the privileged position I gave it in the last chapter. But logical thinking—Reasoning—had to be the pivot of the argument because, of all the claims which the human mind puts forward, the claim of Reasoning to be valid is the only one which the Naturalist cannot deny without (philosophically speaking) cutting his own throat. You cannot, as we saw, prove that there are no proofs. But you can if you wish regard all human ideals as illusions and all human loves as biological bye-products. That is, you can do so without running into flat self-contradiction and nonsense. Whether you can do so without extreme unplausibility—without accepting a picture of things which no one really believes—is another matter.

Besides reasoning about matters of fact, men also make moral judgments—"I ought to do this"—"I ought not to do that"— "This is good"—"That is evil." Two views have been held about moral judgments. Some people think that when we make them we are not using our Reason, but are employing some different power. Other people think that we make them by our Reason. I myself hold this second view. That is, I believe that the primary moral principles on which all others depend are rationally perceived. We "just see" that there is no reason why my neighbour's happiness should be sacrificed to my own, as we "just see" that things which are equal to the same thing are equal to one another. If we cannot prove either axiom, that is not because they are irrational but because they are self-evident and all proofs depend on them. Their intrinsic reasonableness shines by its own light. It is because all morality is based on such self-evident principles that we say to a man, when we would recall him to right conduct, "Be reasonable."

But this is by the way. For our present purpose it does not matter which of these two views you adopt. The important point is to notice that Moral Judgments raise the same sort of difficulty for Naturalism as any other thoughts. We always assume in discussions about morality, as in all other discussions, that the other man's views are worthless if they can be fully accounted for by some non-moral and non-rational cause. When two men differ about good and evil we soon hear this principle being brought into play: "He believes in the santity of property because he's a millionaire"—"He believes in Pacifism because he's a coward" —"He approves of corporal punishment because he's a sadist." Such taunts may often be untrue: but the mere fact that they are made by the one side, and hotly rebutted by the others, shows clearly what principle is being used. Neither side doubts that if they were true they would be decisive. No one (in real life) pays attention to any moral judgment which can be shown to spring from non-moral and non-rational causes. The Freudian and the Marxist attack traditional morality precisely on this ground— and with wide success. All men accept the principle.

But, of course, what discredits particular moral judgments must equally discredit moral judgment as a whole. If the fact that men have such ideas as *ought* and *ought not* at all can be fully explained by irrational and non-moral causes, then those ideas are an illusion. The Naturalist is ready to explain how the illusion arose. Chemical conditions produce life. Life, under the influence of natural selection, produces consciousness. Conscious organisms which behave in one way live longer than those which behave in another. Living longer, they are more likely to have offspring. Inheritance, and sometimes teaching as well, pass on their mode of behaviour to their young. Thus in every species a pattern of behaviour is built up. In the human species conscious teaching plays a larger part in building it up, and the tribe further strengthens it by killing individuals who don't conform. They also invent gods who are said to punish departures from it. Thus, in time, there comes to exist a strong human impulse to conform. But since this impulse is often at variance with the other impulses, a mental conflict arises, and the man expresses it by saying "I want to do A but I ought to do B."

This account may (or may not) explain why men do in fact make moral judgments. It does not explain how they could be right in making them. It excludes, indeed, the very possibility of their being right. For when men say "I ought" they certainly think they are saying something, and something true, about the nature of the proposed action, and not merely about their own feelings. But if Naturalism is true, "I ought" is the same sort of statement as "I itch" or "I'm going to be sick." In real life when a man says "I ought" we may reply, "Yes. You're right. That *is* what you ought to do," or else, "No. I think you're mistaken." But in a world of Naturalists (if Naturalists really remembered their philosophy out of school) the only sensible reply would be, "Oh, are you?" All moral judgments would be statements about the speaker's feelings, mistaken by him for statements about something else (the real moral quality of actions) which does not exist.

Such a doctrine, I have admitted, is not flatly self-contradictory. The Naturalist can, if he chooses, brazen it out. He can say, "Yes. I quite agree that there is no such thing as wrong and right. I admit that no moral judgment can be 'true' or 'correct' and, consequently, that no one system of morality can be better or worse than another. All ideas of good and evil are hallucinations —shadows cast on the outer world by the impulses which we have been conditioned to feel." Indeed many Naturalists are delighted to say this.

But then they must stick to it; and fortunately (though inconsistently) most real Naturalists do not. A moment after they have admitted that good and evil are illusions, you will find them exhorting us to work for posterity, to educate, revolutionise, liquidate, live and die for the good of the human race. A Naturalist like Mr. H. G. Wells has spent a long life doing so with passionate eloquence and zeal. But surely this is very odd? Just as all the books about spiral nebulae, atoms and cave men would really have led you to suppose that the Naturalists claimed to be able to know something, so all the books in which Naturalists tell us what we ought to do would really make you believe that they thought some ideas of good (their own, for example) to be somehow preferable to others. For they write with indignation like men proclaiming what is good in itself and denouncing what is evil in itself, and not at all like men recording that they personally like mild beer but some people prefer bitter. Yet if the "oughts" of Mr. Wells and, say, Franco are both equally the impulses which Nature has conditioned each to have and both tell us nothing about any objective right or wrong, whence is all the fervour? Do you remember while they are writing thus that when they tell us we "ought to make a better world" the words "ought" and "better" must, on their own showing, refer to an irrationally conditioned impulse which cannot be true or false any more than a vomit or a yawn?

My idea is that sometimes they do forget. That is their glory. Holding a philosophy which excludes humanity, they yet remain human. At the sight of injustice they throw all their Naturalism to the winds and speak like men and like men of genius. They know far better than they think they know. But at other times, I suspect, they are trusting in a supposed way of escape from their difficulty.

It works—or *seems* to work—like this. They say to themselves, "Ah, yes. Morality"—or "bourgeois morality" or "conventional morality" or "traditional morality" or some such addition—"Morality *is* an illusion. But we have found out what modes of behaviour will in fact preserve the human race alive. That is the behaviour we are pressing you to adopt. Pray don't mistake us for moralists. We are under an entirely new management" . . . just as if this would help. It would help only if we grant, firstly, that life is better than death and, secondly, that we ought to care for the lives of our descendants as much as, or more than, for our own. And both these are moral judgments which have, like all others, been explained away by Naturalism. Of course, having been conditioned by Nature in a certain way, we do feel thus about life and about posterity. But the Naturalists have cured us of mistaking these feelings for insights into what we once called "real value." Now that I know that my impulse to serve posterity is just the same kind of thing as my fondness for cheese—now that its transcendental pretensions have been exposed for a sham —do you think I shall pay much attention to it? When it happens to be strong (and it has grown considerably weaker since you explained to me its real nature) I suppose I shall obey it. When it is weak, I shall put my money into cheese. There can be no reason for trying to whip up and encourage the one impulse rather than the other. Not now that I know what they both are. The Naturalists must not destroy all my reverence for conscience on Monday and expect to find me still venerating it on Tuesday.

There is no escape along those lines. If we are to continue to make moral judgments (and whatever we say we shall in fact continue) then we must believe that the conscience of man is not a product of Nature. It can be valid only if it is an offshoot of some absolute moral wisdom, a moral wisdom which exists absolutely "on its own" and is not a product of non-moral, non-rational Nature. As the argument of the last chapter led us to acknowledge a supernatural source for rational thought, so the argument of this leads us to acknowledge a supernatural source for our ideas of good and evil. In other words, we now know something more about God. If you hold that moral judgment is a different thing from Reasoning you will express this new knowledge by saying, "We now know that God has at least one other attribute than rationality." If, like me, you hold that moral judgment is a kind of Reasoning, then you will say, "We now know more about the Divine Reason."

And with this we are almost ready to being our main argument. But before doing so it will be well to pause for the consideration of some misgivings or misunderstandings which may have already arisen.

6.

ANSWERS TO MISGIVINGS

For as bats' eyes are to daylight so is our intellectual eye to those truths which are, in their own nature, the most obvious of all.

ARISTOTLE,
Metaphysics, 1 (Brevior) i.

It must be clearly understood that the argument so far leads to no conception of "souls" or "spirits" (words I have avoided) floating about in the realm of Nature with no relation to their environment. Hence we do not deny—indeed we must welcome—certain considerations which are often regarded as proofs of Naturalism. We can admit, and even insist, that Rational Thinking can be shown to be conditioned in its exercise by a natural object (the brain). It is temporarily impaired by alcohol or a blow on the head. It wanes as the brain decays and vanishes when the brain ceases to function. In the same way the moral outlook of a community can be shown to be closely connected with its history, geographical environment, economic structure, and so forth. The moral ideas of the individual are equally related to his general situation: it is no accident that parents and schoolmasters so often tell us that they can stand any vice rather than lying, the lie being the only defensive weapon of the child. All this, far from presenting us with a difficulty, is exactly what we should expect.

The rational and moral element in each human mind is a point of force from the Supernatural working its way into Nature, exploiting at each point those conditions which Nature offers, repulsed where the conditions are hopeless and impeded when they are unfavourable. A man's Rational thinking is *just so much* of his share in eternal Reason as the state of his brain allows to become operative: it represents, so to speak, the bargain struck or the frontier fixed between Reason and Nature at that particular point. A nation's moral outlook is just so much of its share in eternal Moral Wisdom as its history, economics, etc. lets through. In the same way the voice of the Announcer is just so much of a human voice as the receiving set lets through. Of course it varies with the state of the receiving set, and deteriorates as the set wears out and vanishes altogether if I throw a brick at it. It is conditioned by the apparatus but not originated by it. If it were—if we knew that there was no human being at the microphone—we should not attend to the news. The various and complex conditions under which Reason and Morality appear are the twists and turns of the frontier between Nature and Supernature. That is why, if you wish, you can always ignore Supernature and treat the phenomena purely from the Natural side; just as a man studying on a map the boundaries of Cornwall and Devonshire can always say, "What you call a bulge in Devonshire is really a dent in Cornwall." And in a sense you can't refute him. What we call a bulge in Devonshire always *is* a dent in Cornwall. What we call rational thought in a man always involves a state of the brain, in the long run a relation of atoms. But Devonshire is none the less something more than "where Cornwall ends," and Reason is something more than cerebral bio-chemistry.

I now turn to another possible misgiving. To some people the great trouble about any argument for the Supernatural is simply the fact that argument should be needed at all. If so stupendous a thing exists, ought it not to be obvious as the sun in the sky? Is it not intolerable, and indeed incredible, that knowledge of the most basic of all Facts should be accessible only by wiredrawn reasonings for which the vast majority of men have neither leisure nor capacity? I have great sympathy with this point of view. But we must notice two things.

When you are looking at a garden from a room upstairs it is obvious (once you think about it) that you are looking through a window. But if it is the garden that interests you, you may look at it for a long time without thinking of the window. When you

are reading a book it is obvious (once you attend to it) that you
are using your eyes: but unless your eyes begin to hurt you, or
the book is a text book on optics, you may read all evening without once thinking of eyes. When we talk we are obviously using
language and grammar: and when we try to talk a foreign
language we may be painfully aware of the fact. But when we are
talking English we don't notice it. When you shout from the top
of the stairs, "I'm coming in half a moment," you are not usually
conscious that you have made the singular *am* agree with the
singular *I*. There is indeed a story told about a Redskin who,
having learned several other languages, was asked to write a
grammar of the language used by his own tribe. He replied, after
some thought, that it had no grammar. The grammar he had used
all his life had escaped his notice all his life. He knew it (in one
sense) so well that (in another sense) he did not know it existed.

All these instances show that the fact which is in one respect
the most obvious and primary fact, and through which alone
you have access to all the other facts, may be precisely the one
that is most easily forgotten—forgotten not because it is so remote or abstruse but because it is so near and so obvious. And
that is exactly how the Supernatural has been forgotten. The
Naturalists have been engaged in thinking about Nature. They
have not attended to the fact that they were *thinking*. The moment one attends to this it is obvious that one's own thinking
cannot be merely a natural event, and that therefore something other than Nature exists. The Supernatural is not remote
and abstruse: it is a matter of daily and hourly experience, as
intimate as breathimg. Denial of it depends on a certain absent-
mindedness. But this absent-mindedness is in no way surprising. You do not need—indeed you do not wish—to be always
thinking about windows when you are looking at gardens or always thinking about eyes when you are reading. In the same way
the proper procedure for all limited and particular inquiries is
to ignore the fact of your own thinking, and concentrate on the
object. It is only when you stand back from particular inquiries
and try to form a complete philosophy that you must take it into
account. For a complete philosophy must get in *all* the facts. In it
you turn away from specialised or truncated thought to total

thought: and one of the facts total thought must think about is Thinking itself. There is thus a tendency in the study of Nature to make us forget the most obvious fact of all. And since the Sixteenth Century, when Science was born, the minds of men have been increasingly turned outward, to know Nature and to master her. They have been increasingly engaged on those specialised inquiries for which truncated thought is the correct method. It is therefore not in the least astonishing that they should have forgotten the evidence for the Supernatural. The deeply ingrained habit of truncated thought—what we call the "scientific" habit of mind—was indeed certain to lead to Naturalism, unless this tendency were continually corrected from some other source. But no other source was at hand, for during the same period men of science were coming to be metaphysically and theologically uneducated.

That brings me to the second consideration. The state of affairs in which ordinary people can discover the Supernatural only by abstruse reasoning is recent and, by historical standards, abnormal. All over the world, until quite modern times the direct insight of the mystics and the reasonings of the philosophers percolated to the mass of the people by authority and tradition; they could be received by those who were no great reasoners themselves in the concrete form of myth and ritual and the whole pattern of life. In the conditions produced by a century or so of Naturalism, plain men are being forced to bear burdens which plain men were never expected to bear before. We must get the truth for ourselves or go without it. There may be two explanations for this. It might be that humanity, in rebelling against tradition and authority, have made a ghastly mistake; a mistake which will not be the less fatal because the corruptions of those in authority rendered it very excusable. On the other hand, it may be that the Power which rules our species is at this moment carrying out a daring experiment. Could it be intended that the whole mass of the people should now move forward and occupy for themselves those heights which were once reserved only for the sages? Is the distinction between wise and simple to disappear because all are now expected to become wise? If so, our present blunderings would be but growing pains. But let us make no mistake about our necessities. If we are content to go back and become humble plain men obeying a tradition, well. If we are ready to climb and struggle on till we become sages ourselves, better still. But the man who will neither obey wisdom in others nor adventure for her himself is fatal. A society where the simple many obey the few seers can live: a society where all were seers could live even more fully. But a society where the mass is still simple and the seers are no longer attended to can achieve only superficiality, baseness, ugliness, and in the end extinction. On or back we must go; to stay here is death.

One other point that may have raised doubt or difficulty should here be dealt with. I have advanced reasons for believing that a supernatural element is present in every rational man. The presence of human rationality in the world is therefore a Miracle by the definition given in Chapter 2. On realising this the reader may excusably say, "Oh, if *that's* all he means by a Miracle . . ." and fling the book away. But I ask him to have patience. Human Reason and Morality have been mentioned not as instances of Miracle (at least, not of the kind of Miracle you wanted to hear about) but as proofs of the Supernatural: not in order to show that Nature ever is invaded but that there is a possible invader. Whether you choose to call the regular and familiar invasion by human Reason a Miracle or not is largely a matter of words. Its regularity—the fact that it regularly enters by the same door, human sexual intercourse—may incline you not to do so. It looks as if it were (so to speak) the very nature of Nature to suffer *this* invasion. But then we might later find that it was the very nature of Nature to suffer Miracles in general. Fortunately the course of our argument will allow us to leave this question of terminology on one side. We are going to be concerned with other invasions of Nature—with what everyone would call Miracles. Our question could, if you liked, be put in the form, "Does Supernature ever produce particular results in space and time *except* through the instrumentality of human brains acting on human nerves and muscles."

"I have said "*particular* results" because, on our view, Nature as a whole is herself one huge result of the Supernatural: God created her. God pierces her wherever there is a human mind.

God presumably maintains her in existence. The question is whether He ever does anything else to her. Does He, besides all this, ever introduce into her events of which it would not be true to say, "This is simply the working out of the general character which He gave to Nature as a whole in creating her"? Such events are what are popularly called Miracles: and it will be in this sense only that the word Miracle will be used for the rest of the book.

7.

A CHAPTER OF RED HERRINGS

Thence came forth *Maul,* a giant. This *Maul* did use to spoil
young Pilgrims with sophistry.

BUNYAN.

From the admission that God exists and is the author of Nature,
it by no means follows that miracles must, or even can, occur.
God Himself might be a being of such a kind that it was contrary
to His character to work miracles. Or again, He might have made
Nature the sort of thing that cannot be added to, subtracted
from, or modified. The case against Miracles accordingly relies
on two different grounds. You either think that the character of
God excludes them or that the character of Nature excludes
them. We will begin with the second which is the more popular
ground. In this chapter I shall consider forms of it which are, in
my opinion, very superficial—which might even be called misunderstandings or Red Herrings.

The first Red Herring is this. Any day you may hear a man
(and not necessarily a disbeliever in God) say of some alleged
miracle, "No. Or course I don't believe that. We know it is
contrary to the laws of Nature. People could believe it in olden
times because they didn't know the laws of Nature. We know now
that it is a scientific impossibility."

By the "laws of Nature" such a man means, I think, the observed course of Nature. If he means anything more than that
he is not the plain man I take him for but a philosophic Naturalist and will be dealt with in the next chapter. The man I have
in view believes that mere experience (and specially those artificially contrived experiences which we call Experiments) can tell

us what regularly happens in Nature. And he thinks that what we have discovered excludes the possibility of Miracle. This is a confusion of mind.

Granted that miracles *can* occur, it is, of course, for experience to say whether one has done so on any given occasion. But mere experience, even if prolonged for a million years, cannot tell us whether the thing is possible. Experiment finds out what regularly happens in Nature: the norm or rule to which she works. Those who believe in miracles are not denying that there is such a norm or rule: they are only saying that it can be suspended. A miracle is by definition an exception. How can the discovery of the rule tell you whether, granted a sufficient cause, the rule can be suspended? If we said that the rule was A, then experience might refute us by discovering that it was B. If we said that there was no rule, then experience might refute us by observing that there is. But we are saying neither of these things. We agree that there is a rule and that the rule is B. What has that got to do with the question whether the rule can be suspended? You reply, "But experience shows that it never has." We reply, "Even if that were so, this would not prove that it never can. But does experience show that it never has? The world is full of stories of people who say they have experienced miracles. Perhaps the stories are false: perhaps they are true. But before you can decide on that historical question, you must first (as was pointed out in Chapter 1) discover whether the thing is possible, and if possible, how probable."

The idea that the progress of science has somehow altered this question is closely bound up with the idea that people "in olden times" believed in them "because they didn't know the laws of Nature." Thus you will hear people say, "The early Christians believed that Christ was the son of a virgin, but we know that this is a scientific impossibility." Such people seem to have an idea that belief in miracles arose at a period when men were so ignorant of the course of nature that they did not perceive a miracle to be contrary to it. A moment's thought shows this to be nonsense: and the story of the Virgin Birth is a particularly striking example. When St. Joseph discovered that his fiancée was going to have a baby, he not unnaturally decided to repudiate her. Why? Because he knew just as well as any modern gynaecologist that in the ordinary course of nature women do not have babies unless they have lain with men. No doubt the modern gynaecologist knows several things about birth and begetting which St. Joseph did not know. But those things do not concern the main point—that a virgin birth is contrary to the course of nature. And St. Joseph obviously knew *that*. In any sense in which it is true to say now, "The thing is scientifically impossible," he would have said the same: the thing always was, and was always known to be, impossible *unless* the regular processes of nature were, in this particular case, being over-ruled or supplemented by something from beyond nature. When St. Joseph finally accepted the view that his fiancée's pregnancy was due not to unchastity but to a miracle, he accepted the miracle as something contrary to the known order of nature. All records of miracles teach the same thing. In such stories the miracles excite fear and wonder (that is what the very word *miracle* implies) among the spectators, and are taken as evidence of supernatural power. If they were not known to be contrary to the laws of nature how could they suggest the presence of the supernatural? How could they be surprising unless they were seen to be exceptions to the rules? And how can anything be seen to be an exception till the rules are known? If there ever were men who did not know the laws of nature *at all*, they would have no idea of a miracle and feel no particular interest in one if it were performed before them. Nothing can seem extraordinary until you have discovered what is ordinary. Beliefs in miracles, far from depending on an ignorance of the laws of nature, is only possible in so far as those laws are known. We have already seen that if you begin by ruling out the supernatural you will perceive no miracles. We must now add that you will equally perceive no miracles until you believe that nature works according to regular laws. If you have not yet noticed that the sun always rises in the East you will see nothing miraculous about his rising one morning in the West.

If the miracles were offered us as events that normally occurred, then the progress of science, whose business is to tell us what normally occurs, would render belief in them gradually harder and finally impossible. The progress of science has in just this way (and greatly to our benefit) made all sorts of things incredible which our ancestors believed; man-eating ants and gryphons in Scythia, men with one single gigantic foot, magnetic islands that draw all ships toward them, mermaids and fire-breathing dragons. But those things were never put forward as supernatural interruptions of the course of nature. They were put forward as items within her ordinary course—in fact as "science." Later and better science has therefore rightly removed them. Miracles are in a wholly different position. If there were fire-breathing dragons our big-game hunters would find them: but no one ever pretended that the Virgin Birth or Christ's walking on the water could be reckoned on to recur. When a thing professes from the very outset to be a unique invasion of Nature by something from outside, increasing knowledge of Nature can never make it either more or less credible than it was at the beginning. In this sense it is mere confusion of thought to suppose that advancing science has made it harder for us to accept miracles. We always knew they were contrary to the natural course of events; we know still that if there is something beyond Nature, they are possible. Those are the bare bones of the question; time and progress and science and civilisation have not altered them in the least. The grounds for belief and disbelief are the same to-day as they were two thousand—or ten thousand—years ago. If St. Joseph had lacked faith to trust God or humility to perceive the holiness of his spouse, he could have disbelieved in the miraculous origin of her Son as easily as any modern man; and any modern man who believes in God can accept the miracle as easily as St. Joseph did. You and I may not agree, even by the end of this book, as to whether miracles happen or not. But at least let us not talk nonsense. Let us not allow vague rhetoric about the march of science to fool us into supposing that the most complicated account of birth, in terms of genes and spermatozoa, leaves us any more convinced than we were before that *nature* does not send babies to young women who "know not a man."

The second Red Herring is this. Many people say, "They could believe in miracles in olden times because they had a false conception of the universe. They thought the Earth was the largest thing in it and Man the most important creature. It therefore seemed reasonable to suppose that the Creator was specially interested in Man and might even interrupt the course of Nature for his benefit. But now that we know the real immensity of the universe—now that we perceive our own planet and even the whole Solar System to be only a speck—it becomes ludicrous to believe in them any longer. We have discovered our insignificance and can no longer suppose that God is so drastically concerned in our petty affairs."

Whatever its value may be as an argument, it may be stated at once that this view is quiet wrong about facts. The immensity of the universe is not a recent discovery. More than seventeen hundred years ago Ptolemy taught that in relation to the distance of the fixed stars the whole Earth must be regarded as a point with no magnitude. His astronomical system was universally accepted in the Dark and Middle Ages. The insignificance of Earth was as much a commonplace to Boethius, King Alfred, Dante, and Chaucer as it is to Mr. H. G. Wells or Professor Haldane. Statements to the contrary in modern books are due to ignorance.

The real question is quite different from what we commonly suppose. The real question is why the spatial insignificance of Earth, after being asserted by Christian philosophers, sung by Christian poets, and commented on by Christian moralists for some fifteen centuries, without the slightest suspicion that it conflicted with their theology, should suddenly in quite modern times have been set up as a stock argument against Christianity and enjoyed, in that capacity, a brilliant career. I will offer a guess at the answer to this question presently. For the moment, let us consider the strength of this stock argument.

When the doctor at a *post-mortem* looks at the dead man's organs and diagnoses poison he has a clear idea of the different state in which the organs would have been if the man had died a natural death. If from the vastness of the universe and the smallness of Earth we diagnose that Christianity is false we ought to have a clear idea of the sort of universe we should have expected if it were true. But have we? Whatever space may really be, it is certain that our perceptions make it appear three dimensional; and to a three-dimensional space no boundaries are conceivable. By the very forms of our perceptions therefore we must feel as if we lived somewhere in infinite space: and whatever size the Earth happens to be, it must of course be very small in comparison with infinity. And this infinite space must either be empty or contain bodies. If it were empty, or if it contained nothing but our own Sun, then that vast vacancy would certainly be used as an argument against the very existence of God. Why, it would be asked, should He create one speck and leave all the rest of space to nonentity? If, on the other hand, we find (as we actually do) countless bodies floating in space, they must be either habitable or uninhabitable. Now the odd thing is that *both* alternatives are equally used as objections to Christianity. If the universe is teeming with life other than ours, then this, we are told, makes it quite ridiculous to believe that God could be so concerned with the human race as to "come down from Heaven" and be made man for its redemption. If, on the other hand, our planet is really unique in harbouring organic life, then this is thought to prove that life is only an accidental bye-product in the universe and so again to disprove our religion. It seems that we are hard to please. We treat God as the police treat a man when he is arrested; whatever He does will be used in evidence against Him. This kind of objection to the Christian faith is not really based on the observed nature of the actual universe at all. You can make it without waiting to find out what the universe is like, for it will fit any kind of universe we choose to imagine. The doctor here can diagnose poison without looking at the corpse for he has a theory of poison which he will maintain *whatever* the state of the organs turns out to be.

The reason why we cannot even imagine a universe so built as to exclude these objections is, perhaps, as follows. Man is a finite creature who has sense enough to know that he is finite: therefore, on any conceivable view, he finds himself dwarfed by reality as a whole. He is also a derivative being: the cause of his existence lies not in himself but (immediately) in his parents and (ultimately) *either* in the character of Nature as a whole *or* (if there is a God) in God. But there must be something, whether it be God or the totality of Nature, which exists in its own right or goes on "of its own accord": not as the product of causes beyond itself, but simply because it does. In the face of that something, whichever it turns out to be, man must feel his own derived existence to be unimportant, irrelevant, almost accidental. There is no question of religious people fancying that all exists for man and scientific people discovering that it does not. Whether the ultimate and inexplicable being—that which simply *is*—turns out to be God or "the whole show," of course it does not exist for us. On either view we are faced with something which existed before the human race appeared and will exist after the Earth has become uninhabitable; which is utterly independent of us though we are totally dependent on it; and which, through vast ranges of its being, has no relevance to our own hopes and fears. For no man was, I suppose, ever so mad as to think that man, or all creation, *filled* the Divine Mind; if we are a small thing to space and time, space and time are a much smaller thing to God. It is a profound mistake to imagine that Christianity ever intended to dissipate the bewilderment and even the terror, the sense of our own nothingness, which come upon us when we think about the nature of things. It comes to intensify them. Without such sensations there is no religion. Many a man, brought up in the glib profession of some shallow form of Christianity, who comes through reading Astronomy to realise for the first time how majestically indifferent most reality is to man, and who perhaps abandons his religion on that account, may at that moment be having his first genuinely religious experience.

Christianity does not involve the belief that all things were made for man. It does involve the belief that God loves man and for his sake became man and died. I have not yet succeeded in seeing how what we know (and have known since the days of Ptolemy) about the size of the universe affects the credibility of this doctrine one way or the other.

The sceptic asks how we can believe that God so "came down" to this one tiny planet. The question would be embarrassing if we knew (1) that there are rational creatures on any of the other bodies that float in space; (2) that they have, like us, fallen and need redemption; (3) that their redemption must be in the same mode as ours; (4) that redemption in this mode has been withheld from them. But we know none of them. The universe may be full of happy lives that never needed redemption. It may be full of lives that have been redeemed in modes suitable to their condition, of which we can form no conception. It may be full of lives that have been redeemed in the very same mode as our own. It may be full of things quite other than life in which God is interested though we are not.

If it is maintained that anything so small as the Earth must, in any event, be too unimportant to merit the love of the Creator, we reply that no Christian ever supposed we did merit it. Christ did not die for men because they were intrinsically worth dying for, but because He is intrinsically love, and therefore loves infinitely. And what, after all, does the *size* of a world or a creature tell us about its "importance" or value?

There is no doubt that we all *feel* the incongruity of supposing, say, that the planet Earth might be more important than the Great Nebula in Andromeda. On the other hand, we are all equally certain that only a lunatic would think a man six-feet high necessarily more important than a man five-feet, or a horse necessarily more important than a man, or a man's legs than his brain. In other words this supposed ratio of size to importance feels plausible only when one of the sizes involved is very great. And that betrays the true basis of this type of thought. When a relation is perceived by Reason, it is perceived to hold good universally. If our Reason told us that size as proportional to importance, then small differences in size would be accompanied by small differences in importance just as surely as great differences in size were accompanied by great differences in importance. Your six-foot man would have to be slightly more valuable than the man of five feet, and your leg slightly more important than your brain—which everyone knows to be nonsense. The conclusion is inevitable: the importance we attach to great differences of size is an affair not of reason but of emotion—of that peculiar emotion which superiorities in size begin to produce in us only after a certain point of absolute size has been reached.

We are inveterate poets. When a quantity is very great we cease to regard it as a mere quantity. Our imaginations awake.

Instead of mere quantity, we now have a quality—the Sublime. But for this, the merely arithmetical greatness of the Galaxy would be no more impressive than the figures in an account book. To a mind which did not share our emotions and lacked our imaginative energies, the argument against Christianity from the size of the universe would be simply unintelligible. It is therefore from ourselves that the material universe derives its power to overawe us. Men of sensibility look up on the night sky with awe: brutal and stupid men do not. When the silence of the eternal spaces terrified Pascal, it was Pascal's own greatness that enabled them to do so; to be frightened by the bigness of the nebulae is, almost literally, to be frightened at our own shadow. For light years and geological periods are mere arithmetic until the shadow of man, the poet, the maker of myths, falls upon them. As a Christian I do not say we are wrong to tremble at that shadow, for I believe it to be the shadow of an image of God. But if the vastness of Nature ever threatens to overcrow our spirits, we must remember that it is only Nature spiritualised by human imagination which does so.

This suggests a possible answer to the question raised a few pages ago—why the size of the universe, known for centuries, should first in modern times become an argument against Christianity. Has it perhaps done so because in modern times the imagination has become more sensitive to bigness? From this point of view the argument from size might almost be regarded as a bye-product of the Romantic Movement in poetry. In addition to the absolute increase of imaginative vitality on this topic, there has pretty certainly been a decline on others. Any reader of old poetry can see that brightness appealed to ancient and medieval man more than bigness, and more than it does to us. Medieval thinkers believed that the stars must be somehow superior to the Earth because they looked bright and it did not. Moderns think that the Galaxy ought to be more important than the Earth because it is bigger. Both states of mind can produce good poetry. Both can supply mental pictures which rouse very respectable emotions—emotions of awe, humility, or exhilaration. But taken as serious philosophical argument both are ridiculous. The atheist's argument from size is, in fact, an instance of just that picture-thinking to which, as we shall see in a later chapter, the Christian is *not* committed. It is the particular mode in which picture-thinking appears in the twentieth century: for what we fondly call "primitive" errors do not pass away. They merely change their form.

8.

MIRACLE AND THE LAWS OF NATURE

> It's a very odd thing—
> As odd as can be—
> That whatever Miss T. eats
> Turns into Miss T.
>
> W. DE LA MARE.

Having cleared out of the way those objections which are based on a popular and confused notion that the "progress of science" has somehow made the world safe against Miracle, we must now consider the subject on a somewhat deeper level. The question is whether Nature can be known to be of such a kind that supernatural interferences with her are impossible. She is already known to be, in general, regular: she behaves according to fixed laws, many of which have been discovered, and which interlock with one another. There is, in this discussion, no question of mere failure or inaccuracy to keep these laws on the part of Nature, no question of chancey or spontaneous variation.[1] The only question is whether, granting the existence of a Power outside Nature, there is any intrinsic absurdity in the idea of its intervening to produce within Nature events which the regular "going on" of the whole natural system would never have produced.

Three conceptions of the "Laws" of Nature have been held. (1) That they are mere brute facts, known only by observation, with no discoverable rhyme or reason about them. We know *that* Nature behaves thus and thus; we do not know why she does and can see no reason why she should not do the opposite.

---

[1] If any region of reality is in fact chancey or lawless then it is a region which, so far from admitting Miracle with special ease, renders the word "Miracle" meaningless throughout that region.

(2) That they are applications of the law of averages. The foundations of Nature are in the random and lawless. But the numbers of units we are dealing with are so enormous that the behaviour of these crowds (like the behaviour of very large masses of men) can be calculated with practical accuracy. What we call "impossible events" are events so overwhelmingly improbable—by actuarial standards—that we do not need to take them into account. (3) That the fundamental laws of Physics are really what we call "necessary truths" like the truths of mathematics—in other words, that if we clearly understand what we are saying we shall see that the opposite would be meaningless nonsense. Thus it is a "law" that when one billiard ball shoves another the amount of momentum lost by the first ball must exactly equal the amount gained by the second. People who hold that the laws of Nature are necessary truths would say that all we have done is to split up the single event into two halves (adventures of ball A, and adventures of ball B) and then discover that "the two sides of the account balance." When we understand this we see that of course they *must* balance. The fundamental laws are in the long run merely statements that every event is itself and not some different event.

It will at once be clear that the first of these three theories gives no assurance against Miracles—indeed no assurance that, even apart from Miracles, the "laws" which we have hitherto observed will be obeyed to-morrow. If we have no notion why a thing happens, then of course we know no reason why it should not be otherwise, and therefore have no certainty that it might not some day be otherwise. The second theory, which depends on the law of averages, is in the same position. The assurance it gives us is of the same general kind as our assurance that a coin tossed a thousand times will not give the same result, say, nine hundred times: and that the longer you toss it the more nearly the numbers of Heads and Tails will come to being equal. But this is so only provided the coin is an honest coin. If it is a loaded coin our expectations may be disappointed. But the people who believe in miracles are maintaining precisely that the coin *is* loaded. The expectations based on the law of averages will work only for undoctored Nature. And the question whether miracles occur is just the question whether Nature is ever doctored.

The third view (that Laws of Nature are necessary truths) seems at first sight to present an insurmountable obstacle to miracle. The breaking of them would, in that case, be a self-contradiction and not even Omnipotence can do what is self-contradictory. Therefore the Laws cannot be broken. And therefore, shall we conclude, no miracle can ever occur?

We have gone too quickly. It is certain that the billiard balls will behave in a particular way, just as it is certain that if you divide a shilling unequally between two recipients then A's share must exceed the half and B's share fall short of it by exactly the same amount. Provided, of course, that A does not by sleight of hand steal some of B's pennies at the very moment of the transaction. In the same way, you know what will happen to the two billiard balls—provided nothing interferes. If one ball encounters a roughness in the cloth which the other does not, their motion will not illustrate the law in the way you had expected. Of course what happens as a result of the roughness in the cloth will illustrate the law in some other way, but your original prediction will have been false. Or again, if I snatch up a cue and give one of the balls a little help, you will get a third result: and that third result will equally illustrate the laws of physics, and equally falsify your prediction. I shall have "spoiled the experiment." All interferences leave the law perfectly true. But every prediction of what will happen in a given instance is made under the proviso "other things being equal" or "if there are no interferences." Whether other things *are* equal in a given case and whether interferences may occur is another matter. The arithmetician, as an arithmetician, does not know how likely A is to steal some of B's pennies when the shilling is being divided; you had better ask a criminologist. The physicst, as a physicist, does not know how likely I am to catch up a cue and "spoil" his experiment with the billiard balls: you had better ask someone who knows *me*. In the same way the physicist, as such, does not know how likely it is that some supernatural power is going to interfere with them: you had better ask a metaphysician. But the physicist does know, just because he is a physicist, that if the billiard balls are tampered with by any agency, natural or supernatural, which he had not taken into account, then their behaviour must differ from what he expected. Not because the law is false, but because it is true. The more certain we are of the law the more clearly we know that if new factors have been introduced the result will vary accordingly. What we do not know, as physicists, is whether Supernatural power might be one of the new factors.

If the laws of Nature are necessary truths, no miracle can break them: but then no miracle needs to break them. It is with them as with the laws of arithmetic. If I put six pennies into a drawer on Monday and six more on Tuesday, the laws decree that *other things being equal*—I shall find twelve pennies there on Wednesday. But if the drawer has been robbed I may in fact find only two. Something will have been broken (the lock of the drawer or the laws of England) but the laws of arithmetic will not have been broken. The new situation created by the thief will illustrate the laws of arithmetic just as well as the original situation. But if God comes to work miracles, He comes "like a thief in the night." Miracle is, from the point of view of the scientists, a form of doctoring, tampering, (if you like) cheating. It introduces a new factor into the situation, namely supernatural force, which the scientists had not reckoned on. He calculates what will happen, or what must have happened on a past occasion, in the belief that the situation, at that point of space and time, is or was A. But if supernatural force has been added, then the situation really is or was AB. And no one knows better than the scientists that AB *cannot* yield the same result as A. The necessary truth of the laws, far from making it impossible that miracles should occur makes it certain that if the Supernatural is operating they must occur. For if the natural situation by itself, and the natural situation *plus* something else, yielded only the same result, it would be then that we should be faced with a lawless and unsystematic universe. The better you know that two and two make four, the better you know that two and three don't.

This perhaps helps to make a little clearer what the laws of Nature really are. We are in the habit of talking as if they caused events to happen; but they have never caused any event at all.

The laws of motion do not set billiard balls moving: they analyse the motion after something else (say, a man with a cue, or a lurch of the liner, or, perhaps, supernatural power) has provided it. They produce no events: they state the pattern to which every event—if only it can be induced to happen—must conform, just as the rules of arithmetic state the pattern to which all transactions with money must conform—if only you can get hold of any money. Thus in one sense the laws of Nature cover the whole field of space and time; in another, what they leave out is precisely the whole real universe—the incessant torrent of actual events which makes up true history. That must come from somewhere else. To think the laws can produce it is like thinking that you can create real money by simply doing sums. For every law, in the last resort, says "If you have A, then you will get B." But first catch your A: the laws won't do it for you.

It is therefore inaccurate to define a miracle as something that breaks the laws of Nature. It doesn't. If I knock out my pipe I alter the position of a great many atoms: in the long run, and to an infinitesimal degree, of all the atoms there are. Nature digests or assimilates this event with perfect ease and harmonises it in a twinkling with all other events. It is one more bit of raw material for the laws to apply to, and they apply. I have simply thrown one event into the general cataract of events and it finds itself at home there and conforms to all other events. If God annihilates or creates or deflects a unit of matter He has created a new situation at that point. Immediately all Nature domiciles this new situation, makes it at home in her realm, adapts all other events to it. It finds itself conforming to all the laws. If God creates a miraculous spermatozoon in the body of a virgin, it does not proceed to break any laws. The laws at once take it over. Nature is ready. Pregnancy follows, according to all the normal laws, and nine months later a child is born. We see every day that physical nature is not in the least incommoded by the daily inrush of events from biological nature or from psychological nature. If events ever come from beyond Nature altogether, she will be no more incommoded by them. Be sure she will rush to the point where she is invaded, as the defensive forces rush to a cut in our finger, and there hasten to accommodate the newcomer. The moment it enters her realm it obeys all her laws. Miraculous wine will intoxicate, miraculous conception will lead to pregnancy, inspired books will suffer all the ordinary processes of textual corruption, miraculous bread will be digested. The divine art of miracle is not an art of suspending the pattern to which events conform but of feeding new events into that pattern. It does not violate the law's proviso, "If A, then B": it says, "But this time instead of A, A2," and Nature, speaking through all her laws, replies, "Then B2" and naturalises the immigrant, as she well knows how. She is an accomplished hostess.

A miracle is emphatically not an event without cause or without results. Its cause is the activity of God: its results follow according to Natural law. In the forward direction (i.e. during the time which follows its occurrence) it is interlocked with all Nature just like any other event. Its peculiarity is that it is not in that way interlocked backwards, interlocked with the previous history of Nature. And this is just what some people find intolerable. The reason they find it intolerable is that they start by taking Nature to be the whole of reality. And they are sure that all reality must be interrelated and consistent. I agree with them. But I think they have mistaken a partial system within reality, namely Nature, for the whole. That being so, the miracle and the previous history of Nature may be interlocked after all but not in the way the Naturalist expected: rather in a much more roundabout fashion. The great complex event called Nature, and the new particular event introduced into it by the miracle, are related by their common origin in God, and doubtless, if we knew enough, most intricately related in His purpose and design, so that a Nature which had had a different history, and therefore been a different Nature, would have been invaded by different miracles or by none at all. In that way the miracle and the previous course of Nature are as well interlocked as any other two realities, but you must go back as far as their common Creator to find the interlocking. You will not find it *within* Nature. The same sort of thing happens with any partial system. The behaviour of fishes which are being studied in a tank makes a relatively closed system. Now suppose that the tank is shaken by a bomb in the neighbourhood of the laboratory. The behaviour of the fishes will now be no longer fully explicable by what was going on in the tank before the bomb fell: there will be a failure of backward interlocking. This does not mean that the bomb and the previous history of events within the tank are totally and finally unrelated. It does mean that to find their relation you must go back to the much larger reality which includes both the tank and the bomb—the reality of war-time England in which bombs are falling but some laboratories are still at work. You would never find it within the history of the tank. In the same way, the miracle is not *naturally* interlocked in the backward direction. To find how it is interlocked with the previous history of Nature you must replace both Nature and the miracle in a larger context. Everything *is* connected with everything else: but not all things are connected by the short and straight roads we expected.

The rightful demand that all reality should be consistent and systematic does not therefore exclude miracles: but it has a very valuable contribution to make to our conception of them. It reminds us that miracles, if they occur, must, like all events, be revelations of the total harmony of all that exists. Nothing arbitrary, nothing simply "stuck on" and left unreconciled with the texture of total reality, can be admitted. By definition, miracles must of course interrupt the usual course of Nature; but if they are real they must, in the very act of so doing, assert all the more the unity and self-consistency of total reality at some deeper level. They will not be like unmetrical lumps of prose breaking the unity of a poem; they will be like that crowning metrical audacity which, though it may be paralleled nowhere else in the poem, yet, coming just where it does, and effecting just what it effects, is (to those who understand) the supreme revelation of the unity in the poet's conception. If what we call Nature is modified by supernatural power, then we may be sure that the capability of being so modified is of the essence of nature—that the total event, if we could grasp it, would turn out to involve, by its very character, the possibility of such modifications. If Nature brings forth miracles then doubtless it is as "natural" for her to do so when impregnated by the masculine force beyond her as it is for a woman to bear children to a man. In calling them miracles we do not mean that they are contradictions or outrages; we mean that, left to her own resources, she could never produce them.

9.

A CHAPTER NOT STRICTLY NECESSARY

We saw the giants, the sons of Anak; and we were in our own
sight as grasshoppers, and so we were in their sight.
Numbers, XIII, xxxiii.

The last two chapters have been concerned with objections to
Miracle, made, so to speak, from the side of Nature; made on the
ground that she is the sort of system which could not admit miracles. Our next step, if we followed a strict order, would be to
consider objections from the opposite side—in fact, to inquire
whether what is beyond Nature can reasonably be supposed to be
the sort of being that could, or would, work miracles. But I find
myself strongly disposed to turn aside and face first an objection
of a different sort. It is a purely emotional one; severer readers
may skip this chapter. But I know it is one which weighed very
heavily with me at a certain period of my life, and if others have
passed through the same experience they may care to read of it.

One of the things that held me back from Supernaturalism was
a deep repugnance to the view of Nature which, as I thought,
Supernaturalism entailed. I passionately desired that Nature
should exist "on her own." The idea that she had been made,
and could be altered, by God seemed to take from her all that
spontaneity which I found so refreshing. In order to breathe
freely I wanted to feel that in Nature one reached at last something that simply *was:* the thought that she had been manu-
factured or "put there," and put there with a purpose, was suffocating. I wrote a poem in those days about a sunrise, I remember,
in which, after describing the scene, I added that some people

liked to believe there was a Spirit behind it all and that this
Spirit was communicating with them. But, said I, that was exactly what I did not want. The poem was not much good and I
have forgotten most of it: but it ended up by saying how much
rather I would feel

> *That in their own right earth and sky*
> *Continually do dance*
> *For their own sakes—and here crept I*
> *To watch the world by chance.*

"By chance!"—one could not bear to feel that the sunrise had
been in any way "arranged" or had anything to do with oneself.
To find that it had not simply happened, that it had been somehow contrived, would be as bad as finding that the fieldmouse I
saw beside some lonely hedge was really a clockwork mouse put
there to amuse me, or (worse still) to point some moral lesson.
The Greek poet asks, "If water sticks in your throat, what will
you take to wash it down?" I likewise asked, "If Nature herself
proves artificial, where will you go to seek wildness? Where is
the real out-of-doors?" To find that all the woods, and small
streams in the middle of the woods, and odd corners of mountain
valleys, and the wind and the grass were only a sort of *scenery*,
only backcloths for some kind of play, and that play perhaps one
with a moral—what flatness, what an anticlimax, what an unen-
durable bore!

The cure of this mood began years ago: but I must record that
the cure was not complete until I began to study this question of
Miracles. At every stage in the writing of this book I have found
my idea of Nature becoming more vivid and more concrete. I
set out on a work which seemed to involve reducing her status
and undermining her walls at every turn: the paradoxical result
is a growing sensation that if I am not very careful she will become the heroine of my book. She has never seemed to me more
great or more real than at this moment.

The reason is not far to seek. As long as one is a Naturalist,
"Nature" is only a word for "everything." And Everything is not
a subject about which anything very interesting can be said or

(save by illusion) felt. One aspect of things strikes us and we talk of the "peace" of Nature; another strikes us and we talk of her cruelty. And then, because we falsely take her for the ultimate and self-existent Fact and cannot quite repress our high instinct to worship the Self-existent, we are all at sea and our moods fluctuate and Nature means to us whatever we please as the moods select and slur. But everything becomes different when we recognise that Nature is a *creature*, a created thing, with its own particular tang or flavour. There is no need any longer to select and slur. It is not in her, but in Something far beyond her, that all lines meet and all contrasts are explained. It is no more baffling that the creature called Nature should be both fair and cruel than that the first man you meet in the train should be a dishonest grocer and a kind husband. For she is not the Absolute: she is one of the creatures, with her good points and her bad points and her own unmistakable flavour running through them all.

To say that God has created her is not to say that she is unreal, but precisely that she is real. Would you make God less creative than Shakespeare or Dickens? What He creates is created in the round: it is far more concrete than Falstaff or Sam Weller. The theologians certainly tell us that He created Nature freely. They mean that He was not forced to do so by any external necessity. But we must not interpret freedom negatively, as if Nature were a mere construction of parts arbitrarily stuck together. God's creative freedom is to be conceived as the freedom of a poet: the freedom to create a consistent, positive thing with its own inimitable flavour. Shakespeare need not create Falstaff: but if he does, Falstaff *must* be fat. God need not create this Nature. He might have created others, He may have created others. But granted *this* Nature, then doubtless no smallest part of her is there except because it expresses the character He chose to give her. It would be a miserable error to suppose that the dimensions of space and time, the death and re-birth of vegetation, the unity in multiplicity of organisms, the union in opposition of sexes, and the colour of each particular apple in Herefordshire this autumn, were merely a collection of useful devices forcibly welded together. They are the very idiom, almost the facial expression, the smell or taste, of an individual thing. The *quality* of Nature is present in them all just as the Latinity of Latin is present in every inflection or the "Correggiosity" of Correggio in every stroke of the brush.

Nature is by human (and probably by Divine) standards partly good and partly evil. We Christians believe that she has been corrupted. But the same tang or flavour runs through both her corruptions and her excellences. Everything is in character. Falstaff does not sin in the same way as Othello. Othello's fall bears a close relation to his virtues. If Perdita had fallen she would not have been bad in the same way as Lady Macbeth: if Lady Macbeth had remained good her goodness would have been quite different from that of Perdita. The evils we see in Nature are, so to speak, the evils proper to *this* Nature. Her very character decreed that if she were corrupted the corruption would take this form and not another. The horrors of parasitism and the glories of motherhood are good and evil worked out of the same basic theme or idea.

I spoke just now about the Latinity of Latin. It is more evident to us than it can have been to the Romans. The Englishness of English is audible only to those who know some other language as well. In the same way and for the same reason, only Supernaturalists really see Nature. You must go a little away from her, and then turn round, and look back. Then at last the true landscape will become visible. You must have tasted, however briefly, the pure water from beyond the world before you can be distinctly conscious of the hot, salty tang of Nature's current. To treat her as God, or as Everything, is to lose the whole pith and pleasure of her. Come out, look back, and then you will see . . . this astonishing cataract of bears, babies, and bananas: this immoderate deluge of atoms, orchids, oranges, cancers, canaries, fleas, gases, tornadoes and toads. How could you ever have thought this was the ultimate reality? How could you ever have thought that it was merely a stage-set for the moral drama of men and women? She is herself. Offer her neither worship nor contempt. Meet her and know her. If we are immortal, and if she is doomed (as the scientists tell us) to run down and die, we shall miss this half-shy and half-flamboyant creature, this ogress, this hoyden, this incorrigible fairy, this dumb witch. But the theologians tell us that she, like ourselves, is to be redeemed. The "vanity" to which she was subjected was her disease, not her essence. She will be cured, but cured in character: not tamed. (Heaven forbid) nor sterilised. We shall still be able to recognise our old enemy, friend, playfellow and foster-mother, so perfected as to be not less, but more, herself. And that will be a merry meeting.

IO.

"HORRID RED THINGS"

> We can call the attempt to refute theism by displaying the
> continuity of the belief in God with primitive delusion the
> method of Anthropological intimidation.
>
> EDWYN BEVAN,
> *Symbolism and Relief,* chap. ii.

I have argued that there is no security against Miracle to
be found by the study of Nature. She is not the whole of reality
but only a part; for all we know she might be a small part. If that
which is outside her wishes to invade her she has, so far as we
can see, no defences. But of course many who disbelieve in Miracles would admit all this. Their objection comes from the
other side. They think that the Supernatural would not invade:
they accuse those who say that it has done so of having a childish
and unworthy notion of the Supernatural. They therefore reject all forms of Supernaturalism which assert such interferences
and invasions: and specially the form called Christianity, for
in it the Miracles, or at least some Miracles, are more closely
bound up with the fabric of the whole belief than in any other.
All the essentials of Hinduism would, I think, remain unimpaired
if you subtracted the miraculous, and the same is almost true of
Mohammedanism. But you cannot do that with Christianity. It
is precisely the story of a great Miracle. A naturalistic Christianity
leaves out all that is specifically Christian.

The difficulties of the unbeliever do not begin with questions
about this or that particular miracle; they begin much further
back. When a man who has had only the ordinary modern education looks into any authoritative statement of Christian doctrine, he finds himself face to face with what seems to him a

wholly "savage" or "primitive" picture of the universe. He finds that God is supposed to have had a "Son," just as if God were a mythological deity like Jupiter or Odin. He finds that this "Son" is supposed to have "come down from Heaven," just as if God had a palace in the sky from which He had sent down His "Son" like a parachutist. He finds that this "Son" then "descended into Hell"—into some land of the dead under the surface of a (presumably) flat earth—and thence "ascended" again, as if by a balloon, into his Father's sky-palace, where He finally sat down in a decorated chair placed a little to His Father's right. Everything seems to presuppose a conception of reality which the increase of our knowledge has been steadily refuting for the last two thousand years and which no honest man in his senses could return to to-day.

It is this impression which explains the contempt, and even disgust, felt by many people for the writings of modern Christians. When once a man is convinced that Christianity *in general* implies a local "Heaven," a flat earth, and a God who can have children, he naturally listens with impatience to our solutions of particular difficulties and our defences against particular objections. The more ingenious we are in such solutions and defences the more perverse we seem to him. "Of course," he says, "once the doctrines are there, clever people can invent clever arguments to defend them, just as, when once a historian has made a blunder he can go on inventing more and more elaborate theories to make it appear that it was not a blunder. But the real point is that none of these elaborate theories would have been thought of if he had read his documents correctly in the first instance. In the same way, is it not clear that Christian theology would never have come into existence at all if the writers of the New Testament had had the slightest knowledge of what the real universe is actually like?" Thus, at any rate, I used to think myself. The very man who taught me to think—a hard, satirical atheist (ex-Presbyterian) who doted on the *Golden Bough* and filled his house with the products of the Rationalist Press Association—thought in the same way; and he was a man as honest as the daylight, to whom I here willingly acknowledge an immense debt. His attitude to Christianity was for me the starting point of adult thinking; you may say it is bred in my bones. And yet, since those days, I have come to regard that attitude as a total misunderstanding.

Remembering, as I do, from within, the attitude of the impatient sceptic, I realise very well how he is fore-armed against anything I may say for the rest of this chapter. "I know exactly what this man is going to do," he murmurs. "He is going to start explaining all these mythological statements away. It is the invariable practice of these Christians. On any matter whereon science has not yet spoken and on which they cannot be checked, they will tell you some preposterous fairytale. And then, the moment science makes a new advance and shows (as it invariably does) their statement to be untrue, they suddenly turn round and explain that they didn't mean what they said, that they were using a poetic metaphor or constructing an allegory, and that all they really intended was some harmless moral platitude. We are sick of this theological thimble-rigging." Now I have a great deal of sympathy with that sickness and I freely admit that "modernist" Christianity has constantly played just the game of which the impatient sceptic accuses it. But I also think there is a kind of explaining which is not explaining away. In one sense I am going to do just what the sceptic thinks I am going to do: that is, I am going to distinguish what I regard as the "core" or "real meaning" of the doctrines from that in their expression which I regard as inessential and possibly even capable of being changed without damage. But then, what will drop away from the "real meaning" under my treatment will precisely *not* be the miraculous. It is the core itself, the core scraped as clean of inessentials as we can scrape it, which remains for me entirely miraculous, supernatural—nay, if you will, "primitive" and even "magical."

In order to explain this I must now touch on a subject which has an importance quite apart from our present purpose and of which everyone who wishes to think clearly should make himself master as soon as he possibly can. And he ought to begin by reading Mr. Owen Barfield's *Poetic Diction* and Mr. Edwyn Bevan's *Symbolism and Belief*. But for the present argument it will be enough to leave the deeper problems on one side and proceed in a "popular" and unambitious manner.

When I think about London I usually see a mental picture of Euston Station. But when I think (as I do) that London has several million inhabitants, I do not mean that there are several million images of people contained in my image of Euston Station. Nor do I mean that several millions of real people live in real Euston Station. In fact though I have the image while I am thinking about London, what I think or say is not *about* that image, and would be manifest nonsense if it were. It makes sense because it is not about my own mental pictures but about the real London, outside my imagination, of which no one can have an adequate mental picture at all. Or again, when we say that the Sun is ninety-odd million miles away, we understand perfectly clearly what we mean by this number; we can divide and multiply it by other numbers and we can work out how long it would take to travel that distance at any given speed. But this clear *thinking* is accompanied by *imagining* which is ludicrously false to what we know that the reality must be.

To think, then, is one thing, and to imagine is another. What we think or say can be, and usually is, quite different from what we imagine or picture; and what we mean may be true when the mental images that accompany it are entirely false. It is, indeed, doubtful whether anyone except an extreme visualist who is also a trained artist ever has mental images which are particularly like the things he is thinking about.

In these examples the mental image is not only unlike the reality but is known to be unlike it, at least after a moment's reflection. I know that London is not merely Euston Station. Let us now go on to a slightly different predicament. I once heard a lady tell her young daughter that you would die if you ate too many tablets of aspirin. "But why?" asked the child, "it isn't poisonous." "How do you know it isn't poisonous?" said the mother. "Because," said the child, "when you crush an aspirin tablet you don't find horrid red things inside it." Clearly, when this child thought of poison she had a mental picture of Horrid Red Things, just as I have a picture of Euston when I think of London. The difference is that whereas I know my image to be very unlike the real London, the child thought that poison was *really* red. To that extent she was mistaken. But this does not mean that everything she thought or said about poison was necessarily nonsensical. She knew perfectly well that a poison was something which killed you or made you ill if you swallowed it; and she knew, to some extent, which of the substances in her mother's house were poisonous. If a visitor to that house had been warned by the child, "Don't drink that. Mother says it is poison," he would have been ill advised to neglect the warning on the ground that "This child has a primitive idea of poison as Horrid Red Things, which my adult scientific knowledge has long since refuted."

We can now add to our previous statement (that thinking may be sound where the images that accompany it are false) the further statement: thinking may be sound in certain respects where it is accompanied not only by false images but by false images mistaken for true ones.

There is still a third situation to be dealt with. In our two previous examples we have been concerned with thought and imagination, but not with language. I had to picture Euston Station, but I did not need to *mention* it; the child thought that poison was Horrid Red Things, but she could talk about poison without saying so. But very often when we are talking about something which is not perceptible by the five senses we use words which, in one of their meanings, refer to things or actions that are. When a man says that he grasps an argument he is using a verb (*grasp*) which literally means to take something in the hands, but he is certainly not thinking that his mind has hands or that an argument can be seized like a gun. To avoid the word *grasp* he may change the form of expression and say, "I see your point," but he does not mean that a pointed object has appeared in his visual field. He may have a third shot and say, "I follow you," but he does not mean that he is walking behind you along a road. Everyone is familiar with this linguistic phenomenon and the grammarians call it metaphor. But it is a serious mistake to think that metaphor is an optional thing which poets and orators may put into their work as a decoration and plain speakers can do without. The truth is that if we are going to talk at all about things which are not perceived by the senses, we are forced to use language metaphorically. Books on psychology or economics or politics are as continuously metaphorical as books of poetry or devotion. There is no other way of talking, as every philologist is aware. Those who wish can satisfy themselves on the point by reading the books I have already mentioned and the other books to which those two will lead them on. It is a study for a lifetime and I must here content myself with the mere statement; all speech about supersensibles is, and must be, metaphorical in the highest degree.

We have now three guiding principles before us. (1) That thought is distinct from the imagination which accompanies it. (2) That thought may be in the main sound even when the false images that accompany it are mistaken by the thinker for true ones. (3) That anyone who talks about things that cannot be seen, or touched, or heard, or the like, must inevitably talk as *If they could be* seen or touched or heard (e.g. must talk of "complexes" and "repressions" *as if* desires could really be tied up in bundles or shoved back; of "growth" and "development" *as if* institutions could really grow like trees or unfold like flowers; of energy being "released" *as if* it were an animal let out of a cage).

Let us now apply this to the "savage" or "primitive" articles of the Christian creed. And let us admit at once that many Christians (though by no means all) when they make these assertions do have in mind just those crude mental pictures which so horrify the sceptic. When they say that Christ "came down from Heaven" they do have a vague image of something shooting or floating downwards out of the sky. When they say that Christ is the "Son" of "the Father" they may have a picture of two human forms, the one looking rather older than the other. But we now know that the mere presence of these mental pictures does not, of itself, tell us anything about the reasonableness or absurdity of the thoughts they accompany. If absurd images meant absurd thought, then we should all be thinking nonsense all the time. And the Christians themselves make it clear that the images are not to be identified with the thing believed. They may picture the Father as a human form, but they also maintain that He has no body. They may picture Him older than the Son, but they also maintain the one did not exist before the other, both having existed from all eternity. I am speaking, of course, about Christian adults. Christianity is not to be judged from the fancies of children any more than medicine from the ideas of the little girl who believed in horrid red things.

At this stage I must turn aside to deal with a rather simple-minded illusion. When we point out that what the Christians mean is not to be identified with their mental pictures, some people say, "In that case, would it not be better to get rid of the mental pictures, and of the language which suggests them, altogether?" But this is impossible. The people who recommend it have not noticed that when they try to get rid of man-like, or as they are called, "anthropomorphic," images they merely succeed in substituting images of some other kind. "I don't believe in a personal God," says one, "but I do believe in a great spiritual force." What he has not noticed is that the word "force" has let in all sorts of images about winds and tides and electricity and gravitation. "I don't believe in a personal God," says another, "but I do believe we are all parts of one great Being which moves and works through us all"—not noticing that he has merely exchanged the image of a fatherly and royal-looking man for the image of some widely extended gas or fluid. A girl I knew was brought up by "higher thinking" parents to regard God as a perfect "substance"; in later life she realised that this had actually led her to think of Him as something like a vast tapioca pudding. (To make matters worse, she disliked tapioca.) We may feel ourselves quite safe from this degree of absurdity, but we are mistaken. If a man watches his own mind, I believe he will find that what profess to be specially advanced or philosophic conceptions of God are, in his thinking, always accompanied by vague images which, if inspected, would turn out to be even more absurd than the man-like images aroused by Christian theology. For man, after all, is the highest of the things we meet in sensuous experience. He has, at least, conquered the globe, honoured (though not followed) virtue, achieved knowledge, made poetry, music and art. If God exists at all it is not unreasonable to suppose that we are less unlike Him than anything else we know. No doubt we are unspeakably different from Him; to that extent all man-like images are false. But those images of shapeless mists and irrational forces which, unacknowledged, haunt the mind when we think we are rising to the conception of impersonal and absolute Being, must be very much more so. For images, of the one kind or of the other, will come; we cannot jump off our own shadow.

As far, then, as the adult Christian of modern times is concerned, the absurdity of the images does not imply absurdity in the doctrines; but it may be asked whether the early Christian was in the same position. Perhaps he mistook the images for true ones, and really believed in the sky palace or the decorated chair. But as we have seen from the example of the Horrid Red Things, even this would not necessarily invalidate everything that he thought on these subjects. The child in our example might know many truths about poison and even, in some particular cases, truths which a given adult might not know. We can suppose a Galilaean peasant who thought that Christ had literally and physically "sat down at the right hand of the Father." If such a man had then gone to Alexandria and had a philosophical education he would have discovered that the Father had no right hand and did not sit on a thone. Is it conceivable that he would regard this as making any difference to what he had really intended, and valued, in the doctrine during the days of his naivety? For unless we suppose him to have been not only a peasant but a fool (two very different things) physical details about a supposed celestial throne-room would not have been what he cared about. What mattered must have been the belief that a person whom he had known as a man in Palestine had, as a person, survived death and was now operating as the supreme agent of the supernatural Being who governed and maintained the whole field of reality. And that belief would survive substantially unchanged after the falsity of the earlier images had been recognised.

Even if it could be shown, then, that the early Christians accepted their imagery literally, this would not mean that we are justified in relegating their doctrines as a whole to the lumber-room. Whether they actually did, is another matter. The difficulty here is that they were not writing as philosophers to satisfy speculative curiosity about the nature of God and of the universe. They *believed* in God; and once a man does that, philosophical definiteness can never be the *first* necessity. A drowning man does not analyse the rope that is flung him, nor an impassioned lover consider the chemistry of his mistress's complexion. Hence the sort of question we are now considering is never raised by the New Testament writers. When once it is raised, Christianity decides quite clearly that the naif images are false. The sect in the Egyptian desert which thought that God was like a man is condemned: The desert monk who felt he had lost something by its correction is recognised as "muddle-headed." [1] All three Persons of the Trinity are declared "incomprehensible." [2] God is pronounced "Inexpressible, unthinkable, invisible to all created beings." [3] The Second Person is not only bodiless but so unlike man that if self-revelation had been His sole purpose He would not have chosen to be incarnate in a human form.[4] We do not find similar statements in the New Testament, because the issue has not yet been made explicit: but we do find statements which make it certain how that issue will be decided when once it becomes explicit. The title "Son" may sound "primitive" or "naif." But already in the New Testament this "Son" is identified with the Discourse or Reason or Word which was eternally "with God" and yet also *was* God.[5] He is the all-prevasive principle of concretion or cohesion whereby the universe holds together.[6] All things, and specially Life, arose *within* Him,[7] and within Him all things will reach their conclusion—the final statement of what they have been trying to express.[8]

It is, of course, always possible to imagine an earlier stratum of Christianity from which such ideas were absent; just as it is always possible to say that anything you dislike in Shakespeare was put in by an "adapter" and the original play was free from it. But what have such assumptions to do with serious enquiry? And here the fabrication of them is specially perverse, since even

---

[1] *Senex mente confusus* Cassian quoted in Gibbon, cap. xlvii.

[2] Athanasian Creed.

[3] St. Chrysostom *De Incomprehensibili* quoted in Otto, *Idea of the Holy,* Appendix I.

[4] Athanasius *De Incarnatione* viii.

[5] John i. 1.

[6] Col. i. 17.

[7] Col. i. ἐν αὐτῷ ἐκτίσθη. John i. 4.

[8] Eph. 10.

if we go back beyond Christianity into Judaism itself, we shall not find the unambiguous anthropomorphism (or man-likeness) we are looking for. Neither, I admit, shall we find its denial. We shall find, on the one hand, God pictured as living above "in the high and holy place": we shall find, on the other, "Do not I fill heaven and earth? saith the Lord." [1] We shall find that in Ezekiel's vision God appeared (notice the hesitating words) in "the likeness as the appearance of a man." [2] But we shall find also the warning, "Take ye therefore good heed unto yourselves. For ye saw no manner of similitude on the day that the Lord spake unto you in Horeb out of the midst of the fire—lest ye corrupt yourselves and make a graven image." [3] Most baffling of all to a modern literalist, the God who seems to live locally in the sky, also *made* it.[4]

The reason why the modern literalist is puzzled is that he is trying to get out of the old writers something which is not there. Starting from a clear modern distinction between material and immaterial he tries to find out on which side of that distinction the ancient Hebrew conception fell. He forgets that the distinction itself has been made clear only by later thought.

We are often told that primitive man could not conceive pure spirit; but then neither could he conceive mere matter. A throne and a local habitation are attributed to God only at that stage when it is still impossible to regard the throne, or palace even of an earthly king as merely physical objects. In earthly thrones and palaces it was the spiritual significance—as we should say, the "atmosphere"—that mattered to the ancient mind. As soon as the contrast of "spiritual" and "material" was before their minds, they knew God to be "spiritual" and realised that their relgion had implied this all along. But at an earlier stage that contrast was not there. To regard that earlier stage as unspiritual because we find there no clear assertion of unembodied spirit, is a real misunderstanding. You might just as well call it spiritual because it contained no clear consciousness of mere matter. Mr. Barfield

[1] Jer. xxiii. 24.
[2] Ezek. i. 26.
[3] Deut. iv. 15.
[4] Gen. i. 1.

has shown, as regards the history of language, that words did not start by referring merely to physical objects and then get extended by metaphor to refer to emotions, mental states and the like. On the contrary, what we now call the "literal and metaphorical" meanings have both been disengaged by analysis from an ancient unity of meaning which was neither or both. In the same way it is quite erroneous to think that man started with a "material" God or "Heaven" and gradually spiritualised them. He could not have started with something "material" for the "material," as we understand it, comes to be realised only by contrast to the "immaterial," and the two sides of the contrast grow at the same speed. He started with something which was neither and both. As long as we are trying to read back into that ancient unity either the one or the other of the two opposites which have since been analysed out of it, we shall misread all early literature and ignore many states of consciousness which we ourselves still from time to time experience. The point is crucial not only for the present discussion but for any sound literary criticism or philosophy.

The Christian doctrines, and even the Jewish doctrines which preceded them, have always been statements about spiritual reality, not specimens of primitive physical science. Whatever is positive in the conception of the spiritual has always been contained in them; it is only its negative aspect (immateriality) which has had to wait for recognition until abstract thought was fully developed. The material imagery has never been taken literally by anyone who had reached the stage when he could understand what "taking it literally" meant. And now we come to the difference between "explaining" and "explaining away." It shows itself in two ways. (1) Some people when they say that a thing is meant "metaphorically" conclude from this that it is hardly meant at all. They rightly think that Christ spoke metaphorically when he told us to carry the cross; they wrongly conclude that carrying the cross means nothing more than leading a respectable life and subscribing moderately to charities. They reasonably think that hell "fire" is a metaphor—and unwisely conclude that it means nothing more serious than remorse. They say that the story of the Fall in *Genesis* is not literal; and then go on to

say (I have heard them myself) that it was really a fall upwards
—which is like saying that because "My heart is broken" contains
a metaphor, it therefore means "I feel very cheerful." This mode
of interpretation I regard, frankly, as nonsense. For me the Christian doctrines which are "metaphorical"—or which have become
metaphorical with the increase of abstract thought—mean something which is just as "supernatural" or shocking after we have
removed the ancient imagery as it was before. They mean that
in addition to the physical or psycho-physical universe known to
the sciences, there exists an uncreated and unconditioned reality
which causes the universe to be; that this reality has a positive
structure or constitution which is usefully, though doubtless not
completely, described in the doctrine of the Trinity; and that this
reality, at a definite point in time, entered the universe we know
by becoming one of its own creatures and there produced effects
on the historical level which the normal workings of the natural
universe do not produce; and that this has brought about
a change in our relations to the unconditioned reality. It will
be noticed that our colourless "entered the universe" is not a
whit less metaphorical than the more picturesque "came down
from Heaven." We have only substituted a picture of horizontal
or unspecified movement for one of vertical movement. And every
attempt to improve the ancient language will have the same
result. These things not only cannot be asserted—they cannot even be presented for discussion—without metaphor. We can
make our speech duller; we cannot make it more literal.
(2) These statements concern two things—the supernatural, unconditioned reality, and those events on the historical level which
its irruption into the natural universe is held to have produced.
The first thing is indescribable in "literal" speech, and therefore
we rightly interpret all that is said about it metaphorically. But
the second thing is in a wholly different position. Events on the
historical level are the sort of things we can talk about literally.
If they occurred, they were perceived by the senses of men. Legitimate "explanation" degenerates into muddled or dishonest "explaining away" as soon as we start applying to these events the
metaphorical interpretation which we rightly apply to the statements about God. The assertion that God has a Son was never

intended to mean that He is a being propagating His kind by sexual intercourse: and so we do not alter Christianity by rendering explicit the fact that "sonship" is not used of Christ in exactly the same sense in which it is used of men. But the assertion that Jesus turned water into wine was meant perfectly literally, for this refers to something which, if it happened, was well within the reach of our senses and our language. When I say, "My heart is broken," you know perfectly well that I don't mean anything you could verify at a *post-mortem*. But when I say, "My boot-lace is broken," then, if your own observation shows it to be intact, I am either lying or mistaken. The accounts of the "miracles" in first-century Palestine are either lies, or legends, or history. And if all, or the most important, of them are lies or legends then the claim which Christianity has been making for the last two thousand years is simply false. No doubt it might even so contain noble sentiments and moral truths. So does Greek mythology; so does Norse. But that is quite a different affair.

Nothing in this chapter helps us to a decision about the probability or improbability of the Christian claim. We have merely removed a misunderstanding in order to secure for that question a fair hearing.

I I.

CHRISTIANITY AND "RELIGION"

Those who make religion their god will not have God for
their religion.

THOMAS ERSKINE OF LINLATHEN.

Having eliminated the confusions which come from ignoring the
relations of thought, imagination, and speech, we may now return to our question. The Christians say that God has done miracles. The modern world, even when it believes in God, and even
when it has seen the defencelessness of Nature, does not. It thinks
God would not do that sort of thing. Have we any reason for
supposing that the modern world is right? I agree that the sort
of God conceived by the popular "religion" of our own times
would almost certainly work no miracles. The question is whether
that popular religion is at all likely to be true.

I call it "religion" advisedly. We who defend Christianity find
ourselves constantly opposed not by the irreligion of our hearers but by their real religion. Speak about beauty, truth and
goodness, or about a God who is simply the indwelling principle
of these three, speak about a great spiritual force pervading all
things, a common mind of which we are all parts, a pool of gen-
eralised spirituality to which we can all flow, and you will command friendly interest. But the temperature drops as soon as you
mention a God who has purposes and performs particular actions, who does one thing and not another, a concrete, choosing,
commanding, prohibiting God with a determinate character. People become embarrassed or angry. Such a conception seems to
them primitive and crude and even irreverent. The popular "religion" excludes miracles because it excludes the "living God" of
Christianity and believes instead in a kind of God who obviously

would not do miracles, or indeed anything else. This popular "religion" may roughly be called Pantheism, and we must now examine its credentials.

In the first place it is usually based on a quite fanciful picture of the history of religion. According to this picture, Man starts by inventing "spirits" to explain natural phenomena; and at first he imagines these spirits to be exactly like himself. As he gets more enlightened they become less man-like, less "anthropomorphic" as the scholars call it. Their anthropomorphic attributes drop off one by one—first the human shape, then human passions, then personality, will, activity—in the end every concrete or positive attribute whatever. There is left in the end a pure abstraction—mind as such, spirituality as such. God, instead of being a particular entity with a real character of its own, becomes simply "the whole show" looked at in a particular way or the theoretical point at which all the lines of human aspiration would meet if produced to infinity. And since, on the modern view, the final stage of anything is the most refined and civilised stage, this "religion" is held to be a more profound, more spiritual, and more enlightened belief than Christianity.

Now this imagined history of religion is not true. Pantheism certainly is (as its advocates would say) congenial to the modern mind; but the fact that a shoe slips on easily does not prove that it is a new shoe—much less that it will keep your feet dry. Pantheism is congenial to our minds not because it is the final stage in a slow process of enlightenment, but because it is almost as old as we are. It may even be the most primitive of all religions, and the *orenda* of a savage tribe has been interpreted by some to be an "all-pervasive spirit." It is immemorial in India. The Greeks rose above it only at their peak, in the thought of Plato and Aristotle; their successors relapsed into the great Pantheistic system of the Stoics. Modern Europe escaped it only while she remained predominantly Christian; with Giordano Bruno and Spinoza it returned. With Hegel it became almost the agreed philosophy of highly educated people, while the more popular Pantheism of Wordsworth, Carlyle and Emerson conveyed the same doctrine to those on a slightly lower cultural level. So far from being the final religious refinement, Pantheism is in fact the permanent natural bent of the human mind; the permanent ordinary level below which man sometimes sinks, under the influence of priest-craft and superstition, but above which his own unaided efforts can never raise him for very long. Platonism and Judaism, and Christianity (which has incorporated both) have proved the only things capable of resisting it. It is the attitude into which the human mind automatically falls when left to itself. No wonder we find it congenial. If "religion" means simply what man says about God, and not what God does about man, then Pantheism almost *is* religion. And "religion" in that sense has, in the long run, only one really formidable opponent—namely Christianity.[1] Modern philosophy has rejected Hegel and modern science started out with no bias in favour of religion; but they have both proved quite powerless to curb the human impulse towards Pantheism. It is nearly as strong to-day as it was in ancient India or in ancient Rome. Theosophy and the worship of the life-force are both forms of it: even the German worship of a racial spirit is only Pantheism truncated or whittled down to suit barbarians. Yet, by a strange irony, each new relapse into this immemorial "religion" is hailed as the last word in novelty and emancipation.

This native bent of the mind can be paralleled in quite a different field of thought. Men believed in atoms centuries before they had any experimental evidence of their existence. It was apparently natural to do so. And the sort of atoms we naturally believe in are little hard pellets—just like the hard substances we meet in experience, but too small to see. The mind reaches this conception by an easy analogy from grains of sand or of salt. It explains a number of phenomena; and we feel at home with atoms of that sort—we can picture them. The belief would have lasted forever if later science had not been so troublesome as to find out what atoms are *really* like. The moment it does that, all our mental comfort, all the immediate plausibility and obviousness of the old atomic theory, is destroyed. The real atoms turn out to be quite alien from our natural mode of thought. They

[1] Hence, if a Minister of Education professes to value religion and at the same time takes steps to suppress Christianity, it does not necessarily follow that he is a hypocrite or even (in the ordinary this-worldly sense of the word) a fool. He may sincerely desire more "religion" and rightly see that the suppression of Christianity is a necessary preliminary to his design.

are not even made of hard "stuff" or "matter" (as the imagination understands "matter") at all: they are not simple, but have a structure: they are not all the same: and they are unpicturable. The old atomic theory is in physics what Pantheism is in religion —the normal, instinctive guess of the human mind, not utterly wrong, but needing correction. Christian theology, and quantum physics, are both, by comparison with the first guess, hard, complex, dry and repellent. The first shock of the object's real nature, breaking in on our spontaneous dreams of what that object ought to be, always has these characteristics. You must not expect Schrödinger to be as plausible as Democritus; he knows too much. You must not expect St. Athanasius to be as plausible as Mr. Bernard Shaw: he also knows too much.

The true state of the question is often misunderstood because people compare an adult knowedge of Pantheism with a knowledge of Christianity which they acquired in their childhood. They thus get the impression that Christianity gives the "obvious" account of God, the one that is too easy to be true, while Pantheism offers something sublime and mysterious. In reality, it is the other way round. The apparent profundity of Pantheism thinly veils a mass of spontaneous picture-thinking and owes its plausibility to that fact. Pantheists and Christians agree that God is present everywhere. Pantheists conclude that He is "diffused" or "concealed" in all things and therefore a universal medium rather than a concrete entity, because their minds are really dominated by the picture of a gas, or fluid, or space itself. The Christian, on the other hand, deliberately rules out such images by saying that God is totally present at every point of space and time, and *locally* present in none. Again the Pantheist and Christian agree that we are all dependent on God and intimately related to Him. But the Christian defines this relation in terms of Maker and made, whereas the Pantheist (at least of the popular kind) says, we are "parts" of Him, or are contained in Him. Once more, the picture of a vast extended something which can be divided into areas has crept in. Because of this fatal picture Pantheism concludes that God must be equally present in what we call evil and what we call good and therefore indifferent to both (ether permeates the mud and the marble impartially). The Christian has to reply

that this is far too simple; God is present in a great many different modes: not present in matter as He is present in man, not
present in all man as in some, not present in any other man as in
Jesus. Pantheist and Christian also agree that God is super-per-
sonal. The Christian means by this that God has a positive structure which we could never have guessed in advance, any more
than a knowledge of squares would have enabled us to guess at a
cube. He contains "persons" (three of them) while remaining
one God, as a cube combines six squares while remaining one
solid body. We cannot comprehend such a structure any more
than the Flatlanders could comprehend a cube. But we can at
least comprehend our incomprehension, and see that if there is
something beyond personality it *ought* to be incomprehensible in
that sort of way. The Pantheist, on the other hand, though he
may say "super personal" really conceives God in terms of what is
sub personal—as though the Flatlanders thought a cube existed
in *fewer* dimensions than a square.

At every point Christianity has to correct the natural expectations of the Pantheist and offer something more difficult,
just as Schrödinger has to correct Democritus. At every moment
he has to multiply distinctions and rule out false analogies. He
has to substitute the mappings of something that has a positive,
concrete, and highly articulated character for the formless generalities in which Pantheism is at home. Indeed, after the discussion has been going on for some time the Pantheist is apt
to change his ground and where he before accused us of childish naivety now to blame us for the pedantic complexity of our
"cold Christs and tangled Trinities." And we may well sympathise
with him. Christianity, faced with popular "religion" is continuously troublesome. To the large well-meant statements of "religion" it finds itself forced to reply again and again. "Well, not
quite like that," or, "I should hardly put it that way." This
troublesomeness does not of course prove it to be true; but if it
were true it would be bound to have this troublesomeness. The
real musician is similarly troublesome to a man who wishes to
indulge in untaught "musical appreciation"; the real historian is
similarly a nuisance when we want to romance about "the old
days" or "the ancient Greeks and Romans." The ascertained

nature of any real thing is always at first a nuisance to our natural fantasies—a wretched, pedantic, logic-chopping intruder upon a conversation which was getting on famously without it.

But "religion" also claims to base itself on experience. The experiences of the mystics (that ill-defined but popular class) are held to indicate that God is the God of "religion" rather than of Christianity; that He—or It—is not a concrete Being but "being in general" about which nothing can be truly asserted. To everything which we try to say about Him, the mystics tend to reply, "Not thus." What all these negatives of the mystics really mean I shall consider in a moment: but I must first point out why it seems to me impossible that they should be true in the sense popularly understood.

It will be agreed that, however they came there, concrete, individual, determinate things do now exist: things like flamingoes, German generals, lovers, sandwiches, pineapples, comets and kangaroos. These are not mere principles or generalities or theorems, but things—facts—real, resistant existences. One might even say *opaque* existences, in the sense that each contains something which our intelligence cannot completely digest. In so far as they illustrate general laws it can digest them: but then they are never mere illustrations. Above and beyond that there is in each of them the "opaque" brute fact of existence, the fact that it is actually there and is itself. Now this opaque fact, this concreteness, is not in the least accounted for by the laws of Nature or even by the laws of thought. Every law can be reduced to the form "If A, then B." Laws give us only a universe of "Ifs and Ands": not this universe which actually exists. What we know through laws and general principles is a series of connexions. But in order for there to be a real universe the connexions must be given something to connect; a torrent of opaque actualities must be fed into the pattern. If God created the world, then He is precisely the source of this torrent, and it alone gives our truest principles anything to be true *about*. But if God is the ultimate source of all concrete, individual things and events, then God Himself must be concrete, and individual in the highest degree. Unless the origin of all other things were itself concrete and individual, nothing else could be so; for there is no conceivable means whereby what is abstract or general could itself produce concrete reality. Book-keeping, continued to all eternity, could never produce one farthing. Metre, of itself, could never produce a poem. Book-keeping needs something else (namely, real money put into the account) and metre needs something else (real words, fed into it by a poet) before any income or any poem can exist. If anything is to exist at all, then the Original Thing must be, not a principle nor a generality, much less an "ideal" or a "value," but an utterly concrete fact.

Probably no thinking person would, in so many words, deny that God is concrete and individual. But not all thinking people, and certainly not all who believe in "religion," keep this truth steadily before their minds. We must beware, as Professor Whitehead says, of paying God ill-judged "metaphysical compliments." We say that God is "infinite." In the sense that His knowledge and power extend not to some things but to all, this is true. But if by using the word "infinite" we encourage ourselves to think of Him as a formless "everything" about whom nothing in particular and everything in general is true, then it would be better to drop that word altogether. Let us dare to say that God is a particular Thing. Once He was the only Thing: but He is creative, He made other things to be. He is not those other things. He is not "universal being": if He were there would be no creatures, for a generality can make nothing. He is "absolute being"—or rather *the* Absolute Being—in the sense that He alone exists in His own right. But there are things which God is not. In that sense He has a determinate character. Thus He is righteous, not a-moral; creative, not inert. The Hebrew writings here observe an admirable balance. Once God says simply I AM, proclaiming the mystery of self-existence. But times without number He says, "I am the Lord"—I, the ultimate Fact, have *this* determinate character, and not *that*. And men are exhorted to "know the Lord," to discover and experience this particular character.

The error which I am here trying to correct is one of the most sincere and respectable errors in the world; I have sympathy enough with it to feel shocked at the language I have been driven to use in stating the opposite view, which I believe to be the true one. To say that God "is a particular Thing" does seem to obliterate the immeasurable difference not only between what He is and what all other things are but between the very mode of His existence and theirs. I must at once restore the balance by insisting that derivative things, from atoms to archangels, hardly attain to existence at all in comparison with their Creator. Their principle of existence is not in themselves. You can distinguish *what* they are from the fact *that* they are. The definition of them can be understood and a clear idea of them formed without even knowing *whether* they are. Existence is an "opaque" addition to the idea of them. But with God it is not so: if we fully understood *what* God is we should see that there is no question *whether* He is. It would always have been impossible that He should not exist. He is the opaque centre of all existences, the thing that simply and entirely *is*, the fountain of facthood. And yet, now that He has created, there is a sense in which we must say that He is a particular Thing and even one Thing among others. To say this is not to lessen the immeasurable difference between Him and them. On the contrary, it is to recognise in Him a positive perfection which Pantheism has obscured; the perfection of being creative. He is so brim-full of existence that He can give existence away, can cause things to be, and to be really other than Himself, can make it untrue to say that He is everything.

It is clear that there never was a time when nothing existed; otherwise nothing would exist now. But to exist means to be a positive Something, to have (metaphorically) a certain shape or structure, to be this and not that. The Thing which always existed, namely God, has therefore always had His own positive character. Throughout all eternity certain statements about Him would have been true and others false. And from the mere fact of our own existence and Nature's we already know to some extent which are which. We know that He invents, acts, creates. After that there can be no ground for assuming in advance that He does not do miracles.

Why, then, do the mystics talk of Him as they do, and why are many people prepared in advance to maintain that, whatever else God may be, He is not the concrete, living, willing, and acting God of Christian theology? I think the reason is as follows. Let us suppose a mystical limpet, a sage among limpets, who (rapt in vision) catches a glimpse of what Man is like. In reporting it to his disciples, who have some vision themselves (though less than he) he will have to use many negatives. He will have to tell them that Man has no shell, is not attached to a rock, is not surrounded by water. And his disciples, having a little vision of their own to help them, do get some idea of Man. But then there come erudite limpets, limpets who write histories of philosophy and give lectures on comparative religion, and who have never had any vision of their own. What they get out of the prophetic limpet's words is simply and solely the negatives. From these, uncorrected by any positive insight, they build up a picture of Man as a sort of amorphous jelly (he has no shell) existing nowhere in particular (he is not attached to a rock) and never taking nourishment (there is no water to drift it towards him). And having a traditional reverence for Man they conclude that to be a famished jelly in a dimensionless void is the supreme mode of existence, and reject as crude, materialistic superstition any doctrine which would attribute to Man a definite shape, a structure, and organs.

Our own situation is much like that of the erudite limpets. Great prophets and saints have an intuition of God which is positive and concrete in the highest degree. Because, just touching the fringes of His being, they have seen that He is plenitude of life and energy and joy, therefore (and for no other reason) they have to pronounce that He transcends those limitations which we call personality, passion, change, materiality, and the like. The positive quality in Him which repels these limitations is their only ground for all the negatives. But when we come limping after and try to construct an intellectual or "enlightened" religion, we take over these negatives (infinite, immaterial, impassible, immutable, etc.) and use them unchecked by any positive intuition. At each step we have to strip off from our idea of God some human attribute. But the only real reason for stripping off the human attribute is to make room for putting on some positive divine attribute. In St. Paul's language, the purpose of all this unclothing is not that our idea of God should reach nakedness but that it should be re-clothed. But unhappily we have no means of doing the re-clothing. When we have removed from our idea of God some puny human characteristic, we (as merely erudite or intelligent enquirers) have no resources from which to supply that blindingly real and concrete attribute of Deity which ought to replace it. Thus at each step in the process of refinement our idea of God contains less, and the fatal pictures come in (an endless, silent sea, an empty sky beyond all stars, a dome of white radiance) and we reach at last mere zero and worship a nonentity. And the understanding, left to itself, can hardly help following this path. That is why the Christian statement that only He who does the will of the Father will ever know the true doctrine is philosophically accurate. Imagination may help a little: but in the moral life, and (still more) in the devotional life, we touch something concrete which will at once begin to correct the growing emptiness of our idea of God. One moment even of feeble contrition or blurred thankfulness will, at least in some degree, head us off from the abyss of abstraction. It is Reason herself which teaches us not to rely on Reason only in this matter. For Reason knows that she cannot work without materials. When it becomes clear that you cannot find out by reasoning whether the cat is in the linen-cupboard, it is Reason herself who whispers, "Go and look. This is not my job: it is a matter for the senses." So here. The materials for correcting our abstract conception of God cannot be supplied by Reason: she will be the first to tell you to go and try experience—"Oh, taste and see!" For of course she will have already pointed out that your present position is absurd. As long as we remain Erudite Limpets we are forgetting that if no-one had ever seen more of God than we, we should have no reason even to believe Him immaterial, immutable, impassible and all the rest of it. Even that negative knowledge which seems to us so enlightened is only a relic left over from the positive knowledge of better men—only the pattern which that heavenly wave left on the sand when it retreated.

"A Spirit and a Vision," said Blake, "are not, as the modern philosophy supposes, a cloudy vapour, or a nothing. They are organised and minutely articulated beyond all that the mortal and perishing nature can produce." [1] He is speaking only of how to draw pictures of apparitions which may well have been illu-

[1] *A Descriptive Catalogue*. Number IV.

sory, but his words suggest a truth on the metaphysical level also. God is basic Fact or Actuality, the source of all other facthood. At all costs therefore He must not be thought of as a featureless generality. If He exists at all, He is the most concrete thing there is, the most individual, "organised and minutely articulated." He is unspeakable not by being indefinite but by being too definite for the unavoidable vagueness of language. The words *incorporeal* and *impersonal* are misleading, because they suggest that He lacks some reality which we possess. It would be safer to call Him *trans-corporeal, trans-personal*. Body and personality as we know them are the real negatives—they are what is left of positive being when it is sufficiently diluted to appear in temporal or finite forms. Even our sexuality should be regarded as the transposition into a minor key of that creative joy which in Him ins unceasing and irresistible. Grammatically the things we say of Him are "metaphorical": but in a deeper sense it is our physical and psychic energies that are mere "metaphors" of the real life which is God. Divine Sonship is, so to speak, the solid of which biological sonship is merely a diagrammatic representation on the flat.

And here the subject of imagery, which crossed our path in the last chapter, can be seen in a new light. For it is just the recognition of God' positive and concrete reality which the religious imagery preserves. The crudest Old Testament picture of Jahweh thundering and lightning out of dense smoke, making mountains skip like rams, threatening, promising, pleading, even changing His mind, transmits that sense of *living* Deity which evaporates in abstract thought. Even sub-Christian images—even a Hindoo idol with a hundred hands—gets in *something* which mere "religion" in our own days has left out. We rightly reject it, for by itself it would encourage the most blackguard of superstitions, the adoration of mere power. Perhaps we may rightly reject much of the Old Testament imagery. But we must be clear why we are doing so: not because the images are too strong but because they are too weak. The ultimate spiritual reality is not vaguer, more inert, more transparent than the images, but more positive, more dynamic, more opaque. Confusion between Spirit and soul (or "ghost") has here done much harm. Ghosts must be pictured, if we are to picture them at all, as shadowy and tenuous, for ghosts are half-men, one element abstracted from a creature that ought to have flesh. But Spirit, if pictured at all, must be pictured in the very opposite way. Neither God nor even the gods are "shadowy" in traditional imagination: even the human dead, when glorified in Christ, cease to be "ghosts" and become "saints." The difference of atmosphere which even now surrounds the words "I saw a ghost" and the words "I saw a saint"—all the pallor and insubstantiality of the one, all the gold and blue of the other—contains more wisdom than whole libraries of "religion." If we must have a mental picture to symbolise Spirit, we should represent it as something *heavier* than matter.

And if we say that we are rejecting the old images in order to do more justice to the moral attributes of God, we must again be careful of what we are really meaning. When we wish to learn of the love and goodness of God by *analogy*—by imagining parallels to them in the realm of human relations—we turn of course to the parables of Christ. But when we try to conceive the reality as it may be in itself, we must beware lest we interpret "moral attributes" in terms of mere conscientiousness or abstract benevolence. The mistake is easily made because we (correctly) deny that God has passions; and with us a love that is not passionate means a love that is something less. But the reason why God has no passions is that passions imply passivity and intermission. The passion of love is something that happens to us, as "getting wet" happens to a body: and God is exempt from that "passion" in the same way that water is exempt from "getting wet." He cannot be affected with love, because He *is* love. To imagine that love as something less torrential or less sharp than our own temporary and derivative "passions" is a most disastrous fantasy.

Again, we may find a violence in some of the traditional imagery which tends to obscure the changelessness of God, the peace, which nearly all who approach Him have reported—the "still, small voice." And it is here, I think, that the pre-Christian imagery is least suggestive. Yet even here, there is a danger lest the half conscious picture of some huge thing at rest—a clear, still ocean, a dome of "white radiance"—should smuggle in ideas of inertia or vacuity. The stillness in which the mystics approach Him is intent and alert—at the opposite pole from sleep or reverie. They are becoming like Him. Silences in the physical world occur in empty places: but the ultimate Peace is silent through very density of life. Saying is swallowed up in being. There is no movement because His action (which is Himself) is timeless. You might, if you wished, call it movement at an infinite speed, which is the same thing as rest, but reached by a different—perhaps a less misleading—way of approach.

Men are reluctant to pass over from the notion of an abstract and negative deity to the living God. I do not wonder. Here lies the deepest tap-root of Pantheism and of the objection to traditional imagery. It was hated not, at bottom, because it pictured Him as man but because it pictured Him as king, or even as warrior. The Pantheist's God does nothing, demands nothing. He is there if you wish for Him, like a book on a shelf. He will not pursue you. There is no danger that at any time heaven and earth should flee away at His glance. If He were the truth, then we could really say that all the Christian images of kingship were a historical accident of which our religion ought to be cleansed. It is with a shock that we discover them to be indispensable. You have had a shock like that before, in connection with smaller matters—when the line pulls at your hand, when something breathes beside you in the darkness. So here; the shock comes at the precise moment when the thrill of *life* is communicated to us along the clue we have been following. It is always shocking to meet life where we thought we were alone. "Look out!" we cry, "it's *alive*." And therefore this is the very point at which so many draw back—I would have done so myself if I could—and proceed no further with Christianity. An "impersonal God"—well and good. A subjective God of beauty, truth and goodness, inside our own heads—better still. A formless life-force surging through us, a vast power which we can tap—best of all. But God Himself, alive, pulling at the other end of the cord, perhaps approaching at an infinite speed, the hunter, king, husband—that is quite another matter. There comes a moment when the children who have been playing at burglars hush suddenly: was that a *real* footstep in the hall? There comes a moment when people who have been dabbling in religion ("Man's search for God"!) suddenly draw back. Supposing we really found Him? We never meant it to come to *that!* Worse still, supposing He had found us?

So it is a sort of Rubicon. One goes across; or not. But if one does, there is no manner of security against miracles. One may be in for *anything*.

12.

THE PROPRIETY OF MIRACLES

The Principle at the same moment that it explains the Rules
supersedes them.

SEELEY,
Ecce Homo, chap. XVI.

If the ultimate Fact is not an abstraction but the living
God, opaque by the very fulness of His blinding actuality, then
He might do things. He might work miracles. But would He?
Many people of sincere piety feel that He would not. They think
it unworthy of Him. It is petty and capricious tyrants who break
their own laws: good and wise kings obey them. Only an incompetent workman will produce work which needs to be interfered
with. And people who think in this way are not satisfied by the
assurance given them in Chapter 8 that miracles do not, in fact,
break the laws of Nature. That may be undeniable. But it will
still be felt (and justly) that miracles interrupt the orderly march
of events, the steady development of Nature according to her own
inherent genius or character. That regular march seems to such
critics as I have in mind more impressive than any miracle.
Looking up (like Lucifer in Meredith's sonnet) at the night sky,
they feel it almost impious to suppose that God should sometimes
unsay what He has once said with such magnificence. This feeling springs from deep and noble sources in the mind and must
always be treated with respect. Yet it is, I believe, founded on an
error.

When schoolboys begin to be taught to make Latin verses at
school they are very properly forbidden to have what is technically called "a spondee in the fifth foot." It is a good rule for boys
because the normal hexameter does not have a spondee there: if

boys were allowed to use this abnormal form they would be constantly doing it for convenience and might never get the typical
music of the hexameter into their heads at all. But when the
boys come to read Virgil they find that Virgil does the very thing
they have been forbidden to do—not very often, but not so very
rarely either. In the same way, young people who have just
learned how to write English rhyming verse, may be shocked at
finding "bad" rhymes (i.e. half-rhymes) in the great poets. Even
in carpentry or car-driving or surgery there are, I expect, "licenses"—abnormal ways of doing things—which the master will
use himself both safely and judiciously but which he would
think it unwise to teach his pupils.

Now one often finds that the beginner, who has just mastered
the strict formal rules, is over-punctilious and pedantic about
them. And the mere critic, who is never going to begin himself,
may be more pedantic still. The classical critics were shocked at
the "irregularity" or "licenses" of Shakespeare. A stupid schoolboy might think that the abnormal hexameters in Virgil, or the
half-rhymes in English poets, were due to incompetence. In
reality, of course, every one of them is there for a purpose and
breaks the superficial regularity of the metre in obedience to a
higher and subtler law: just as the irregularities in *The Winter's Tale* do not impair, but embody and perfect, the inward
unity of its spirit.

In other words, there are rules behind the rules, and a unity
which is deeper than uniformity. A supreme workman will never
break by one note or one syllable or one stroke of the brush the
living and inward law of the work he is producing. But he will
break without scruple any number of those superficial regularities and orthodoxies which little, unimaginative critics mistake
for its laws. The extent to which one can distinguish a just "li-
cense" from a mere botch or failure of unity depends on the extent to which one has grasped the real and inward significance
of the work as a whole. If we had grasped as a whole the innermost spirit of that "work which God worketh from the beginning to the end," and of which Nature is only a part and perhaps
a small part, we should be in a position to decide whether miraculous interruptions of Nature's history were mere improprieties

unworthy of the Great Workman or expressions of the truest and deepest unity in His total work. In fact, of course, we are in no such position. The gap between God's mind and ours must, on any view, be incalculably greater than the gap between Shakespeare's mind and that of the most peddling critics of the old French school.

For who can suppose that God's eternal act, seen from within, would be that same complexity of mathematical relations which Nature, scientifically studied, reveals? It is like thinking that a poet builds up his line out of those metrical feet into which we can analyse it, or that living speech takes grammar as its starting point. But the best illustration of all is Bergson's. Let us suppose a race of people whose peculiar mental limitation compels them to regard a painting as something made up of little coloured dots which have been put together like a mosaic. Studying the brushwork of a great painting, through their magnifying glasses, they discover more and more complicated relations between the dots, and sort these relations out, with great toil, into certain regularities. Their labour will not be in vain. These regularities will in fact "work"; they will cover most of the facts. But if they go on to conclude that any departure from them would be unworthy of the painter, and an arbitrary breaking of his own rules, they will be far astray. For the regularities they have observed never were the rule the painter was following. What they painfully reconstruct from a million dots, arranged in an agonising complexity, he really produced with a single lightning-quick turn of the wrist, his eye meanwhile taking in the canvas as a whole and his mind obeying laws of composition which the observers, counting their dots, have not yet come within sight of, and perhaps never will. I do not say that the normalities of Nature are unreal. The living fountain of divine energy, solidified for purposes of this spatio-temporal Nature into bodies moving in space and time, and thence, by our abstract thought, turned into mathematical formulae, does in fact, for us, commonly fall into such and such patterns. In finding out those patterns we are therefore gaining real, and often useful, knowledge. But to think that a disturbance of them would constitute a breach of the living rule and organic unity whereby God, from His own point of view, works, is a mistake. If miracles do occur then we may be sure that *not* to have wrought them would be the real inconsistency.

How a miracle can be no inconsistency, but the highest consistency, will be clear to those who have read Miss Dorothy Sayers' indispensable book, *The Mind of the Maker*. Miss Sayers' thesis is based on the analogy between God's relation to the world, on the one hand, and an author's relation to his book on the other. If you are writing a story, miracles or abnormal events may be bad art, or they may not. If, for example, you are writing an ordinary realistic novel and have got your characters into a hopeless muddle, it would be quite intolerable if you suddenly cut the knot and secured a happy ending by having a fortune left to the hero from an unexpected quarter. On the other hand there is nothing against taking as your subject from the outset the adventures of a man who inherits an unexpected fortune. The unusual event is perfectly permissible if it is what you are really writing *about*: it is an artistic crime if you simply drag it in by the heels to get yourself out of a hole. The ghost story is a legitimate form of art; but you must not bring a ghost into an ordinary novel to get over a difficulty in the plot. Now there is no doubt that a great deal of the modern objection to miracles is based on the suspicion that they are marvels of the wrong sort; that a story of a certain kind (Nature) is arbitrarily interfered with, to get the characters out of a difficulty, by events that do not really belong to that kind of story. Some people probably think of the Resurrection as a desperate last moment expedient to save the Hero from a situation which had got out of the Author's control.

The reader may set his mind at rest. If I thought miracles were like that, I should not believe in them. If they have occurred, they have occurred because they are the very thing this universal story is about. They are not exceptions (however rarely they occur) nor irrelevancies. They are precisely those chapters in this great story on which the plot turns. Death and Resurrection are what the story is about; and had we but eyes to see it, this has been hinted on every page, met us, in some disguise, at every turn, and even been muttered in conversations between such minor characters (if they are minor characters) as the vegetables. If you have hitherto disbelieved in miracles, it is worth pausing a moment to consider whether this is not chiefly because you thought you had discovered what the story was really about?— that atoms, and time and space and economics and politics were the main plot? And is it certain you were right? It is easy to make mistakes in such matters. A friend of mine wrote a play in which the main idea was that the hero had a pathological horror of trees and a mania for cutting them down. But naturally other things came in as well; there was some sort of love story mixed up with it. And the trees killed the man in the end. When my friend had written it, he sent it to an older man to criticise. It came back with the comment, "Not bad. But I'd cut out those bits of *padding* about the trees." To be sure, God might be expected to make a better story than my friend. But it is a very *long* story, with a complicated plot; and we are not, perhaps, very attentive readers.

13.

ON PROBABILITY

Probability is founded on the presumption of a resemblance between those objects of which we have had experience and those of which we have had none; and therefore it is impossible that this presumption can arise from probability.

HUME,
Treatise of Human Nature, I, III, vi.

The argument up to date shows that miracles are possible and that there is nothing antecedently ridiculous in the stories which say that God has sometimes performed them. This does not mean, of course, that we are committed to believing all stories of miracles. Most stories about miraculous events are probably false: if it comes to that, most stories about natural events are false. Lies, exaggerations, misunderstandings and hearsay make up perhaps more than half of all that is said and written in the world. We must therefore find a criterion whereby to judge any particular story of the miraculous.

In one sense, of course, our criterion is plain. Those stories are to be accepted for which the historical evidence is sufficiently good. But then, as we saw at the outset, the answer to the question, "How much evidence should we require for this story?" depends on our answer to the question, "How far is this story intrinsically probable?" We must therefore find a criterion of probability.

The ordinary procedure of the modern historian, even if he admits the possibility of a miracle, is to admit no particular instance of it until every possibility of "natural" explanation has been tried and failed. That is, he will accept the most improbable "natural" explanations rather than say that a miracle occurred. Collective hallucination, hypnotism of unconsenting spectators, widespread instantaneous conspiracy in lying by persons not otherwise known to be liars and not likely to gain by the lie —all these are known to be very improbable events: so improbable that, except for the special purpose of excluding a miracle, they are never suggested. But they are preferred to the admission of a miracle.

Such a procedure is, from the purely historical point of view, sheer midsummer madness *unless* we start by knowing that any Miracle whatever is more improbable than the most improbable natural event. Do we know this?

We must distinguish the different kinds of improbability. Since miracles are, by definition, rarer than other events, it is obviously improbable beforehand that one will occur at any given place and time. In that sense every miracle is improbable. But that sort of improbability does not make the story that a miracle *has* happened incredible; for in the same sense all events whatever were once improbable. It is immensely improbable beforehand that a pebble dropped from the stratosphere over London will hit any given spot, or that any one particular person will win a large lottery. But the report that the pebble has landed outside such and such a shop or that Mr. So-and-So has won the lottery is not at all incredible. When you consider the immense number of meetings and fertile unions between ancestors which were necessary in order that you should be born, you perceive that it was once immensely improbable that such a person as you should come to exist: but once you are here, the report of your existence is not in the least incredible. With probability of this kind—antecedent probability of chances—we are not here concerned. Our business is with historical probability.

Ever since Hume's famous *Essay* it has been believed that historical statements about miracles are the most intrinsically improbable of all historical statements. According to Hume, probability rests on what may be called the majority vote of our past experiences. The more often a thing has been known to happen, the more probable it is that it should happen again; and the less often the less probable. Now the regularity of Nature's course, says Hume, is supported by something better than the majority vote of past experiences: it is supported by their unanimous vote, or, as Hume says, by "firm and unalterable experience." There is, in fact, "uniform experience" against Miracle; otherwise, says Hume, it would not be Miracle. A Miracle is therefore the most improbable of all events. It is always more probable that the witnesses were lying or mistaken than that a Miracle occurred.

Now of course we must agree with Hume that if there is absolutely "uniform experience" against miracles, if in other words they have never happened, why then they never have. Unfortunately we know the experience against them to be uniform only if we know that all the reports of them are false. And we can know all the reports to be false only if we know already that miracles have never occurred. In fact, we are arguing in a circle.

There is also an objection to Hume which leads us deeper into our problem. The whole idea of Probability (as Hume understands it) depends on the principle of the Uniformity of Nature. Unless Nature always goes on in the same way, the fact that a thing had happened ten million times would not make it a whit more probable that it would happen again. And how do we know the Uniformity of Nature? A moment's thought shows that we do not know it by experience. We observe many regularities in Nature. But of course all the observations that men have made or will make while the race lasts cover only a minute fraction of the events that actually go on. Our observations would therefore be of no use unless we felt sure that Nature when we are not watching her behaves in the same way as when we are: in other words, unless we believed in the Uniformity of Nature. Experience therefore cannot prove uniformity, because uniformity has to be assumed before experience proves anything. And mere length of experience does not help matters. It is no good saying, "Each fresh experience confirms our belief in uniformity and therefore we reasonably expect that it will always be confirmed"; for that argument works only on the assumption that the future will resemble the past—which is simply the assumption of Uniformity under a new name. Can we say that Uniformity is at any rate very probable? Unfortunately not. We have just seen that all probabilities depend on *it*. Unless Nature is uniform, nothing is either probable or improbable. And clearly the assumption which you have to make before there is any such thing as probability cannot itself be probable.

The odd thing is that no man knew this better than Hume. His *Essay on Miracles* is quite inconsistent with the more radical, and honourable, scepticism of his main work.

The question, "Do miracles occur?" and the question, "Is the course of Nature absolutely uniform?" are the same question asked in two different ways. Hume, by sleight of hand, treats them as two different questions. He first answers, "Yes," to the question whether Nature is absolutely uniform: and then uses this "Yes" as a ground for answering, "No," to the question, "Do miracles occur?" The single real question which he set out to answer is never discussed at all. He gets the answer to one form of the question by assuming the answer to another form of the same question.

Probabilities of the kind that Hume is concerned with hold inside the framework of an assumed Uniformity of Nature. When the question of miracles is raised we are asking about the validity or perfection of the frame itself. No study of probabilities inside a given frame can ever tell us how probable it is that the frame itself can be violated. Granted a school time-table with French on Tuesday morning at ten o'clock, it is really probable that Jones, who always skimps his French preparation, will be in trouble next Tuesday, and that he was in trouble on any previous Tuesday. But what does this tell us about the probability of the time-table's being altered? To find that out you must eavesdrop in the master's common-room. It is no use studying the time-table.

If we stick to Hume's method, far from getting what he hoped (namely, the conclusion that all miracles are infinitely improbable) we get a complete deadlock. The only kind of probability he allows holds exclusively within the frame of uniformity. When uniformity is itself in question (and it is in question the moment we ask whether miracles occur) this kind of probability is suspended. And Hume knows no other. By his method, therefore, we cannot say that uniformity is either probable or improbable; and equally we cannot say that miracles are either probable or improbable. We have impounded *both* uniformity *and* miracles in a sort of limbo where probability and improbability can never come. This result is equally disastrous for the scientist and the theologian; but along Hume's lines there is nothing whatever to be done about it.

Our only hope, then, will be to cast about for some quite different kind of Probability. Let us for the moment cease to ask what right we have to believe in the Uniformity of Nature, and ask why in fact men do believe in it. I think the belief has three causes, two of which are irrational. In the first place we are creatures of habit. We expect new situations to resemble old ones. It is a tendency which we share with animals; one can see it working, often to very comic results, in our dogs and cats. In the second place, when we plan our actions, we have to leave out of account the theoretical possibility that Nature might not behave as usual to-morrow, because we can do nothing about it. It is not worth bothering about because no action can be taken to meet it. And what we habitually put out of our minds we soon forget. The picture of uniformity thus comes to dominate our minds without rival and we believe it. Both these causes are irrational and would be just as effective in building up a false belief as in building up a true one.

But I am convinced that there is a third cause. "In science," said the late Sir Arthur Eddington, "we sometimes have convictions which we cherish but cannot justify; we are influenced by some innate sense of the fitness of things." This may sound a perilously subjective and aesthetic criterion; but can one doubt that it is a principal source of our belief in Uniformity? A universe in which unprecedented and unpredictable events were at every moment flung into Nature would not merely be inconvenient to us: it would be profoundly repugnant. We will not accept such a universe on any terms whatever. It is utterly detestable to us. It shocks our "sense of the fitness of things." In advance of experience, in the teeth of many experiences, we are already enlisted on the side of uniformity. For of course science actually proceeds by concentrating not on the regularities of Nature but on her apparent irregularities. It is the apparent irregularity that prompts each new hypothesis. It does so because we refuse to acquiesce in irregularities: we never rest till we have formed and verified a hypothesis which enables us to say that they were not really irregularities at all. Nature as it comes to us looks at first like a mass of irregularities. The stove which lit alright yesterday won't light to-day; the water which was wholesome last year is poisonous this year. The whole mass of seemingly irregular experience could never have been turned into scientific knowledge at all unless from the very start we had brought to it a faith in uniformity which almost no number of disappointments can shake.

This faith—the preference—is it a thing we can trust? Or is it only the way our minds happen to work? It is useless to say that it has hitherto always been confirmed by the event. That is no good unless you (at least silently) add, "And therefore always will be": and you cannot add that unless you know already that our faith in uniformity is well rounded. And that is just what we are now asking. Does this sense of fitness of ours correspond to anything in external reality?

The answer depends on the Metaphysic one holds. If all that exists is Nature, the great mindless interlocking event, if our own deepest convictions are merely the bye-products of an irrational process, then clearly there is not the slightest ground for supposing that our sense of fitness and our consequent faith in uniformity tell us anything about a reality external to ourselves. Our convictions are simply a fact *about us*—like the colour of our hair. If Naturalism is true we have no reason to trust our conviction that Nature is uniform. It can be trusted only if quite a different Metaphysic is true. If the deepest thing in reality, the Fact which is the source of all other facthood, is a thing in some degree like ourselves—if it is a Rational Spirit and we derive our rational spirituality from It—then indeed our conviction can be trusted. Our repugnance to disorder is derived from Nature's Creator and ours. The disorderly world which we cannot endure to believe in is the disorderly world He would not have endured to create. Our conviction that the time-table will not be perpetually or meaninglessly altered is sound because we have (in a sense) eavesdropped in the Masters' common-room.

The sciences logically require a metaphysic of this sort. Our greatest natural philosopher thinks it is also the metaphysic out of which they originally grew. Professor Whitehead points out[1] that centuries of belief in a God who combined "the personal energy of Jehovah" with "the rationality of a Greek philosopher" first produced that firm expectation of systematic order which rendered possible the birth of modern science. Men became scientific because they expected Law in Nature, and they expected Law in Nature because they believed in a Legislator. In most modern scientists this belief has died: it will be interesting to see how long their confidence in uniformity survives it. Two significant developments have already appeared—the hypothesis of a lawless sub-nature, and the surrender of the claim that science is true. We may be living nearer than we suppose to the end of the Scientific Age.

But if we admit God, must we admit Miracle? Indeed, indeed, you have no security against it. That is the bargain. Theology says to you in effect, "Admit God and with Him the risk of a few miracles, and I in return will ratify your faith in uniformity as regards the overwhelming majority of events." The philosophy which forbids you to make uniformity absolute is also the philosophy which offers you solid grounds for believing it to be general, to be *almost* absolute. The Being who threatens Nature's claim to omnipotence confirms her in her lawful occasions. Give us this ha'porth of tar and we will save the ship. The alternative is really much worse. Try to make Nature absolute and you find that her uniformity is not even probable. By claiming too much, you get nothing. You get the deadlock, as in Hume. Theology offers you a working arrangement, which leaves the scientist free to continue his experiments and the Christian to continue his prayers.

We have also, I suggest, found what we were looking for—a criterion whereby to judge the intrinsic probability of an alleged miracle. We must judge it by our "innate sense of the fitness of things," that same sense of fitness which led us to anticipate that the universe would be orderly. I do not mean, of course, that we are to use this sense in deciding whether miracles in general are possible: we know that they are on philosophical grounds. Nor

[1] *Science and the Modern World*. Chapter II.

do I mean that a sense of fitness will do instead of close inquiry into the historical evidence. As I have repeatedly pointed out, the historical evidence cannot be estimated unless we have first estimated the intrinsic probability of the recorded event. It is in making that estimate as regards each story of the miraculous that our sense of fitness comes into play.

If in giving such weight to the sense of fitness I were doing anything new, I should feel rather nervous. In reality I am merely giving formal acknowledgment to a principle which is always used. Whatever men may *say,* no one really thinks that the Christian doctrine of the Resurrection is exactly on the same level with some pious tittle-tattle about how Mother Egarée Louise miraculously found her second best thimble by the aid of St. Antony. The religious and the irreligious are really quite agreed on the point. The whoop of delight with which the sceptic would unearth the story of the thimble, and the "rosy pudency" with which the Christian would keep it in the background, both tell the same tale. Even those who think all stories of miracles absurd think some very much more absurd than others: even those who believe them all (if anyone does) think that some require a specially robust faith. The criterion which both parties are actually using is that of fitness. More than half the disbelief in miracles that exists is based on a sense of their *unfitness:* a conviction (due, as I have argued, to false philosophy) that they are unsuitable to the dignity of God or Nature or else to the indignity and insignificance of man.

In the three following chapters I will try to present the central miracles of the Christian Faith in such a way as to exhibit their "fitness." I shall not, however, proceed by formally setting out the conditions which "fitness" in the abstract ought to satisfy and then dovetailing the Miracles into that scheme. Our "sense of fitness" is too delicate and elusive a thing to submit to such treatment. If I succeed, the fitness—and if I fail, the unfitness— of these miracles will of itself become apparent while we study them.

14.

THE GRAND MIRACLE

A light that shone from behind the sun; the sun was not so
fierce as to pierce where that light could.

CHARLES WILLIAMS.

The central miracle asserted by Christians is the Incarnation.
They say that God became Man. Every other miracle prepares
for this, or exhibits this, or results from this. Just as every natural
event is the manifestation at a particular place and moment of
Nature's total character, so every particular Christian miracle
manifests at a particular place and moment the character and
significance of the Incarnation. There is no question in
Christianity of arbitrary interferences just scattered about. It
relates not a series of disconnected raids on Nature but the various steps of a strategically coherent invasion—an invasion which
intends complete conquest and "occupation." The fitness, and
therefore credibility, of the particular miracles depends on their
relation to the Grand Miracle; all discussion of them in isolation
from it is futile.

The fitness or credibility of the Grand Miracle itself cannot,
obviously, be judged by the same standard. And let us admit at
once that it is very difficult to find a standard by which it can be
judged. If the thing happened, it was the central event in the
history of the Earth—the very thing that the whole story has
been about. Since it happened only once, it is by Hume's
standards infinitely improbable. But then the whole history of
the Earth has also happened only once; is it therefore incredible?
Hence the difficulty, which weighs upon Christian and atheist
alike, of estimating the probability of the Incarnation. It is like
asking whether the existence of Nature herself is intrinsically

306

probable. That is why it is easier to argue, on historical grounds, that the Incarnation actually occurred than to show, on philosophical grounds, the probability of its occurrence. The historical difficulty of giving for the life, sayings and influence of Jesus any explanation that is not harder than the Christian explanation, is very great. The discrepancy between the depth and sanity and (let me add) *shrewdness* of His moral teaching and the rampant megalomania which must lie behind His theological teaching unless He is indeed God, has never been satisfactorily got over. Hence the non-Christian hypotheses succeed one another with the restless fertility of bewilderment. To-day we are asked to regard all the theological elements as later accretions to the story of a "historical" and merely human Jesus: yesterday we were asked to believe that the whole thing began with vegetation myths and mystery religions and that the pseudo-historical Man was only fadged up at a later date. But this historical inquiry is outside the scope of my book.

Since the Incarnation, if it is a fact, holds this central position, and since we are assuming that we do not yet know it to have happened on historical grounds, we are in a position which may be illustrated by the following analogy. Let us suppose we possess parts of a novel or a symphony. Someone now brings us a newly discovered piece of manuscript and says, "This is the missing part of the work. This is the chapter on which the whole plot of the novel really turned. This is the main theme of the symphony." Our business would be to see whether the new passage, if admitted to the central place which the discoverer claimed for it, did actually illuminate all the parts we had already seen and "pull them together." Nor should we be likely to go very far wrong. The new passage, if spurious, however attractive it looked at the first glance, would become harder and harder to reconcile with the rest of the work the longer we considered the matter. But if it were genuine, then at every fresh hearing of the music or every fresh reading of the book, we should find it settling down, making itself more at home, and eliciting significance from all sorts of details in the whole work which we had hitherto neglected. Even though the new central chapter or main theme contained great difficulties in itself, we should still think it genuine provided that it continually removed difficulties elsewhere. Something like this we must do with the doctrine of the Incarnation. Here, instead of a symphony or a novel, we have the whole mass of our knowledge. The credibility will depend on the extent to which the doctrine, if accepted, can illuminate and integrate that whole mass. It is much less important that the doctrine itself should be fully comprehensible. We believe that the sun is in the sky at midday in summer not because we can clearly see the sun (in fact, we cannot) but because we can see everything else.

The first difficulty that occurs to any critic of the doctrine lies in the very centre of it. What can be meant by "God becoming Man?" In what sense is it conceivable that eternal self-existent Spirit, basic Fact-hood, should be so combined with a natural human organism as to make one person? And this would be a fatal stumbling-block if we had not already discovered that in every human being a wholly supernatural entity is thus united with a part of Nature: so united that the composite creature calls itself "I" and "Me." I am not, of course, suggesting that what happened when God became Man was simply another instance of this process. In other men a supernatural *creature* thus becomes, in union with the natural creature, one human being. In Jesus, it is held, the Supernatural Creator Himself did so. I do not think anything we can do will enable us to imagine the mode of consciousness of the incarnate God. That is where the doctrine is not fully comprehensible. But the difficulty which we felt in the mere idea of the Supernatural descending into the Natural is apparently non-existent, or is at least overcome in the person of every man. If we did not know by experience what it feels like to be a rational animal—how all these natural facts, all this bio-chemistry and instinctive affection or repulsion and sensuous perception, can become the medium of rational thought and moral will which understand necessary relations and acknowledge modes of behaviour as universally binding, we could not conceive, much less imagine, the thing happening. The discrepancy between a movement of atoms in an astronomer's cortex, and his understanding that there must be a still unobserved planet beyond Uranus, is already so immense that the

Incarnation of God Himself is, in one sense, scarcely more startling. We cannot conceive how the Divine Spirit dwelled within the created and human spirit of Jesus: but neither can we conceive how His human spirit, or that of any man, dwells within his natural organism. What we can understand, if the Christian doctrine is true, is that our own composite existence is not the sheer anomaly it might seem to be, but a faint image of the Divine Incarnation itself—the same theme in a very minor key. We can understand that if God so descends into a human spirit, and human spirit so descends into Nature, and our thoughts into our senses and passions, and if adult minds (but only the best of them) can descend into sympathy with children, and men into sympathy with beasts, then everything hangs together and the total reality, both Natural and Supernatural, in which we are living is more multifariously and subtly harmonious than we had suspected. We catch sight of a new key principle—the power of the Higher, just in so far as it is truly Higher, to come down, the power of the greater to include the less. Thus solid bodies exemplify many truths of plane geometry, but plane figures no truths of solid geometry: many inorganic propositions are true of organisms but no organic propositions are true of minerals; Montaigne became kittenish with his kitten but she never talked philosophy to him.[1] Everywhere the great enters the little—its power to do so is almost the test of its greatness.

In the Christian story God descends to re-ascend. He comes down; down from the heights of absolute being into time and space, down into humanity; down further still, if embryologists are right, to recapitulate in the womb ancient and pre-human phases of life; down to the very roots and sea-bed of the Nature He had created. But He goes down to come up again and bring the whole ruined world up with Him. One has the picture of a strong man stooping lower and lower to get himself underneath some great complicated burden. He must stoop in order to lift, he must almost disappear under the load before he incredibly straightens his back and marches off with the whole mass swaying on his back and marches off with the whole mass swaying on his shoulders. Or one may think of a diver, first reducing himself

---

[1] *Essays*, I, xii, Apology for Raimond de Sebonde.

to nakedness, then glancing in mid-air, then gone with a splash, vanished, rushing down through green and warm water into black and cold water, down through increasing pressure into the deathlike region of ooze and slime and old decay; then up again, back to colour and light, his lungs almost bursting, till suddenly he breaks surface again, holding in his hand the dripping, precious thing that he went down to recover. He and it are both coloured now that they have come up into the light: down below, where it lay colourless in the dark, he lost his colour too.

In this descent and re-ascent everyone will recognise a familiar pattern: a thing written all over the world. It is the pattern of all vegetable life. It must belittle itself into something hard, small and deathlike, it must fall into the ground: thence the new life re-ascends. It is the pattern of all animal generation too. There is descent from the full and perfect organisms into the spermatozoon and ovum, and in the dark womb a life at first inferior in kind to that of the species which is being reproduced: then the slow ascent to the perfect embryo, to the living, conscious baby, and finally to the adult. So it is also in our moral and emotional life. The first innocent and spontaneous desires have to submit to the deathlike process of control or total denial: but from that there is a re-ascent to fully formed character in which the strength of the original material all operates but in a new way. Death and Re-birth—go down to go up—it is a key principle. Through this bottleneck, this belittlement, the highroad nearly always lies.

The doctrine of the Incarnation, if accepted, puts this principle even more emphatically at the centre. The pattern is there in Nature because it was first there in God. All the instances of it which I have mentioned turn out to be but transpositions of the Divine theme into a minor key. I am not now referring simply to the Crucifixion and Resurrection of Christ. The total pattern, of which they are only the turning point, is the real Death and Re-birth: for certainly no seed ever fell from so fair a tree into so dark and cold a soil as would furnish more than a faint analogy to this huge descent and re-ascension in which God dredged the salt and oozy bottom of Creation.

From this point of view the Christian doctrine makes itself so

quickly at home amid the deepest apprehensions of reality
which we have from other sources, that doubt may spring up in a
new direction. Is it not fitting in too well? So well that it must
have come into men's minds from seeing this pattern elsewhere,
particularly in the annual death and resurrection of the corn?
For there have, of course, been many religions in which that annual drama (so important for the life of the tribe) was almost
admittedly the central theme, and the deity—Adonis, Osiris,
or another—almost undisguisedly a personification of the corn,
a "corn-king" who died and rose again each year. Is not Christ
simply another corn-king?

Now this brings us to the oddest thing about Christianity. In a
sense the view which I have just described is actually true. From a
certain point of view Christ is "the same sort of thing" as Adonis
or Osiris (always, of course, waiving the fact that they lived nobody knows where or when, while He was executed by a Roman
magistrate we know in a year which can be roughly dated. And
that is just the puzzle. If Christianity is a religion of that kind
why is the analogy of the seed falling into the ground so seldom
mentioned (twice only if I mistake not) in the New Testament?
Corn-religions are popular and respectable: if that is what the
first Christian teachers were putting across, what motive could
they have for concealing the fact? The impression they make is
that of men who simply don't know how close they are to the
corn-religions: men who simply overlook the rich sources of relevant imagery and association which they must have been on the
verge of tapping at every moment. If you say they suppressed it
because they were Jews, that only raises the puzzle in a new form.
Why should the only religion of a "dying God" which has actually survived and risen to unexampled spiritual heights occur
precisely among those people to whom, and to whom almost
alone, the whole circle of ideas that belong to the "dying God"
was foreign? I myself, who first seriously read the New Testament
when I was, imaginatively and poetically, all agog for the Death
and Re-birth pattern and anxious to meet a corn-king, was chilled
and puzzled by the almost total absence of such ideas in the
Christian documents. One moment particularly stood out. A
"dying God"—the only dying god who might possibly be his-

torical—holds bread, that is, corn, in His hand and says, "This is my body." Surely here, even if nowhere else—or surely if not here, at least in the earliest comments on this passage and through all later devotional usage in ever swelling volume—the truth must come out; the connection between this and the annual drama of the crops must be made. But it is not. It is there for me. There is no sign that it was there for the disciples or (humanly speaking) for Christ Himself. It is almost as if He didn't realise what He had said.

The records, in fact, show us a Person who *enacts* the part of the Dying God, but whose thoughts and words remain quite outside the circle of religious ideas to which the Dying God belongs. The very thing which the Nature-religions are all about seems to have really happened once: but it happened in a circle where no trace of Nature-religion was present. It is as if you met the sea-serpent and found that it disbelieved in sea-serpents: as if history recorded a man who had done all the things attributed to Sir Launcelot but who had himself never apparently heard of chivalry.

There is, however, one hypothesis which, if accepted, makes everything easy and coherent. The Christians are not claiming that simply "God" was incarnate in Jesus. They are claiming that the one true God is He whom the Jews worshipped as Jahweh, and that it is He who has descended. Now the double character of Jahweh is this. On the one hand He is the God of Nature, her glad Creator. It is He who sends rain into the furrows till the valleys stand so thick with corn that they laugh and sing. The trees of the wood rejoice before Him and His voice causes the wild deer to bring forth their young. He is the God of wheat and wine and oil. In that respect He is constantly doing all the things that nature-gods do: He is Bacchus, Venus, Ceres all rolled into one. There is no trace in Judaism of the idea found in some pessimistic and Pantheistic religions that Nature is some kind of illusion or disaster, that finite existence is in itself an evil and that the cure lies in the relapse of all things into God. Compared with such anti-natural conceptions Jahweh might almost be mistaken for a nature-god.

On the other hand, Jahweh is clearly *not* a nature-god. He

does not die and come to life each year as a true corn-king should. He may give wine and fertility, but must not be worshipped with bacchanalian or aphrodisiac rites. He is not the soul of Nature nor of any part of Nature. He inhabits eternity: He dwells in the high and holy place: heaven is His throne, not His vehicle; earth is His footstool, not His vesture. One day He will dismantle both and make a new heaven and earth. He is not to be identified even with the "divine spark" in man. He is "God and not man": His thoughts are not our thoughts: all our righteousness is filthy rags. His appearance to Ezekiel is attended with imagery that does not borrow from Nature, but (it is a mystery too seldom noticed [1]) from those machines which men were to make centuries after Ezekiel's death. The prophet saw something suspiciously like a *dynamo*.

Jahweh is neither the soul of Nature nor her enemy. She is neither His body nor a declension and falling away from Him. She is His creature. He is not a nature-god, but the God of Nature—her inventor, maker, owner, and controller. To everyone who reads this book the conception has been familiar from childhood; we therefore easily think it is the most ordinary conception in the world. "If people are going to believe in a God at all," we ask, "what other kind would they believe in?" But the answer of history is, "Almost any other kind." We mistake our privileges for our instincts: just as one meets ladies who believe their own refined manners to be natural to them. They don't remember being taught.

Now if there is such a God and if He descends to rise again, then we can understand why Christ is at once so like the corn-king and so silent about him. He is like the corn-king because the corn-king is a portrait of Him. The similarity is not in the least unreal or accidental. For the corn-king is derived (through human imagination) from the facts of Nature, and the facts of Nature from her Creator; the Death and Re-birth pattern is in her because it was first in Him. On the other hand, elements of Nature-religion are strikingly absent from the teaching of Jesus and from the Judaic preparation which led up to it precisely because in them Nature's Original is manifesting Itself. In them

[1] I owe this point to Canon Adam Fox.

you have from the very outset got in behind Nature-religion and behind Nature herself. Where the real God is present the shadows of that God do not appear; that which the shadows resembled does. The Hebrews throughout their history were being constantly headed off from the worship of nature-gods; not because the nature-gods were in all respects unlike the God of Nature but because, at best, they were merely like, and it was the destiny of that nation to be turned away from likenesses to the thing itself.

The mention of that nation turns our attention to one of those features in the Christian story which is repulsive to the modern mind. To be quite frank, we do not at all like the idea of a "chosen people." Democrats by birth and education, we should prefer to think that all nations and individuals start level in the search for God, or even that all religions are equally true. It must be admitted at once that Christianity makes no concessions to this point of view. It does not tell of a human search for God at all, but of something done by God for, to, and about, Man. And the way in which it is done is selective, undemocratic, to the highest degree. After the knowledge of God had been universally lost or obscured, one man from the whole earth (Abraham) is picked out. He is separated (miserably enough, we may suppose) from his natural surroundings, sent into a strange country, and made the ancestor of a nation who are to carry the knowledge of the true God. Within this nation there is further selection: some die in the desert, some remain behind in Babylon. There is further selection still. The process grows narrower and narrower, sharpens at last into one small bright point like the head of a spear. It is a Jewish girl at her prayers. All humanity (so far as concerns its redemption) has narrowed to that.

Such a process is very unlike what modern feeling demands: but it is startlingly like what Nature habitually does. Selectiveness, and with it (we must allow) enormous wastage, is her method. Out of enormous space a very small portion is occupied by matter at all. Of all the stars, perhaps very few, perhaps only one, have planets. Of the planets in our own system probably only one supports organic life. In the transmission of organic life, countless seeds and spermatozoa are emitted: some few are selected for the distinction of fertility. Among the species only one is rational. Within that species only a few attain excellence of beauty, strength, or intelligence.

At this point we come perilously near the argument of Butler's famous *Analogy*. I say "perilously" because the argument of that book very nearly admits parodying in the form "You say that the behaviour attributed to the Christian God is both wicked and foolish: but it is no less likely to be true on that account for I can show that Nature (which He created) behaves just as badly." To which the atheist will answer—and the nearer he is to Christ in his heart, the more certainly he will do so—"If there is a God like that I despise and defy Him." But I am not saying that Nature, as we know her, is good; that is a point we must return to in a moment. Nor am I saying that a God whose actions were no better than Nature's would be a proper object of worship for any honest man. The point is a little finer than that. This selective or undemocratic quality in Nature, at least in so far as it affects human life, is neither good nor evil. According as spirit exploits or fails to exploit this Natural situation, it gives rise to one or the other. It permits, on the one hand, ruthless competition, arrogance, and envy: it permits, on the other, modesty and (one of our greatest pleasures) admiration. A world in which I was *really* (and not merely by a useful legal fiction) "as good as everyone else," in which I never looked up to anyone wiser or cleverer or braver or more learned than I, would be insufferable. The very "fans" of the cinema stars and the famous footballers know better than to desire that! What the Christian story does is not to instate on the Divine level a cruelty and wastefulness which have already disgusted us on the Natural, but to show us in God's act, working neither cruelly nor wastefully, the same principle which is in Nature also, though down there it works sometimes in one way and sometimes in the other. It illuminates the Natural scene by suggesting that a principle which at first looked meaningless may yet be derived from a principle which is good and fair, may indeed be a depraved and blurred copy of it—the pathological form which it would take in a *spoiled* Nature.

For when we look into the Selectiveness which the Christians attribute to God we find in it none of that "favouritism" which we were afraid of. The "chosen" people are chosen not for their own sake (certainly not for their own honour or pleasure; but for the sake of the unchosen. Abraham is told that "in his seed" (the chosen nation) "all nations shall be blest." That nation has been chosen to bear a heavy burden. Their sufferings are great: but, as Isaiah recognised, their sufferings heal others. On the finally selected Woman falls the utmost depth of maternal anguish. Her Son, the incarnate God, is a "man of sorrows"; the one Man into whom Deity descended, the one Man who can be lawfully adored, is pre-eminent for suffering.

But, you will ask, does this much mend matters? Is not this still injustice, though now the other way round? Where, at the first glance, we accused God of undue favour to His "chosen," we are now tempted to accuse Him of undue disfavour. (The attempt to keep up both charges at the same time had better be dropped.) And certainly we have here come to a principle very deep-rooted in Christianity: what may be called the principle of *Vicariousness*. The Sinless Man suffers for the sinful, and, in their degree, all good men for all bad men. And this Vicariousness—no less than Death and Rebirth or Selectiveness—is also a characteristic of Nature. Self-sufficiency, living on one's own resources, is a thing impossible in her realm. Everything is indebted to everything else, sacrificed to everything else, dependent on everything else. And here too we must recognise that the principle is in itself neither good nor bad. The cat lives on the mouse in a way I think bad: the bees and the flowers live on one another in a more pleasing manner. The parasite lives on its "host": but so also the unborn child on its mother. In social life without Vicariousness there would be no exploitation or oppression; but also no kindness or gratitude. It is a fountain both of love and hatred, both of misery and happiness. When we have understood this we shall no longer think that the depraved examples of Vicariousness in Nature forbid us to suppose that the principle itself is of divine origin.

At this point it may be well to take a backward glance and notice how the doctrine of the Incarnation is already acting on the rest of our knowledge. We have already brought it into contact with four other principles: the composite nature of man, the

pattern of descent and reascension, Selectiveness, and Vicariousness. The first may be called a fact about the frontier between
Nature and Supernature; the other three are characteristics of
Nature herself. Now most religions, when brought face to face
with the facts of Nature, either simply re-affirm them, give them
(just as they stand) a transcendent prestige, or else simply ne-
gate them, promise us release from such facts and from Nature
altogether. The Nature Religions take the first line. They sanc-
tify our agricultural concerns and indeed our whole biological
life. We get really drunk in the worship of Dionysus and lie with
real women in the temple of the fertility goddess. In Life-force
worship, which is the modern and western type of Nature-religion, we take over the existing trend towards "development" or
increasing complexity in organic, social, and industrial life, and
make it a god. The anti-Natural or pessimistic religions, which
are more civilised and sensitive, such as Buddhism or higher Hinduism, tell us that Nature is evil and illusory, that there is an
escape from this incessant change, this furnace of striving and
desire. Neither the one nor the other sets the facts of Nature in a
new light. The Nature religions merely reinforce that view of
Nature which we spontaneously adopt in our moments of rude
health and cheerful brutality; the anti-natural religions do the
same for the view we take in moments of compassion, fastidious-
ness, or lassitude. The Christian doctrine does neither of these
things. If any man approaches it with the idea that because Jahweh is the God of fertility our lasciviousness is going to be authorised or that the Selectiveness and Vicariousness of God's method
will excuse us for imitating (as "Heroes," "Supermen" or social
parasites) the lower Selectiveness and Vicariousness of Nature, he
will be stunned and repelled by the inflexible Christian demand
for chastity, humility, mercy and justice. On the other hand if
we come to it regarding the death which precedes every re-birth,
or the fact of inequality, or our dependence on others and their
dependence on us, as the mere odious necessities of an evil cos-
mos, and hoping to be delivered into transparent and "enlightened" spirituality where all these things just vanish, we shall be
equally disappointed. We shall be told that, in one sense, and
despite enormous differences, it is "the same all the way up"; that

hierarchical inequality, the need for self surrender, the willing sacrifice of self to others, and the thankful and loving (but unashamed) acceptance of others' sacrifice to us, hold sway in the realm beyond Nature. It is indeed only love that makes the difference: all those very same principles which are evil in the world of selfishness and necessity are good in the world of love and understanding. Thus, as we accept this doctrine of the higher world we make new discoveries about the lower world. It is from that hill that we first really understand the landscape of this valley. Here, at last, we find (as we do not find either in the Nature religions or in the religions that deny Nature) a real illumination: Nature is being lit up by a light from beyond Nature. Someone is speaking who knows more about her than can be known from inside her.

Throughout this doctrine it is, of course, implied that Nature is infected with evil. Those great key-principles which exist as modes of goodness in the Divine Life, take on, in her operations, not merely a less perfect form (that we should, on any view, expect) but forms which I have been driven to describe as morbid or depraved. And this depravity could not be totally removed without the drastic re-making of Nature. Complete human virtue could indeed banish from human life all the evils that now arise in it from Vicariousness and Selectiveness and retain only the good: but the wastefulness and painfulness of non-human Nature would remain—and would, of course, continue to infect human life in the form of disease. And the destiny which Christianity promises to man clearly involves a "redemption" or "remaking" of Nature which could not stop at Man, or even at this planet. We are told that "the whole creation" is in travail, and that Man's re-birth will be the signal for hers. This gives rise to several problems, the discussion of which puts the whole doctrine of the Incarnation in a clearer light.

In the first place, we ask how the Nature created by a good God comes to be in this condition? By which question we may mean either how she comes to be imperfect—to leave "room for improvement" as the schoolmasters say in their reports—or else, how she comes to be positively depraved. If we ask the question in the first sense, the Christian answer (I think) is that God, from the first, created her such as to reach her perfection by a process in time. He made an Earth at first "without form and void" and brought it by degrees to its perfection. In this, as elsewhere, we see the familiar pattern—descent from God to the formless Earth and re-ascent from the formless to the finished. In that sense a certain degree of "evolutionism" or "developmentalism" is inherent in Christianity. So much for Nature's imperfection; her positive depravity calls for a very different explanation. According to the Christians this is all due to sin: the sin both of men and of powerful, non-human beings, supernatural but created. The unpopularity of this doctrine arises from the widespread Naturalism of our age—the belief that nothing but Nature exists and that if anything else did she is protected from it by a Maginot Line—and will disappear as this error is corrected. To be sure, the morbid inquisitiveness about such beings which led our ancestors to a pseudo-science of Demonology, is to be sternly discouraged: our attitude should be that of the sensible citizen in wartime who believe that there are enemy spies in our midst but disbelieves nearly every particular spy story. We must limit ourselves to the general statement that beings in a different, and higher, "Nature" which is *partially* interlocked with ours have, like men, fallen and have tampered with things inside our frontier. The doctrine, besides proving itself fruitful of good in each man's spiritual life, helps to protect us from shallowly optimistic or pessimistic views of Nature. To call her either "good" or "evil" is boys' philosophy. We find ourselves in a world of transporting pleasures, ravishing beauties, and tantalising possibilities, but all constantly being destroyed, all coming to nothing. Nature has all the air of a good thing spoiled.

The sin, both of men and of angels, was rendered possible by the fact that God gave them free will; thus surrendering a portion of His omnipotence (it is again a deathlike or descending movement) because He saw that from a world of free creatures, even though they fell, He could work out (and this is the re-ascent) a deeper happiness and a fuller splendour than any world of automata would admit.

Another question that arises is this. If the redemption of Man is the beginning of Nature's redemption as a whole, must we then conclude after all that Man is the most important thing in Nature? If I had to answer "Yes" to this question I should not be embarrassed. Supposing Man to be the only rational animal in the universe, then (as has been shown) his small size and the small size of the globe he inhabits would not make it ridiculous to regard him as the hero of the cosmic drama: Jack after all is the smallest character in *Jack the Giant-Killer*. Nor do I think it in the least improbable that Man is in fact the only rational creature in the spatio-temporal Nature. That is just the sort of lonely pre-eminence—just the disproportion between picture and frame —which all that I know of Nature's "selectiveness" would lead me to anticipate. But I do not need to assume that it actually exists. Let Man be only one among a myriad of rational species, and let him be the only one that has fallen. Because he has fallen, for him God does the great deed; just as in the parable it is the one lost sheep for whom the shepherd hunts. Let Man's pre-eminence or solitude be one not of superiority but of misery and evil: then, all the more, Man will be the very species into which Mercy will descend. For this prodigal the fatted calf, or, to speak more suitably, the eternal lamb, is killed. But once the Son of God, drawn hither not by our merits but by our unworthiness, has put on human nature, then our species (whatever it may have been before) does become in one sense the central face in all Nature: our species, rising after its long descent, will drag all Nature up with it because in our species the Lord of Nature is now included. And it would be all of a piece with what we already know if ninety and nine righteous races inhabiting distant planets that circle distant suns, and needing no redemption on their own account, were re-made and glorified by the glory which had descended into our race. For God is not merely mending, not simply restoring a *status quo*. Redeemed humanity is to be something more glorious than unfallen humanity would have been, more glorious than any unfallen race now is (if at this moment the night sky conceals any such). The greater the sin, the greater the mercy: the deeper the death the brighter the re-birth. And this super-added glory will, with true vicariousness, exalt all creatures and those who have never fallen will thus bless Adam's fall.

I write so far on the assumption that the Incarnation was occasioned only by the Fall. Another view has, of course, been sometimes held by Christians. According to it the descent of God into Nature was not in itself occasioned by sin. It would have occurred for Glorification and Perfection even if it had not been required for Redemption. Its attendant circumstances would have been very different: the divine humility would not have been a divine humiliation, the sorrows, the gall and vinegar, the crown of thorns and the cross, would have been absent. If this view is taken, then clearly the Incarnation, wherever and however it occurred, would always have been the beginning of Nature's rebirth. The fact that it has occurred in the human species, summoned thither by that strong incantation of misery and abjection which Love has made Himself unable to resist, would not deprive it of its universal significance.

This doctrine of a universal redemption spreading outwards from the redemption of Man, mythological as it will seem to modern minds, is in reality far more philosophical than any theory which holds that God, having once entered Nature, should leave her, and leave her substantially unchanged, or that the glorification of one creature could be realised without the glorification of the whole system. God never undoes anything but evil, never does good to undo it again. The union between God and Nature in the Person of Christ admits no divorce. He will not *go out of* Nature again and she must be glorified in all ways which this miraculous union demands. When spring comes it "leaves no corner of the land untouched"; even a pebble dropped in a pond sends circles to the margin. The question we want to ask about Man's "central" position in this drama is really on a level with the disciples' question, "Which of them was the greatest?". It is the sort of question which God does not answer. If from Man's point of view the re-creation of non-human and even inanimate Nature appears a mere bye-product of his own redemption, then equally from some remote, non-human point of view man's redemption may seem merely the preliminary to this more widely diffused springtime, and the very permission of Man's fall may be supposed to have had that larger end in view. Both attitudes will be right if they will consent to drop the words *mere* and *merely*. Where a God who is totally purposive and totally foreseeing acts upon a Nature which is totally interlocked, there can be no accidents or loose ends, nothing whatever of which we can safely use the word *merely*. Nothing is "merely a bye-product" of anything else. All results are intended from the first. What is subservient from one point of view is the main purpose from another. No thing or event is first or highest in a sense which forbids it to be also last and lowest. The partner who bows to Man in one movement of the dance receives Man's reverences in another. To be high or central means to abdicate continually: to be low means to be raised: all good masters are servants: God washes the feet of men. The concepts we usually bring to the consideration of such matters are miserably political and prosaic. We think of flat repetitive equality and arbitrary privilege as the only two alternatives—thus missing all the overtones, the counterpoint, the vibrant sensitiveness, the inter-inanimations of reality.

For this reason I do not think it at all likely that there have been (as Alice Meynell suggested in an interesting poem) many Incarnations to redeem many different kinds of creature. One's sense of *style*—of the divine idiom—rejects it. The suggestion of mass-production and of waiting queues comes from a level of thought which is here hopelessly inadequate. If other natural creatures than Man have sinned we must believe that they are redeemed: but God's Incarnation as Man will be one unique act in the drama of total redemption and other species will have witnessed wholly different acts, each equally unique, equally necessary and differently necessary to the whole process, and each (from a certain point of view) justifiably regarded as "the great scene" of the play. To those who live in Act II, Act III looks like an epilogue: to those who live in Act III, Act II looks like a prologue. And both are right until they add the fatal word *merely,* or else try to avoid it by the dullard's supposition that both acts are the same.

It ought to be noticed at this stage that the Christian doctrine, if accepted, involves a particular view of Death. There are two attitudes towards Death which the human mind naturally adopts. One is the lofty view, which reached its greatest intensity among the Stoics, that Death "doesn't matter," that it is "kind nature's signal for retreat," and that we ought to regard it with indifference. The other is the "natural" point of view, implicit in nearly all private conversations on the subject, and in much modern thought about the survival of the human species, that Death is the greatest of all evils; Hobbes is perhaps the only philosopher who erected a system on this basis. The first idea simply negates, the second simply affirms, our instinct for self-preservation; neither throws any new light on Nature, and Christianity countenances neither. Its doctrine is subtler. On the one hand Death is the triumph of Satan, the punishment of the Fall, and the last enemy. Christ shed tears at the grave of Lazarus and sweated blood in Gethsemane: the Life of Lives that was in Him detested this penal obscenity not less than we do, but more. On the other hand, only he who loses his life will save it. We are baptized into the *death* of Christ, and it is the remedy for the Fall. Death is, in fact, what some modern people call "ambivalent." It is Satan's great weapon and also God's great weapon: it is holy and unholy; our supreme disgrace and our only hope; the thing Christ came to conquer and the means by which He conquered.

To penetrate the whole of this mystery is, of course, far beyond my intention. If the pattern of Descent and Re-ascent is (as looks not unlikely) the very formula of reality, then in the mystery of Death the secret of secrets lies hid. But something must be said in order to put the Grand Miracle in its proper light. We need not discuss Death on the highest level of all: the mystical slaying of the Lamb "before the foundation of the world" is above our speculations. Nor need we consider Death on the lowest level. The death of organisms which are nothing more than organisms, which have developed no personality, does not concern us. Of it we may truly say, as some spiritually minded people would have us say of human Death, that it "doesn't matter." But the startling Christian doctrine of human Death cannot be passed over.

Human Death, according to the Christians, is a result of human sin; Man, as originally created, was immune from it: Man, when redeemed, and recalled to a new life (which will, in some undefined sense, be a bodily life) in the midst of a more organic and more fully obedient Nature, will be immune from it again. This doctrine is of course simply nonsense if a man is nothing but a

Natural organism. But if he were, then, as we have seen, all thoughts would be equally nonsensical, for all would have irrational causes. Man must therefore be a composite being—a natural organism tenanted by, or in a state of *symbiosis* with, a supernatural spirit. The Christian doctrine, startling as it must seem to those who have not fully cleared their minds of Naturalism, states that the relations which we now observe between that spirit and that organism, are abnormal or pathological ones. At present spirit can retain its foothold against the incessant counter-attacks of Nature (both physiological and psychological) only by perpetual vigilance, and physiological Nature always defeats it in the end. Sooner or later it becomes unable to resist the disintegrating processes at work in the body and death ensues. A little later the Natural organism (for it does not long enjoy its triumph) is similarly conquered by merely physical Nature and returns to the inorganic. But, on the Christian view, this was not always so. The spirit was once not a garrison, maintaining its post with difficulty in a hostile Nature, but was fully "at home" with its organism, like a king in his own country or a rider on his own horse—or better still, as the human part of a Centaur was "at home" with the equine part. Where spirit's power over the organism was complete and unresisted, death would never occur. No doubt, spirit's permanent triumph over natural forces which, if left to themselves, would kill the organism, would involve a continued miracle: but only the same sort of miracle which occurs every day—for whenever we think rationally we are, by direct spiritual power, forcing certain atoms in our brain and certain psychological tendencies in our natural soul to do what they would never have done if left to Nature. The Christian doctrine would be fantastic only if the present frontier-situation between spirit and Nature in each human being were so intelligible and self explanatory that we just "saw" it to be the only one that could ever have existed. But is it?

In reality the frontier situation is so odd that nothing but custom could make it seem natural, and nothing but the Christian doctrine can make it fully intelligible. There is certainly a state of war. But not a war of mutual destruction. Nature by dominating spirit wrecks all spiritual activities: Spirit by dominating Nature confirms and improves natural activities. The brain does not become less a brain by being used for rational thought. The emotions do not become weak or jaded by being organised in the service of a moral will—indeed they grow richer and stronger as a beard is strengthened by being shaved or a river is deepened by being banked. The body of the reasonable and virtuous man, other things being equal, is a better body than that of the fool or the debauchee, and his sensuous pleasures better simply as sensuous pleasures: for the slaves of the senses, after the first bait, are starved by their master. Everything happens as if what we saw was not war, but rebellion: that rebellion of the lower against the higher by which the lower destroys both the higher and itself. And if the present situation is one of rebellion, then reason cannot reject but will rather demand the belief that there was a time before the rebellion broke out and may be a time after it has been settled. And if we thus see grounds for believing that the supernatural spirit and the natural organism in Man have quarrelled, we shall immediately find it confirmed from two quite unexpected quarters.

Almost the whole of Christian theology could perhaps be deduced from the two facts (*a*) That men make coarse jokes, and (*b*) That they feel the dead to be uncanny. The coarse joke proclaims that we have here an animal which finds its own animality either objectionable or funny. Unless there had been a quarrel between the spirit and the organism I do not see how this could be: it is the very mark of the two not being "at home" together. But it is very difficult to imagine such a state of affairs as original —to suppose a creature which from the very first was half shocked and half tickled to death at the mere fact of being the creature it is. I do not perceive that dogs see anything funny about being dogs: I suspect that angels see nothing funny about being angels. Our feeling about the dead is equally odd. It is idle to say that we dislike corpses because we are afraid of ghosts. You might say with equal truth that we fear ghosts because we dislike corpses— for the ghost owes much of its horror to the associated ideas of pallor, decay, coffins, shrouds, and worms. In reality we hate the division which makes possible the conception of either corpse or ghost. Because the thing ought not to be divided, each of the halves into which it falls by division is detestable. The explanations which Naturalism gives both of bodily shame and of our feeling about the dead are not satisfactory. It refers us to primitive taboos and superstitions—as if these themselves were not obviously results of the thing to be explained. But once accept the Christian doctrine that man was originally a unity and that the present division is unnatural, and all the phenomena fall into place. It would be fantastic to suggest that the doctrine was devised to explain our enjoyment of a chapter in Rabelais, a good ghost story, or the *Tales* of Edgar Allan Poe. It does so none the less.

I ought, perhaps, to point out that the argument is not in the least affected by the value-judgments we make about ghost stories or coarse humour. You may hold that both are bad. You may hold that both, though they result (like clothes) from the Fall, are (like clothes) the proper way to deal with the Fall once it has occurred: that while perfected and recreated Man will no longer experience that kind of laughter or that kind of shudder, yet here and now not to feel the horror and not to see the joke is to be less than human. But either way the facts bear witness to our present maladjustment.

So much for the sense in which human Death is the result of sin and the triumph of Satan. But it is also the means of redemption from sin, God's medicine for Man and His weapon against Satan. In a general way it is not difficult to understand how the same thing can be a masterstroke on the part of one combatant and also the very means whereby the superior combatant defeats him. Every good general, every good chess-player, takes what is precisely the strong point of his opponent's plan and makes it the pivot of his own plan. Take that castle of mine if you insist. It was not my original intention that you should—indeed, I thought you would have had more sense. But take it by all means. For now I move thus . . . and thus . . . and it is mate in three moves. Something like this must be supposed to have happened about Death. Do not say that such metaphors are too trivial to illustrate so high a matter: the unnoticed mechanical and mineral metaphors which, in this age, will dominate our whole minds (without being recognised as metaphors at all) the moment we relax our vigilance against them, must be incomparably less adequate.

And one can see how it might have happened. The Enemy persuades Man to rebel against God: Man, by doing so, loses power to control that other rebellion which the Enemy now raises in Man's organism (both psychical and physical) against Man's spirit: just as that organism, in its turn, loses power to maintain itself against the rebellion of the inorganic. In that way, Satan produced human Death. But when God created Man he gave him such a constitution that, if the highest part of it rebelled against Himself, it would be bound to lose control over the lower parts: i.e. in the long run to suffer Death. This provision may be regarded equally as a punitive sentence ("In the day ye eat of that fruit ye shall die"), as a mercy, and as a safety device. It is punishment because Death—that Death of which Martha says to Christ, "But . . . Sir . . . it'll *smell*"—is horror and ignominy. ("I am not so much afraid of death as ashamed of it," said Sir Thomas Browne.) It is mercy because by willing and humble surrender to it Man undoes his act of rebellion and makes even this depraved and monstrous mode of Death an instance of that higher and mystical Death which is eternally good and a necessary ingredient in the highest life. "The readiness is all"—not, of course, the merely heroic readiness but that of humility and self-renunciation. Our enemy, so welcomed, becomes our servant: bodily Death, the monster, becomes blessed spiritual Death to self, if the spirit so wills—or rather if it allows the Spirit of the willingly dying God so to will in it. It is a safety-device because, once Man has fallen, natural immortality would be the one utterly hopeless destiny for him. Aided to the surrender that he must make by no external necessity of Death, free (if you call it freedom) to rivet faster and faster about himself through unending centuries the chains of his own pride and lust and of the nightmare civilisations which these build up in ever-increasing power and complication, he would progress from being merely a fallen man to being a fiend, possibly beyond all modes of redemption. This danger was averted. The sentence that those who ate of the forbidden fruit would be driven away from the Tree of Life was implicit in the com-

posite nature with which Man was created. But to convert this
penal death into the means of eternal life—to add to its
negative and preventive function a positive and saving function
—it was further necessary that death should be *accepted*. Humanity must embrace death freely, submit to it with total humility,
drink it to the dregs, and so convert it into that mystical death
which is the secret of life. But only a Man who did not need to
have been a Man at all unless He had chosen, only one who
served in our sad regiment as a volunteer, yet also one who was
perfectly a Man, could perform this perfect dying; and thus
(which way you put it is unimportant) either defeat Death or
redeem it. He tasted death on behalf of all others. He is the representative "Die-er" of the universe: and for that very reason the
Resurrection and the Life. Or conversely, because He truly lives,
He truly dies, for that is the very pattern of reality. Because the
higher can descend into the lower He who from all eternity has
been incessantly plunging Himself in the blessed death of self-
surrender to the Father can also most fully descend into the horrible and (for us) involuntary death of the body. Because Vicariousness is the very idiom of the reality He has created, His death
can become ours. The whole Miracle, far from denying what we
already know of reality, writes the comment which makes that
crabbed text plain: or rather, proves itself to be the text on which
Nature was only the commentary. In science we have been reading only the notes to a poem; in Christianity we find the poem
itself.

With this our sketch of the Grand Miracle may end. Its credibility does not lie in Obviousness. Pessimism, Optimism, Pantheism, Materialism, all have this "obvious" attraction. Each is
confirmed at the first glance by multitudes of facts: later on, each
meets insuperable obstacles. The doctrine of the Incarnation
works into our minds quite differently. It digs beneath the surface, works through the rest of our knowledge by unexpected
channels, harmonises best with our deepest apprehensions and
our "second thoughts," and in union with these undermines our
superficial opinions. It has little to say to the man who is still
certain that everything is going to the dogs, or that everything
is getting better and better, or that everything is God, or that

everything is electricity. Its hour comes when these wholesale creeds have begun to fail us. Whether the thing really happened is a historical question. But when you turn to history, you will not demand for it that kind and degree of evidence which you would rightly demand for something intrinsically improbable; only that kind and degree which you demand for something which, if accepted, illuminates and orders all other phenomena, explains both our laughter and our logic, our fear of the dead and our knowledge that it is somehow good to die, and which at one stroke covers what multitudes of separate theories will hardly cover for us if this is rejected.

15.

MIRACLES OF THE OLD CREATION

The Son can do nothing of himself, but what he seeth the
Father do.

John v. 19.

If we open such books as Grimm's *Fairy Tales* or Ovid's *Meta-
morphoses* or the Italian epics we find ourselves in a world of
miracles so diverse that they can hardly be classified. Beasts turn
into men and men into beasts or trees, trees talk, ships become
goddesses, and a magic ring can cause tables richly spread with
food to appear in solitary places. Some people cannot stand this
kind of story, others find it fun. But the least suspicion that it
was true would turn the fun into nightmare. If such things
really happened they would, I suppose, show that Nature was
being invaded. But they would show that she was being invaded
by an alien power. The fitness of the Christian miracles, and
their difference from these mythological miracles, lies in the fact
that they show invasion by a Power which is not alien. They are
what might be expected to happen when she is invaded not simply by a god, but by the God of Nature: by a Power which is outside her jurisdiction not as a foreigner but as a sovereign. They
proclaim that He who has come is not merely a king, but *the*
King, her King and ours.

It is this which, to my mind, puts the Christian miracles in a
different class from most other miracles. I do not think that it is
the duty of a Christian apologist (as many sceptics suppose) to disprove all stories of the miraculous which fall outside the Christian records, nor of a Christian man to disbelieve them. I am in
no way committed to the assertion that God has never worked

miracles through and for Pagans or never permitted created supernatural beings to do so. If, as Tacitus, Suetonius, and Dion Cassius relate, Vespasian performed two cures, and if modern doctors tell me that they could not have been performed without miracle, I have no objection. But I claim that the Christian miracles have a much greater intrinsic probability in virtue of their organic connection with one another and with the whole structure of the religion they exhibit. If it can be shown that one particular Roman emperor—and, let us admit, a fairly good emperor as emperors go—once was empowered to do a miracle, we must of course put up with the fact. But it would remain a quite isolated and anomalous fact. Nothing comes of it, nothing leads up to it, it establishes no body of doctrine, explains nothing, is connected with nothing. And this, after all, is an unusually favourable instance of a non-Christian miracle. The immoral, and sometimes almost idiotic interferences attributed to gods in Pagan stories, even if they had a trace of historical evidence, could be accepted only on the condition of our accepting a wholly meaningless universe. What raises infinite difficulties and solves none will be believed by a rational man only under absolute compulsion. Sometimes the credibility of the miracles is in an inverse ratio to the credibility of the religion. Thus miracles are (in late documents, I believe) recorded of the Buddha. But what could be more absurd than that he who came to teach us that Nature is an illusion from which we must escape should occupy himself in producing effects on the Natural level—that he who comes to wake us from a nightmare should *add* to the nightmare? The more we respect his teaching the less we could accept his miracles. But in Christianity, the more we understand what God it is who is said to be present and the purpose for which He is said to have appeared, the more credible the miracles become. That is why we seldom find the Christian miracles denied except by those who have abandoned some part of the Christian doctrine. The mind which asks for a non-miraculous Christianity is a mind in process of relapsing from Christianity into mere "religion."[1]

[1] A consideration of the Old Testament miracles is beyond the scope of this book and would require many kinds of knowledge which I do not possess. My present view—which is tentative and liable to any amount of correction

The miracles of Christ can be classified in two ways. The first system yields the classes (1) Miracles of Fertility (2) Miracles of Healing (3) Miracles of Destruction (4) Miracles of Dominion over the Inorganic (5) Miracles of Reversal (6) Miracles of Perfecting or Glorification. The second system, which cuts across the first, yields two classes only: they are (1) Miracles of the Old Creation, and (2) Miracles of the New Creation.

I contend that in all these miracles alike the incarnate God does suddenly and locally something that God has done or will do in general. Each miracle writes for us in small letters something that God has already written, or will write, in letters almost too large to be noticed, across the whole canvas of Nature. They focus at a particular point either God's actual, or His future, operations on the universe. When they reproduce operations we have already seen on the large scale they are miracles of the Old Creation: when they focus those which are still to come they are

---

—would be that just as, on the factual side, a long preparation culminates in God's becoming incarnate as Man, so, on the documentary side, the truth first appears in *mythical* form and then by a long process of condensing or focussing finally becomes incarnate as History. This involves the belief that Myth in general is not merely misunderstood history (as Euhemerus thought) nor diabolical illusion (as some of the Fathers thought) nor priestly lying (as the philosophers of the Enlightenment thought) but, at its best, a real though unfocussed gleam of divine truth falling on human imagination. The Hebrews, like other peoples, had mythology: but as they were the chosen people so their mythology was the chosen mythology—the mythology chosen by God to be the vehicle of the earliest sacred truths, the first step in that process which ends in the New Testament where truth has become completely historical. Whether we can ever say with certainty where, in this process of crystalisation, any particular Old Testament story falls, is another matter. I take it that the memoirs of David's court come at one end of the scale and are scarcely less historical than *St. Mark* or *Acts;* and that the Book *of Jonah* is at the opposite end. It should be noted that on this view (*a*) Just as God, in becoming Man, is "emptied" of His glory, so the truth, when it comes down from the "heaven" of myth to the "earth of history, undergoes a certain humiliation. Hence the New Testament is, and ought to be, more prosaic, in some ways less *splendid,* than the Old; just as the Old Testament is and ought to be less rich in many kinds of imaginative beauty than the Pagan mythologies. (*b*) Just as God is none the less God by being Man, so the Myth remains Myth even when it becomes Fact. The story of Christ demands from us, and repays, not only a religious and historical but also an imaginative response. It is directed to the child, the poet, and the savage in us as well as to the conscience and to the intellect. One of its functions is to break down dividing walls.

miracles of the New. Not one of them is isolated or anomalous: each carries the signature of the God whom we know through conscience and from Nature. Their authenticity is attested by the *style*.

Before going any further I should say that I do not propose to raise the question, which has before now been asked, whether Christ was able to do these things only because He was God or also because He was perfect man; for it is a possible view that if Man had never fallen all men would have been able to do the like. It is one of the glories of Christianity that we can say of this question, "It doesn't matter." Whatever may have been the powers of unfallen man, it appears that those of redeemed Man will be almost unlimited.[1] Christ, re-ascending from His great dive, is bringing up Human Nature with Him. Where He goes, it goes too. It will be made "like Him."[2] If in His miracles He is not acting as the Old Man might have done before his Fall, then He is acting as the New Man, every new man, will do after his redemption. When humanity, borne on His shoulders, passes with Him up from the cold dark water into the green warm water and out at last into the sunlight and the air, it also will be bright and coloured.

Another way of expressing the real character of the Miracles would be to say that though isolated from other actions, they are not isolated in either of the two ways we are apt to suppose. They are not, on the one hand, isolated from other Divine acts: they do close and small and, as it were, in focus what God at other times does so large that men do not attend to it. Neither are they isolated exactly as we suppose from other human acts: they anticipate powers which all men will have when they also are "sons" of God and enter into that "glorious liberty." Christ's isolation is not that of a prodigy but of a pioneer. He is the first of His kind; He will not be the last.

Let us return to our classification and firstly to Miracles of *Fertility*. The earliest of these was the conversion of water into wine at the wedding feast in Cana. This miracle proclaims that

---

[1] Matt. xvii. 20, xxi. 21, Mark xi. 23, Luke x. 19, John xiv. 12, 1 Cor. iii. 22, 2 Tim. ii. 12.

[2] Phil. iii. 21, 1 John iii. 12.

the God of all wine is present. The vine is one of the blessings sent by Jahweh: He is the reality behind the false god Bacchus. Every year, as part of the Natural order, God makes wine. He does so by creating a vegetable organism that can turn water, soil, and sunlight into a juice which will, under proper conditions, become wine. Thus, in a certain sense, He constantly turns water into wine, for wine, like all drinks, is but water modified. Once, and in one year only, God, now incarnate, short circuits the process: makes wine in a moment: uses earthenware jars instead of vegetable fibres to hold the water. But uses them to do what He is always doing. The Miracle consists in the short cut; but the event to which it leads is the usual one. If the thing happened, then we know that what has come into Nature is no anti-Natural spirit, no God who loves tragedy and tears and fasting *for their own sake* (however He may permit or demand them for special purposes) but the God of Israel who has through all these centuries given us wine to gladden the heart of man.

Other miracles that fall in this class are the two instances of miraculous feeding. They involve the multiplication of a little bread and a little fish into much bread and much fish. Once in the desert Satan had tempted Him to make bread of stones: He refused the suggestion. "The Son does nothing except what He sees the Father do"; perhaps one may without boldness surmise that the direct change from stone to bread appeared to the Son to be not quite in the hereditary style. Little bread into much bread is quite a different matter. Every year God makes a little corn into much corn: the seed is sown and there is an increase. And men say, according to their several fashions, "It is the laws of Nature," or, "It is Ceres, it is Adonis, it is the Corn-King." But the laws of Nature are only a pattern: nothing will come of them unless they can, so to speak, take over the universe as a going concern. And as for Adonis, no man can tell us where he died or when he rose again. Here, at the feeding of the five thousand, is He whom we have ignorantly worshipped: the *real* Corn-King who will die once and rise once at Jerusalem during the term of office of Pontius Pilate.

That same day He also multiplied fish. Look down into every bay and almost every river. This swarming, undulating fecundity

shows He is still at work "thronging the seas with spawn innumerable." The ancients had a god called Genius; the god of animal and human fertility, the patron of gynaecology, embryology,
and the marriage bed—the "genial" bed as they called it after its
god Genius. But Genius is only another mask for the God of Israel, for it was He who at the beginning commanded all species
"to be fruitful and multiply and replenish the earth." And now,
that day, at the feeding of the thousands, incarnate God does the
same: does close and small, under His human hands, a workman's
hands, what He has always been doing in the seas, the lakes and
the little brooks.

With this we stand on the threshold of that Miracle which for
some reason proves hardest of all for the modern mind to accept. I can understand the man who denies miracles altogether:
but what is one to make of people who will believe other miracles
and "draw the line" at the Virgin Birth? Is it that for all their lip
service to the laws of Nature there is only one natural process in
which they really believe? Or is it that they think they see in this
miracle a slur upon sexual intercourse (though they might just
as well see in the feeding of the five thousand an insult to bakers)
and that sexual intercourse is the one thing still venerated in this
unvenerating age? In reality the Miracle is no less, and no more,
surprising than any others.

Perhaps the best way to approach it is from the remark I saw
in one of the most archaic of our anti-god papers. The remark
was that Christians believed in a God who had "committed adultery with the wife of a Jewish carpenter." The writer was probably merely "letting off steam" and did not really think that God,
in the Christian story, had assumed human form and lain with a
mortal woman, as Zeus lay with Alcmena. But if one had to answer this person, one would have to say that if you called the
miraculous conception divine adultery you would be driven to
find a similar divine adultery in the conception of every child
—nay, of every animal too. I am sorry to use expressions which
will offend pious ears, but I do not know how else to make my
point.

In a normal act of generation the father has no creative function. A microscopic particle of matter from his body, and a mi-

croscopic particle from the woman's body, meet. And with that there passes the colour of his hair and the hanging lower lip of her grandfather and the form of humanity in all its complexity of bones, sinews, nerves, liver and heart, and the form of those pre-human organisms which the embryo will recapitulate in the womb. Behind every spermatozoon lies the whole history of the universe: locked within it lies no inconsiderable part of the world's future. The weight or drive behind it is the momentum of the whole interlocked event which we call Nature up-to-date. And we know now that the "laws of Nature" cannot supply that momentum. If we believe that God created Nature that momentum comes from Him. The human father is merely an instrument, a carrier, often an unwilling carrier, always simply the last in a long line of carriers—a line that stretches back far beyond his ancestors into pre-human and pre-organic deserts of time, back to the creation of matter itself. That line is in God's hand. It is the instrument by which He normally creates a man. For He is the reality behind both Genius and Venus; no woman ever conceived a child, no mare a foal, without Him. But once, and for a special purpose, He dispensed with that long line which is His instrument: once His life-giving finger touched a woman without passing through the ages of interlocked events. Once the great glove of Nature was taken off His hand. His naked hand touched her. There was of course an unique reason for it. That time He was creating not simply a man but the Man who was to be Himself: was creating Man anew: was beginning, at this divine and human point, the New Creation of all things. The whole soiled and weary universe quivered at this direct injection of essential life—direct, uncontaminated, not drained through all the crowded history of Nature. But it would be out of place here to explore the religious significance of the miracle. We are here concerned with it simply as Miracle—that and nothing more. As far as concerns the creation of Christ's human nature (the Grand Miracle whereby His divine begotten nature enters into it is another matter) the miraculous conception is one more witness that here is Nature's Lord. He is doing now, small and close, what He does in a different fashion for every woman who conceives. He does it this time without a line of human ancestors: but even where He uses human ancestors it is not the less He who gives life.[1] The bed is barren where that great third party, Genius, is not present.

The miracles of *Healing*, to which I turn next, are now in a peculiar position. Men are ready to admit that many of them happened but are inclined to deny that they were miraculous. The symptoms of very many diseases can be aped by hysteria, and hysteria can often be cured by "suggestion." It could, no doubt, be argued that such suggestion is a spiritual power, and therefore (if you like) a supernatural power, and that all instances of "faith healing" are therefore Miracles. But in our terminology they would be miraculous only in the same sense in which every instance of human reason is miraculous: and what we are now looking for is miracles other than that. My own view is that it would be unreasonable to ask a person who has not yet embraced Christianity in its entirety to allow that all the healings mentioned in the Gospels were miracles—that is, that they go beyond the possibilities of human "suggestion." It is for the doctors to decide as regards each particular case—supposing that the narratives are sufficiently detailed to allow even probable diagnosis. We have here a good example to what was said in an earlier chapter. So far from belief in miracles depending upon ignorance of natural law, we are here finding for ourselves that ignorance of law makes miracle unascertainable.

Without deciding in detail which of the healings must (apart from acceptance of the Christian faith) be regarded as miraculous, we can however indicate the kind of miracle involved. Its character can easily be obscured by the somewhat magical view which many people still take of ordinary and medical healing. There is a sense in which no doctor ever heals. The doctors themselves would be the first to admit this. The magic is not in the medicine but in the patient's body—in the *vis medicatrix naturae,* the recuperative or self-corrective energy of Nature. What the treatment does is to stimulate Natural functions or to remove what hinders them. We speak for convenience of the doctor, or the dressing, healing a cut. But in another sense every cut heals itself: no cut can be healed in a corpse. That same mysterious force which we

[1] Cf. Matt. xxiii. 9.

call gravitational when it steers the planets and biochemical when it heals a live body, is the efficient cause of all recoveries. And that energy proceeds from God in the first instance. All who are cured are cured by Him, not merely in the sense that His providence provides them with medical assistance and wholesome environments, but also in the sense that their very tissues are repaired by the far-descended energy which, flowing from Him, energises the whole system of Nature. But once He did it visibly to the sick in Palestine, a Man meeting with men. What in its general operations we refer to laws of Nature or once referred to Apollo or Asclepius thus reveals itself. The Power that always was behind all healings puts on a face and hands. Hence, of course, the apparent chanciness of the miracles. It is idle to complain that He heals those whom He happens to meet, not those whom He doesn't. To be a man means to be in one place and not in another. The world which would not know Him as present everywhere was saved by His becoming *local*.

Christ's single miracle of Destruction, the withering of the fig-tree, has proved troublesome to some people, but I think its significance is plain enough. The miracle is an acted parable, a symbol of God's sentence on all that is "fruitless" and specially, no doubt, on the official Judaism of that age. That is its moral significance. As a miracle, it again does in focus, repeats small and close, what God does constantly and throughout Nature. We have seen in the previous chapter how God, twisting Satan's weapon out of his hand, had become, since the Fall, the God even of human death. But much more, and perhaps ever since the creation, He has been the God of the death of organisms. In both cases, though in somewhat different ways, He is the God of death because He is the God of Life: the God of human death because through it increase of life now comes—the God of merely organic death because death is part of the very mode by which organic life spreads itself out in Time and yet remains new. A forest a thousand years deep is still collectively alive because some trees are dying and others are growing up. His human face, turned with negation in its eyes upon that one fig tree, did once what His unincarnate actions does to all trees. No tree died that year in

Palestine, or any year anywhere, except because God did—or rather ceased to do—something to it.

All the miracles which we have considered so far are Miracles of the Old Creation. In all of them we see the Divine Man focussing for us what the God of Nature has already done on a larger scale. In our next class, the Miracles of Dominion over the Inorganic, we find some that are of the Old Creation and some that are of the New. When Christ stills the storm He does what God has often done before. God made Nature such that there would be both storms and calms: in that way all storms (except those that are still going on at this moment) have been stilled by God. It is unphilosophical, if you have once accepted the Grand Miracle, to reject the stilling of the storm. There is really no difficulty about adapting the weather conditions of the rest of the world to this one miraculous calm. I myself can still a storm in a room by shutting the window. Nature must make the best she can of it. And to do her justice she makes no trouble at all. The whole system, far from being thrown out of gear (which is what some nervous people seem to think a miracle would do) digests the new situation as easily as an elephant digests a drop of water. She is, as I have said before, an accomplished hostess. But when Christ walks on the water we have a miracle of the New Creation. God had not made the Old Nature, the world before the Incarnation, of such a kind that water would support a human body. This miracle is the foretaste of a Nature that is still in the future. The New Creation is just breaking in. For a moment it looks as if it were going to spread. For a moment two men are living in that new world. St. Peter also walks on the water—a pace or two: then his trust fails him and he sinks. He is back in Old Nature. That momentary glimpse was a snowdrop of a miracle. The snowdrops show that we have turned the corner of the year. Summer is coming. But it is a long way off and the snowdrops do not last long.

The miracles of Reversal all belong to the New Creation. It is a miracle of Reversal when the dead are raised. Old Nature knows nothing of this process: it involves playing backwards a film that we have always seen played forwards. The one or two instances of it in the Gospels are early flowers—what we call spring flowers, because they are prophetic, although they really bloom while it is still winter. And the miracles of Perfecting or of Glory, the Transfiguration, the Resurrection, and the Ascension, are even more emphatically of the New Creation. These are the true spring, or even the summer, of the world's new year. The Captain, the forerunner is already in May or June, though His followers on earth are still living in the frosts and east winds of Old Nature—for "spring comes slowly up this way."

None of the Miracles of the New Creation can be considered apart from the Resurrection and Ascension: and that will require another chapter.

16.

MIRACLES OF THE NEW CREATION

Beware; for fiends in triumph laugh
O'er him who learns the truth by half!
Beware; for God will not endure
For men to make their hope more pure
Than His good promise, or require
Another than the five-stringed lyre[1]
Which He has vowed again to the hands
Devout of him who understands
To tune it justly here!

C. PATMORE,
The Victories of Love.

In the earliest days of Christianity an "apostle" was first and foremost a man who claimed to be an eye-witness of the Resurrection. Only a few days after the Crucifixion when two candidates were nominated for the vacancy created by the treachery of Judas, their qualification was that they had known Jesus personally both before and after His death and could offer first-hand evidence of the Resurrection in addressing the outer world (Acts i. 22). A few days later St. Peter, preaching the first Christian sermon, makes the same claim—"God raised Jesus, of which we all (we Christians) are witnesses" (Acts ii. 32). In the first *Letter to the Corinthians* St. Paul bases his claim to apostleship on the same ground—"Am I not an apostle? Have I not seen the Lord Jesus?"

As this qualification suggests, to preach Christianity meant primarily to preach the Resurrection. Thus people who had heard only fragments of St. Paul's teaching at Athens got the impres-

---

i e. the Body with its five senses.

341

sion that he was talking about two new gods, Jesus and Anastasis (i.e. Resurrection) (Acts xvii. 18). The Resurrection is the central theme in every Christian sermon reported in the Acts. The Resurrection, and its consequences, were the "gospel" or good news which the Christians brought: what we call the "gospels," the narratives of Our Lord's life and death, were composed later for the benefit of those who had already accepted the *gospel*. They were in no sense the basis of Christianity: they were written for those already converted. The miracle of the Resurrection, and the theology of that miracle, comes first: the biography comes later as a comment on it. Nothing could be more unhistorical than to pick out selected sayings of Christ from the gospels and to regard those as the datum and the rest of the New Testament as a construction upon it. The first fact in the history of Christendom is a number of people who say they have seen the Resurrection. If they had died without making anyone else believe this "gospel" no gospels would ever have been written.

It is very important to be clear about what these people meant. When modern writers talk of the Resurrection they usually mean one particular moment—the discovery of the Empty Tomb and the appearance of Jesus a few yards away from it. The story of that moment is what Christian apologists now chiefly try to support and sceptics chiefly try to impugn. But this almost exclusive concentration on the first five minutes or so of the Resurrection would have astonished the earliest Christian teachers. In claiming to have seen the Resurrection they were not necessarily claiming to have seen *that*. Some of them had, some of them had not. It had no more importance than any of the other appearances of the risen Jesus—apart from the poetic and dramatic importance which the beginnings of things must always have. What they were claiming was that they had all, at once time or another, met Jesus during the six or seven weeks that followed His death. Sometimes they seem to have been alone when they did so, but on one occasion twelve of them saw Him together, and on another occasion about five hundred of them. St. Paul says that the majority of the five hundred were still alive when he wrote the *First Letter to the Corinthians*, i.e. in about 55 A.D.

The "Resurrection" to which they bore witness was, in fact, not the action of rising from the dead but the state of having risen; a state, as they held, attested by intermittent meetings during a limited period (except for the special, and in some ways different, meeting vouchsafed to St. Paul). This termination of the period is important, for, as we shall see, there is no possibility of isolating the doctrine of the Resurrection from that of the Ascension.

The next point to notice is that the Resurrection was not regarded simply or chiefly as evidence for the immortality of the soul. It is, of course, often so regarded to-day: I have heard a man maintain that "the importance of the Resurrection is that it proves *survival*." Such a view cannot at any point be reconciled with the language of the New Testament. On such a view Christ would simply have done what all men do when they die: the only novelty would have been that in His case we were allowed to see it happening. But there is not in Scripture the faintest suggestion that the Resurrection was new evidence for something that had *in fact* been always happening. The New Testament writers speak as if Christ's achievement in rising from the dead was the first event of its kind in the whole history of the universe. He is the "first fruits," the "pioneer of life." He has forced open a door that has been locked since the death of the first man. He has met, fought, and beaten the King of Death. Everything is different because He has done so. This is the beginning of the New Creation: a new chapter in cosmic history has opened.

I do not mean, of course, that the writers of the New Testament disbelieved in "survival." On the contrary they believed in it so readily that Jesus on more than one occasion had to assure them that He was not a ghost. From the earliest times the Jews, like many other nations, had believed that man possessed a "soul" or *Nephesh* separable from the body, which went at death into the shadowy world called *Sheol:* a land of forgetfulness and imbecility where none called upon Jehovah any more, a land half unreal and melancholy like the Hades of the Greeks or the Niflheim of the Norsemen. From it shades could return and appear to the living, as Samuel's shade had done at the command of the Witch of Endor. In much more recent times there had arisen a more cheerful belief that the righteous passed at death to "heaven." Both doctrines are doctrines of "the immortality of the soul" as a Greek or a modern Englishman understands it: and both are quite irrelevant to the story of the Resurrection. The writers look upon this event as an absolute novelty. Quite clearly they do not think they have been haunted by a ghost from Sheol, nor even that they have had a vision of a "soul" in "heaven." It must be clearly understood that if the Psychical Researchers succeeded in proving "survival" and showed that the Resurrection was an instance of it, they would not be supporting the Christian faith but refuting it. If that were all that had happened the original "gospel" would have been untrue. What the apostles claimed to have seen did not corroborate, nor exclude, and had indeed nothing to do with, either the doctrine of "heaven" or the doctrine of Sheol. Insofar as it corroborated anything it corroborated a third Jewish belief which is quite distinct from both these. This third doctrine taught that in "the day of Jahweh" peace would be restored and world dominion given to Israel under a righteous King: and that when this happened the righteous dead, or some of them, would come back to earth—not as floating wraiths but as solid men who cast shadows in the sunlight and made a noise when they tramped the floors. "Awake and sing, ye that dwell in the dust," said Isaiah, "And the earth shall cast out the dead" (xxvi. 19). What the apostles thought they had seen was, if not that, at any rate a lonely first instance of that: the first movement of a great wheel beginning to turn in the direction opposite to that which all men hitherto had observed. Of all the ideas entertained by man about death it is this one, and this one only, which the story of the Resurrection tends to confirm. If the story is false then it is this Hebrew myth of resurrection which begot it. If the story is true then the hint and anticipation of the truth is to be found not in popular ideas about ghosts nor in eastern doctrines of re-incarnation nor in philosophical speculations about the immortality of the soul, but exclusively in the Hebrew prophecies of the return, the restoration, the great reversal. Immortality simply as immortality is irrelevant to the Christian claim.

There are, I allow, certain respects in which the risen Christ resembles the "ghost" of popular tradition. Like a ghost He "appears" and "disappears": locked doors are no obstacle to Him. On the other hand He Himself vigorously asserts that He is corporeal (Luke xxiv. 39-40) and eats boiled fish. It is at this point that the modern reader becomes uncomfortable. He becomes more uncomfortable still at the words, "Don't touch me; I have not yet gone up to the Father" (John xx. 17). For voices and apparitions we are, in some measure, prepared. But what is this that must not be touched? What is all this about going "up" to the Father? Is He not already "with the Father" in the only sense that matters? What can "going up" be except a metaphor for *that?* And if so, why has He "not yet" gone? These discomforts arise because the story the "apostles" actually had to tell begins at this point to conflict with the story we expect and are determined beforehand to read into their narrative.

We expect them to tell of a risen life which is purely "spiritual" in the negative sense of that word: that is, we use the word "spiritual" to mean not what it is but what it is not. We mean a life without space, without history, without environment, with no sensuous elements in it. We also, in our heart of hearts, tend to slur over the risen *manhood* of Jesus, to conceive Him, after death, simply returning into Deity, so that the Resurrection would be no more than the reversal or undoing of the Incarnation. That being so, all references to the risen *body* make us uneasy: they raise awkward questions. For as long as we hold the negatively spiritual view, we have not really been believing in that body at all. We have thought (whether we acknowledged it or not) that the body was not objective: that it was an appearance sent by God to assure the disciples of truths otherwise incommunicable. But what truths? If the truth is that after death there comes a negatively spiritual life, an eternity of mystical experience, what more misleading way of communicating it could possibly be found than the appearance of a human form which eats boiled fish? Again, on such a view, the body would really be a hallucination. And any theory of hallucination breaks down on the fact (and if it is invention it is the oddest invention that ever entered the mind of man) that on three separate occasions this hallucination was not immediately recognised as Jesus (Luke xxiv. 13-31; John xx. 15, xxi. 4). Even granting that God sent a

holy hallucination to teach truths already widely believed without it, and far more easily taught by other methods, and certain
to be completely obscured by this, might we not at least hope that
He would get the face of the hallucination *right?* Is He who
made all faces such a bungler that He cannot even work up a recognisable likeness of the Man who was Himself?

It is at this point that awe and trembling fall upon us as we
read the records. If the story is false, it is at least a much stranger
story than we expected, something for which philosophical "religion," psychical research, and popular superstition have all
alike failed to prepare us. If the story is true, then a wholly new
mode of being has arisen in the universe.

The body, which lives in that new mode is like, and yet unlike,
the body His friends knew before the execution. It is differently
related to space and probably to time, but by no means cut off
from all relation to them. It can perform the animal act of eating.
It is so related to matter, as we know it, that it can be touched,
though at first it had better not be touched. It has also a history
before it which is in view from the first moment of the Resurrection; it is presently going to become different or go somewhere
else. That is why the story of the Ascension cannot be separated
from that of the Resurrection. All the accounts suggest that the
appearances of the Risen Body came to an end; some describe an
abrupt end about six weeks after the death. And they describe
this abrupt end in a way which presents greater difficulties to the
modern mind than any other part of Scripture. For here,
surely, we get the implication of all those primitive crudities to
which I have said that Christians are not committed: the vertical
ascent like a balloon, the local Heaven, the decorated chair to the
right of the Father's throne. "He was caught up into the sky (*our-
anos*)," says St. Mark's Gospel, "and sat down at the right hand
of God." "He was lifted up," says the author of *Acts,* "and a cloud
cut Him off from their sight."

It is true that if we wish to get rid of these embarrassing passages we have the means to do so. The Marcan one probably
formed no part of the earliest text of St. Mark's Gospel: and you
may add that the Ascension, though constantly implied throughout the New Testament, is described only in these two places.

Can we then simply drop the Ascension story? The answer is that we can do so only if we regard the Resurrection appearances as those of a ghost or hallucination. For a phantom can just fade away; but an objective entity must go somewhere—something must happen to it. And if the Risen Body were not objective, then all of us (Christian or not) must invent some explanation for the disappearance of the corpse. And all Christians must explain why God sent or permitted a "vision" or "ghost" whose behaviour seems almost exclusively directed to convincing the disciples that it was not a vision or a ghost but a really corporeal being. If it were a vision then it was the most systematically deceptive and lying vision on record. But if it were real, then something happened to it after it ceased to appear. You cannot take away the Ascension without putting something else in its place.

The records represent Christ as passing after death (as no man had passed before) neither into a purely, that is, negatively, "spiritual" mode of existence nor into a "natural" life such as we know, but into a life which has its own, new Nature. It represents Him as withdrawing six weeks later, into some different mode of existence. It says—He says—that He goes "to prepare a place for us." This presumably means that He is about to create that whole new Nature which will provide the environment or conditions for His glorified humanity and, in Him, for ours. The picture is not what we expected—though whether it is less or more probable and philosophical on that account is another question. It is not the picture of an escape from any and every kind of Nature into some unconditioned and utterly transcendent life. It is the picture of a new human nature, and a new Nature in general, being brought into existence. We must, indeed, believe the risen body to be extremely different from the mortal body: but the existence, in that new state, of anything that could in any sense be described as "body" at all, involves some sort of spatial relations and in the long run a whole new universe. That is the picture—not of unmaking but of remaking. The old field of space, time, matter, and the senses is to be weeded, dug, and sown for a new crop. We may be tired of that old field: God is not.

And yet the very way in which this new Nature begins to shine in has a certain affinity with the habits of old Nature. In Nature as we know her, things tend to be anticipated. Nature is fond of "false dawns," of precursors: thus, as I said before, some flowers come before true spring: sub-men (the evolutionists would have it) before the true men. So, here also, we get Law before Gospel, animal sacrifices foreshadowing the great sacrifice of God to God, the Baptist before the Messiah, and those "miracles of the New Creation" which come before the Resurrection. Christ's walking on the water, and His raising of Lazarus fall in this class. Both give us hints of what the New Nature will be like.

In the Walking on the Water we see the relations of spirit and Nature so altered that Nature can be made to do whatever spirit pleases. This new obedience of Nature is, of course, not to be separated even in thought from spirit's own obedience to the Father of Spirits. Apart from that proviso such obedience by Nature, if it were possible, would result in chaos: the evil dream of Magic arises from finite spirit's longing to get that power without paying that price. The evil reality of lawless applied science (which is Magic's son and heir) is actually reducing large tracts of Nature to disorder and sterility at this very moment. I do not know how radically Nature herself would need to be altered to make her thus obedient to spirits, when spirits have become wholly obedient to their source. One thing at least we must observe. If we are in fact spirits, not Nature's offspring, then there must be some point (probably the brain) at which created spirit even now can produce effects on matter not by manipulation or technics but simply by the wish to do so. If that is what you mean by Magic then Magic is a reality manifested every time you move your hand or think a thought. And Nature, as we have seen, is not destroyed but rather perfected by her servitude.

The raising of Lazarus differs from the Resurrection of Christ Himself because Lazarus, so far as we know, was not raised to a new and more glorious mode of existence but merely restored to the sort of life he had had before. The fitness of the miracle lies in the fact that He who will raise all men at the general resurrection here does it small and close, and in an inferior—a merely anticipatory—fashion. For the mere restoration of Lazarus is as inferior in splendour to the *glorious* resurrection of the New

Humanity as stone jars are to the green and growing vine for five little barley loaves to all the waving bronze and gold of a fat valley ripe for harvest. The resuscitation of Lazarus, so far as we can see, is simple reversal: a series of changes working in the direction opposite to that we have always experienced. At death, matter which has been organic, begins to flow away into the inorganic, to be finally scattered and used (some of it) by other organisms. The resurrection of Lazarus involves the reverse process. The general resurrection involves the reverse process universalised—a rush of matter towards organisation at the call of spirits which require it. It is presumably a foolish fancy (not justified by the words of Scripture) that each spirit should recover those particular units of matter which he ruled before. For one thing, they would not be enough to go round: we all live in second-hand suits and there are doubtless atoms in my chin which have served many another man, many a dog, many an eel, many a dinosaur. Nor does the unity of our bodies, even in this present life, consist in retaining the same particles. My form remains one, though the matter in it changes continually. I am, in that respect, like a curve in a waterfall.

But the miracle of Lazarus, though only anticipatory in one sense, belongs emphatically to the New Creation, for nothing is more definitely excluded by Old Nature than any return to a *status quo.* The pattern of Death and Rebirth never restores the previous individual organism. And similarly, on the inorganic level, we are told that Nature never restores order where disorder has once occurred. "Shuffling," said Professor Eddington, "is the thing Nature never undoes." Hence we live in a universe where organisms are always getting more disordered. These laws between them—irreversible death and irreversible entropy—cover almost the whole of what St. Paul calls the "vanity" of Nature: her futility, her ruinousness. And the film is never reversed. The movement from more order to less almost serves to determine the direction in which Time is flowing. You could almost define the future as the period in which what is now living will be dead and in which what order still remains will be diminished

But entropy by its very character assures us that though it may be the universal rule in the Nature we know, it cannot be universal absolutely. If a man says, "Humpty Dumpty is falling," you see at once that this is not a complete story. The bit you have been told implies both a later chapter in which Humpty Dumpty will have reached the ground, and an earlier chapter in which he was still seated on the wall. A Nature which is "running down" cannot be the whole story. A clock can't run down unless it has been wound up. Humpty Dumpty can't fall off a wall which never existed. If a Nature which disintegrates order were the whole of reality, where would she find any order to disintegrate? Thus on any view there must have been a time when processes the reverse of those we now see were going on: a time of winding up. The Christian claim is that those days are not gone forever. Humpty Dumpty is going to be replaced on the wall—at least in the sense that what has died is going to recover life, probably in the sense that the inorganic universe is going to be reordered. Either Humpty Dumpty will never reach the ground (being caught in mid-fall by the everlasting arms) or else when he reaches it he will be put together again and replaced on a new and better wall. Admittedly, science discerns no "king's horses and men" who can "put Humpty Dumpty together again." But you would not expect her to. She is based on observation: and all our observations are observations of Humpty Dumpty in mid-air. They do not reach either the wall above or the ground below— much less the King with His horses and men hastening towards the spot.

The Transfiguration or "Metamorphosis" of Jesus is also, no doubt, an anticipatory glimpse of something to come. He is seen conversing with two of the ancient dead. The change which His own human form had undergone is described as one to luminosity, to "shining whiteness." A similar whiteness characterises His appearances at the beginning of the book of Revelation. One rather curious detail is that this shining or whiteness affected His clothes as much as His body. St. Mark indeed mentions the clothes more explicitly than the face, and adds, with his inimitable naivety, that "no laundry could do anything like it." Taken by itself this episode bears all the marks of a "vision": that is, of an experience which, though it may be divinely sent and may reveal great truth, yet is not, objectively speaking, the experience it seems to be. But if the theory of "vision" (or holy hallucination) will not cover the Resurrection appearances, it would be only a multiplying of hypotheses to introduce it here. We do not know to what phase or feature of the New Creation this episode points. It may reveal some special glorifying of Christ's manhood at some phase of its history (since history it apparently has) or it may reveal the glory which that manhood always has in its New Creation: it may even reveal a glory which all risen men will inherit. We do not know.

It must indeed be emphasised throughout that we know and can know very little about the New Nature. The task of the imagination here is not to forecast it but simply, by brooding on many possibilities, to make room for a more complete and circumspect agnosticism. It is useful to remember that even now senses responsive to different vibrations would admit us to quite new worlds of experience: that a multi-dimensional space would be different, almost beyond recognition, from the space we are now aware of, yet not discontinuous from it: that time may not always be for us, as it now is, unilinear and irreversible: that other parts of Nature might some day obey us as our cortex now does. It is useful not because we can trust these fancies to give us any positive truths about the New Creation but because they teach us not to limit, in our rashness, the vigour and variety of the new crops which this old field might yet produce. We are therefore compelled to believe that nearly all we are told about the New Creation is metaphorical. But not quite all. That is just where the story of the Resurrection suddenly jerks us back like a tether. The local appearances, the eating, the touching, the claim to be corporeal, must be either reality or sheer illusion. The New Nature is, in the most troublesome way, interlocked at some points with the Old. Because of its novelty we have to think of it, for the most part, metaphorically: but because of the partial interlocking, some facts about it come through into our present experience in all their literal facthood—just as some facts about an organism are inorganic facts, and some facts about a solid body are facts of linear geometry.

Even apart from that, the mere idea of a New Nature, a Nature beyond Nature, a systematic and diversified reality which is "supernatural" in relation to the world of our five present senses but "natural" from its own point of view, is profoundly shocking to a certain philosophical preconception from which we all suffer. I think Kant is at the root of it. It may be expressed by saying that we are prepared to believe either in a reality with one floor or in a reality with two floors, but not in a reality like a skyscraper with several floors. We are prepared, on the one hand, for the sort of reality that Naturalists believe in. That is a one-floor reality: this present Nature is all that there is. We are also prepared for reality as "religion" conceives it: a reality with a ground floor (Nature) and then above that one other floor and one only —an eternal, spaceless, timeless, spiritual Something of which we can have no images and which, if it presents itself to human consciousness at all, does so in a mystical experience which shatters all our categories of thought. What we are not prepared for is anything in between. We feel quite sure that the first step beyond the world of our present experience must lead either nowhere at all or else into the blinding abyss of undifferentiated spirituality, the unconditioned, the absolute. That is why many believe in God who cannot believe in angels and an angelic world. That is why many believe in immortality who cannot believe in the resurrection of the body. That is why Pantheism is more popular than Christianity, and why many desire a Christianity stripped of its miracles. I cannot now understand, but I well remember, the passionate conviction with which I myself once defended this prejudice. Any rumour of floors or levels intermediate between the Unconditioned and the world revealed by our present senses I rejected without trial as "mythology."

Yet it is very difficult to see any rational grounds for the dogma that reality must have no more than two levels. There cannot, from the nature of the case, be evidence that God never created and never will create, more than one system. Each of them would be at least extra-natural in relation to all the others: and if any of them is more concrete, more permanent, more excellent, and richer than another it will be to that other *super*-natural. Nor will a partial contact between any two obliterate their distinctness. In that way there might be Natures piled upon Natures to any height God pleased, each Supernatural to that below it and

Sub-natural to that which surpassed it. But the tenor of Christian teaching is that we are actually living in a situation even more complex than that. A new Nature is being not merely made but made out of an old one. We live amid all the anomalies, inconveniences, hopes, and excitements of a house that is being rebuilt. Something is being pulled down and something going up in its place.

To accept the idea of intermediate floors—which the Christian story will, quite simply, force us to do if it is not a falsehood—does not of course involve losing our spiritual apprehension of the top floor of all. Most certainly, beyond all worlds, unconditioned and unimaginable, transcending discursive thought, there yawns forever the ultimate Fact, the fountain of all other facthood, the burning and undimensioned depth of the Divine Life. Most certainly also, to be united with that Life in the eternal Sonship of Christ is, strictly speaking, the only thing worth a moment's consideration. And in so far as *that* is what you mean by *Heaven,* Christ's divine Nature never left it, and therefore never returned to it: and His human nature ascended thither not at the moment of the Ascension but at every moment. In that sense not one word that the spiritualisers have uttered will, please God, ever be unsaid by me. But it by no means follows that there are not other truths as well. I allow, indeed I insist, that Christ cannot be at "the right hand of God" except in a metaphorical sense. I allow and insist that the Eternal Word, the Second Person of the Trinity, can never be, nor have been, confined to any place at all: it is rather in Him that all places exist. But the records say that the glorified, but still in some sense corporeal, Christ withdrew into some different mode of being about six weeks after the Crucifixion: and that He is "preparing a place" for us. The statement in St. Mark that He sat down at the right hand of God we must take as a metaphor: it was indeed, even for the writer, a poetical quotation, from Psalm CX. But the statement that the holy Shape went up and vanished does not permit the same treatment.

What troubles us here is not simply the statement itself but what (we feel sure) the author meant by it. Granted that there are different Natures, different levels of being, distinct but not always discontinuous—granted that Christ withdrew from one of these to another, that His withdrawal from one was indeed the first step in His creation of the other—what precisely should we expect the onlookers to see? Perhaps mere instantaneous vanishing would make us most comfortable. A sudden break between the perceptible and the imperceptible would worry us less than any kind of joint. But if the spectators say they saw first a short vertical movement and then a vague luminosity (that is what "cloud" presumably means here as it certainly does in the account of the Transfiguration) and then nothing—have we any reason to object? We are well aware that increased distance from the centre of this planet could not *in itself* be equated with increase of power or beatitude. But this is only saying that *if* the movement had no connection with such spiritual events, why then it had no connection with them.

Movement (in any direction but one) away from the position momentarily occupied by our moving Earth will certainly be to us movement "upwards." To say that Christ's passage to a new "Nature" could involve no such movement, or no movement at all, within the "Nature" he was leaving, is very arbitrary. Where there is passage, there is departure; and departure is an event in the region from which the traveller is departing. All this, even on the assumption that the Ascending Christ is in a three-dimensional space. If it is not that kind of body, and space is not that kind of space, then we are even less qualified to say what the spectators of this entirely new event might or might not see or feel as if they had seen. There is, of course, no question of a human body as we know it existing in interstellar space as we know it. The Ascension belongs to a new Nature. We are discussing only what the "joint" between the old Nature and the new, the precise moment of transition, would look like.

But what really worries us is the conviction that, whatever we say, the New Testament writers meant something quite different. We feel sure that they thought they had seen their Master setting off on a journey for a local "Heaven" where God sat in a throne and where there was another throne waiting for Him. And I believe that in a sense that is just what they did think. And I believe that, for this reason, whatever they had actually seen (sense perception, almost by hypothesis, would be confused at such a mo-

ment) they would almost certainly have remembered it as a vertical movement. What we must not say is that they "mistook"
local "Heavens" and celestial throne-rooms and the like for the
"spiritual" Heaven of union with God and supreme power and
beatitude. You and I have been gradually disentangling different
senses of the word *Heaven* throughout this chapter. It may be
convenient here to make a list. *Heaven* can mean (1) The unconditioned Divine Life beyond all worlds. (2) Blessed participation in that Life by a created spirit. (3) The whole Nature or
system of conditions in which redeemed human spirits, still remaining human, can enjoy such participation fully and forever.
This is the Heaven Christ goes to "prepare" for us. (4) The physical Heaven, the sky, the space in which Earth moves. What enables us to distinguish these senses and hold them clearly apart
is not any special spiritual purity but the fact that we are the
heirs to centuries of logical analysis: not that we are sons to Abraham but that we are sons to Aristotle. We are not to suppose that
the writers of the New Testament mistook Heaven in sense four
or three for Heaven in sense two or one. You cannot mistake a
half sovereign for a sixpence until you know the English system
of coinage—that is, until you know the difference between them.
In their idea of Heaven all these meanings were latent, ready to
be brought out by later analysis. They never thought merely of
the blue sky or merely of a "spiritual" heaven. When they looked
up at the blue sky they never doubted that there, whence light
and heat and the precious rain descended, was the home of God:
but on the other hand, when they thought of one ascending
to that Heaven they never doubted He was "ascending" in what
we should call a "spiritual" sense. The real and pernicious period of literalism comes far later, in the Middle Ages and the seventeenth century, when the distinctions have been made and
heavy-handed people try to force the separated concepts together
again in wrong ways. The fact that Galilaean shepherds could
not distinguish what they saw at the Ascension from that kind of
ascent which, by its very nature, could never be seen at all, does
not prove on the one hand that they were unspiritual, nor on
the other that they saw nothing. A man who really believes that
"Heaven" is in the sky may well, in his heart, have a far truer and

more spiritual conception of it than many a modern logician who could expose that fallacy with a few strokes of his pen. For he who does the will of the Father shall know the doctrine. Irrelevant material splendours in such a man's idea of the vision of God will do no harm, for they are not there for their own sakes. Purity from such images in a merely theoretical Christian's idea will do no good if they have been banished only by logical criticism.

But we must go a little further than this. It is not an accident that simple-minded people, however spiritual, should blend the ideas of God and Heaven and the blue sky. It is a fact, not a fiction, that light and life-giving heat do come down from the sky to Earth. The analogy of the sky's rôle to begetting and of the Earth's rôle to bearing is sound as far as it goes. The huge dome of the sky is of all things sensuously perceived the most like infinity. And when God made space and worlds that move in space, and clothed our world with air, and gave us such eyes and such imaginations as those we have, He knew what the sky would mean to us. And since nothing in His work is accidental, if He knew, He intended. We cannot be certain that this was not indeed one of the chief purposes for which Nature was created; still less that it was not one of the chief reasons why the withdrawal was allowed to affect human senses as a movement upwards. (A disappearance into the Earth would beget a wholly different religion.) The ancients, in letting the spiritual symbolism of the sky flow straight into their minds without stopping to discover by analysis that it was a symbol, were not entirely mistaken. In one way they were perhaps less mistaken than we.

For we have fallen into an opposite difficulty. Let us confess that probably every Christian now alive finds a difficulty in reconciling the two things he has been told about "heaven"—that it is, on the one hand, a life in Christ, a vision of God, a ceaseless adoration, and that it is, on the other hand, a bodily life. When we seem nearest to the vision of God in this life, the body seems almost an irrelevance. And if we try to conceive our eternal life as one in a body (any kind of body) we tend to find that some vague dream of Platonic paradises and gardens of the Hesperides has substituted itself for that mystical approach which we feel (and I think rightly) to be more important. But if that discrepancy were final then it would follow—which is absurd—that God was originally mistaken when He introduced our spirits into the Natural order at all. We must conclude that the discrepancy itself is precisely one of the disorders which the New Creation comes to heal. The fact that the body, and locality and locomotion and time, now feel irrelevant to the highest reaches of the spiritual life is (like the fact that we can think of our bodies as "coarse") a *symptom*. Spirit and Nature have quarrelled in us; that is our disease. Nothing we can yet do enables us to imagine its complete healing. Some glimpses and faint hints we have: in the Sacraments, in the use made of sensuous imagery by the great poets, in the best instances of sexual love, in our experiences of the earth's beauty. But the full healing is utterly beyond our present conceptions. Mystics have got as far in contemplation of God as the point at which the senses are banished: the further point, at which they will be put back again, has (to the best of my knowledge) been reached by no one. The destiny of redeemed man is not less but more unimaginable than mysticism would lead us to suppose—because it is full of semi-imaginables which we cannot at present admit without destroying its essential character.

One point must be touched on because, though I kept silence, it would none the less be present in most readers' minds. The letter and spirit of scripture, and of all Christianity, forbid us to suppose that life in the New Creation will be a sexual life; and this reduces our imagination to the withering alternative either of bodies which are hardly recognisable as human bodies at all or else of a perpetual fast. As regards the fast, I think our present outlook might be like that of a small boy who, on being told that the sexual act was the highest bodily pleasure, should immediately ask whether you ate chocolates at the same time. On receiving the answer "No," he might regard absence of chocolates as the chief characteristic of sexuality. In vain would you tell him that the reason why lovers in their carnal raptures don't bother about chocolates is that they have something better to think of. The boy knows chocolate: he does not know the positive thing that excludes it. We are in the same position. We know the sexual life; we do not know, except in glimpses, the other thing

which, in Heaven, will leave no room for it. Hence where fulness
awaits us we anticipate fasting. In denying that sexual life, as we
now understand it, makes any part of the final beatitude, it is not
of course necessary to suppose that the distinction of sexes will disappear. What is no longer needed for biological purposes may
be expected to survive for splendour. Sexuality is the instrument
both of virginity and of conjugal virtue; neither men nor women
will be asked to throw away weapons they have used victoriously.
It is the beaten and the fugitives who throw away their swords.
The conquerors sheathe theirs and retain them. "Trans-sexual"
would be a better word than "sexless" for the heavenly life.

I am well aware that this last paragraph may seem to many
readers unfortunate and to some comic. But that very comedy, as
I must repeatedly insist, is the symptom of our estrangement, as
spirits, from Nature and our estrangement, as animals, from
Spirit. The whole conception of the New Creation involves the
belief that this estrangement will be healed. A curious consequence will follow. The archaic type of thought which could not
clearly distinguish spiritual "Heaven" from the sky, is from our
point of view a confused type of thought. But it also resembles
and anticipates a type of thought which will one day be true.
That archaic sort of thinking will become simply the correct
sort when Nature and Spirit are fully harmonised—when Spirit
rides Nature so perfectly that the two together make rather a
Centaur than a mounted knight. I do not mean necessarily that
the blending of Heaven and sky, in particular, will turn out to be
specially true, but that the kind of blending will accurately mirror the reality which will then exist. There will be no room to
get the finest razor-blade of thought in between Spirit and Nature. Every state of affairs in the New Nature will be the perfect expression of a spiritual state and every spiritual state the
perfect informing of, and bloom upon, a state of affairs; one
with it as the perfume with a flower or the "spirit" of great poetry
with its form. There is thus in the history of human thought, as
elsewhere, a pattern of death and rebirth. The old, richly imaginative thought which still survives in Plato has to submit to the
deathlike, but indispensable, process of logical analysis: nature
and spirit, matter and mind, fact and myth, the literal and the

metaphorical, have to be more and more sharply separated, till at last a purely mathematical universe and a purely subjective mind confront one another across an unbridgeable chasm. But from this descent also, if thought itself is to survive, there must be re-ascent and the Christian conception provides for it. Those who attain the glorious resurrection will see the dry bones clothed again with flesh, the fact and the myth re-married, the literal and the metaphorical rushing together.

The remark so often made that "Heaven is a state of mind" bears witness to the wintry and deathlike phase of this process in which we are now living. The implication is that if Heaven is a state of mind—or, more correctly, of the spirit—then it must be only a state of the spirit, or at least that anything else, if added to that state of spirit, would be irrelevant. That is what every great religion *except* Christianity would say. But Christian teaching by saying that God made the world and called it good teaches that Nature or environment cannot be simply irrelevant to spiritual beatitude in general, however far in one particular Nature, during the days of her bondage, they may have drawn apart. By teaching the resurrection of the body it teaches that Heaven is not merely a state of the spirit but a state of the body as well: and therefore a state of Nature as a whole. Christ, it is true, told His hearers that the Kingdom of Heaven was "within" or "among" them. But His hearers were not *merely* in "a state of mind." The planet He had created was beneath their feet, His sun above their heads; blood and lungs and guts were working in the bodies He had invented, photons and sound waves of His devising were blessing them with the sight of His human face and the sound of His voice. We are never *merely* in a state of mind. The prayer and the meditation made in howling wind or quiet sunshine, in morning alacrity or evening resignation, in youth or age, good health or ill, may be equally, but are differently, blessed. Already in this present life we have all seen how God can take up all these seeming irrelevancies into the spiritual fact and cause them to bear no small part in making the blessing of that moment to be the particular blessing it was—as fire can burn coal and wood equally but a wood fire is different from a coal one. From this factor of environment Christianity does not teach us to desire a total release. We desire, like St. Paul, not to be un-clothed but to be re-clothed: to find not the formless Everywhere-and-Nowhere but the promised land, that Nature which will be always and perfectly—as present Nature is partially and intermittently—the instrument for that music which will then arise between Christ and us.

And what, you ask, does it matter? Do not such ideas only excite us and distract us from the more immediate and more certain things, the love of God and our neighbours, the bearing of the daily cross? If you find that they so distract you, think of them no more. I most fully allow that it is of more importance for you or me to-day to refrain from one sneer or to extend one charitable thought to an enemy than to know all that angels and archangels know about the mysteries of the New Creation. I write of these things not because they are the most important but because this book is about miracles. From the title you cannot have expected a book of devotion or of ascetic theology. Yet I will not admit that the things we have been discussing for the last few pages are of no importance for the practice of the Christian life. For I suspect that our conception of Heaven as *merely* a state of mind is not unconnected with the fact that the specifically Christian virtue of Hope has in our time grown so languid. Where our fathers, peering into the future, saw gleams of gold, we see only the mist, white, featureless, cold and never moving.

The thought at the back of all this negative spirituality is really one forbidden to Christians. They, of all men, must not conceive spiritual joy and worth as things that need to be rescued or tenderly protected from time and place and matter and the senses. Their God is the God of corn and oil and wine. He is the glad Creator. He has become Himself incarnate. The sacraments have been instituted. Certain spiritual gifts are offered us only on condition that we perform certain bodily acts. After that we cannot really be in doubt of His intention. To shrink back from all that can be called Nature into negative spirituality is as if we ran away from horses instead of learning to ride. There is in our present pilgrim condition plenty of room (more room than most of us like) for abstinence and renunciation and mortifying our natural desires. But behind all asceticism the thought should be, "Who will trust us with the true wealth if we cannot be trusted even with the wealth that perishes?" Who will trust me with a spiritual body if I cannot control even an earthly body? These small and perishable bodies we now have were given to us as ponies are given to schoolboys. We must learn to manage: not that we may some day be free of horses altogether but that some day we may ride bare-back, confident and rejoicing, those greater mounts, those winged, shining and world-shaking horses which perhaps even now expect us with impatience, pawing and snorting in the King's stables. Not that the gallop would be of any value unless it were a gallop with the King; but how else—since He has retained His own charger—should we accompany Him?

17.

EPILOGUE

> "If you leave a thing alone you leave it to a torrent of change.
> If you leave a white post alone it will soon be a black post."
>
> G. K. CHESTERTON,
> *Orthodoxy*.

My work ends here. If, after reading it, you now turn to study the historical evidence for yourself, begin with the New Testament and not with the books about it. If you do not know Greek get it in a modern translation. Moffat's is probably the best: Monsignor Knox is also good. I do not advise the *Basic English* version. And when you turn from the New Testament to modern scholars, remember that you go among them as a sheep among wolves. Naturalistic assumptions, beggings of the question such as that which I noted on the first page of this book, will meet you on every side—even from the pens of clergymen. This does not mean (as I was once tempted to suspect) that these clergymen are disguised apostates who deliberately exploit the position and the livelihood given them by the Christian Church to undermine Christianity. It comes partly from what we may call a "hangover." We all have Naturalism in our bones and even conversion does not at once work the infection out of our system. Its assumptions rush back upon the mind the moment vigilance is relaxed. And in part the procedure of these scholars arises from the feeling which is greatly to their credit—which indeed is honourable to the point of being Quixotic. They are anxious to allow to the enemy every advantage he can with any show of fairness claim. They thus make it part of their method to eliminate the supernatural whenever it is even remotely possible to do so, to strain natural explanation even to the breaking point be-

362

fore they admit the least suggestion of miracle. Just in the same spirit some examiners tend to overmark any candidate whose opinions and character, as revealed by his work, are revolting to them. We are so afraid of being led into unfairness by our instant dislike of the man that we are liable to overshoot the mark and treat him too kindly. Many modern Christian scholars overshoot the mark for a similar reason.

In using the books of such people you must therefore be continually on guard. You must develop a nose like a bloodhound for those steps in the argument which depend not on historical and linguistic knowledge but on the concealed assumption that miracles are impossible, improbable, or improper. And this means that you must really re-educate yourself: must work hard and consistently to eradicate from your mind the whole type of thought in which we have all been brought up. It is the type of thought which, under various disguises, has been our adversary throughout this book. It is technically called *Monism;* but perhaps the unlearned reader will understand me best if I call it *Everythingism.* I mean by this the belief that "everything," or "the whole show," must be self-existent, must be more important than every particular thing, and must contain all particular things in such a way that they cannot be really very different from one another—that they must be not merely "at one," but one. Thus the Everythingist, if he starts from God, becomes a Pantheist; there must be nothing that is not God. If he starts from Nature he becomes a Naturalist; there must be nothing that is not Nature. He thinks that everything is in the long run "merely" a precursor or a development or a relic or an instance or a disguise, of everything else. This philosophy I believe to be profoundly untrue. One of the moderns has said that reality is "incorrigibly plural." I think he is right. All things come from One. All things are related—related in different and complicated ways. But all things are not one. The word "everything" should mean simply the total (a total to be reached, if we knew enough, by enumeration) of all the things that exist at a given moment. It must not be given a mental capital letter; must not (under the influence of picture thinking) be turned into a sort of pool in which particular things sink or even a cake in which they are the

Miracles

currants. Real things are sharp and knobbly and complicated and different. Everythingism is congenial to our minds because it is the natural philosophy of a totalitarian, mass-producing, conscripted age. That is why we must be perpetually on our guard against it.

And yet . . . and yet . . . it is that *and yet* which I fear more than any positive argument against miracles: that soft, tidal return of your habitual outlook as you close the book and the familiar four walls about you and the familiar noises from the street re-assert themselves. Perhaps (if I dare suppose so much) you have been led on at times while you were reading, have felt ancient hopes and fears astir in your heart, have perhaps come almost to the threshold of belief—but now? No. It just won't do. Here is the ordinary, here is the "real" world, round you again. The dream is ending; as all other similar dreams have always ended. For of course this is not the first time such a thing has happened. More than once in your life before this you have heard a strange story, read some odd book, seen something queer or imagined you have seen it, entertained some wild hope of terror: but always it ended in the same way. And always you wondered how you could, even for a moment, have expected it not to. For that "real world" when you came back to it is so unanswerable. *Of course* the strange story was false, of course the voice was really subjective, of course the apparent portent was a coincidence. You are ashamed of yourself for having ever thought otherwise: ashamed, relieved, amused, disappointed, and angry all at once. You ought to have known that, as Arnold says, "Miracles don't happen."

About this state of mind I have just two things to say. First, that it is precisely one of those counter-attacks by Nature which, on my theory, you ought to have anticipated. Your rational thinking has no foothold in your merely natural consciousness except what it wins and maintains by conquest. The moment rational thought ceases, imagination, mental habit, temperament, and the "spirit of the age" take charge of you again. New thoughts, until they have themselves become habitual, will affect your consciousness as a whole only while you are actually thinking them. Reason has but to nod at his post, and instantly

Nature's patrols are infiltrating. Therefore, while counterarguments against miracle are to be given full attention (for if I am wrong, then the sooner I am refuted the better not only for you but for me), the mere gravitation of the mind back to its habitual outlook must be discounted. Not only in this enquiry but in every enquiry. That same familiar room, re-asserting itself as one closes the book, can make other things *feel* incredible besides miracles. Whether the book has been telling you that the end of all civilisation is at hand, that you are kept in your chair by the curvature of space, or even that you are upside down in relation to Australia, it may still seem a little unreal as you yawn and think of going to bed. I have found even a simple truth (e.g. that my hand, this hand now resting on the book, will one day be a skeleton's hand) singularly unconvincing at such a moment. "Belief-feelings," as Dr. Richards calls them, do not follow reason except by long training: they follow Nature, follow the grooves and ruts which already exist in the mind. The firmest theoretical conviction in favour of materialism will not prevent a particular kind of man, under certain conditions, from being afraid of ghosts. The firmest theoretical conviction in favour of miracles will not prevent another kind of man, in other conditions, from *feeling* a heavy, inescapable certainty that no miracle can ever occur. But the feelings of a tired and nervous man, unexpectedly reduced to passing a night in a large empty country house at the end of a journey on which he has been reading a ghost-story, are no evidence that ghosts exist. Your feelings at this moment are no evidence that miracles do not occur.

The second thing is this. You are probably quite right in thinking that you will never see a miracle done: you are probably equally right in thinking that there was a natural explanation of anything in your past life which seemed, at the first glance, to be "rum" or "odd." God does not shake miracles into Nature at random as if from a pepper-caster. They come on great occasions: they are found at the great ganglions of history—not of political or social history, but of that spiritual history which cannot be fully known by men. If your own life does not happen to be near one of those great ganglions, how should you expect to see one? If we were heroic missionaries, apostles, or martyrs, it would be a different matter. But why you or I? Unless you live near a railway, you will not see trains go past your windows. How likely is it that you or I will be present when a peace-treaty is signed, when a great scientific discovery is made, when a dictator commits suicide? That we should see a miracle is even less likely. Nor, if we understand, shall we be anxious to do so. "Nothing almost sees miracles but misery." Miracles and martyrdoms tend to bunch about the same areas of history—areas we have naturally no wish to frequent. Do not, I earnestly advise you, demand an ocular proof unless you are already perfectly certain that it is not forthcoming.

On the Words "Spirit"
and "Spiritual"

The reader should be warned that the angle from which Man is approached in chapter 4 is quite different from that which would be proper in a devotional or practical treatise on the spiritual life. The kind of analysis which you make of any complex thing depends on the purpose you have in view. Thus in a society the important distinctions, from one point of view, would be those of male and female, children and adults, and the like. From another point of view the important distinctions would be those of rulers and ruled. From a third point of view distinctions of class or occupation might be the most important. All these different analyses might be equally correct, but they would be useful for different purposes. When we are considering Man as evidence for the fact that this spatio-temporal Nature is not the only thing in existence, the important distinction is between that part of Man which belongs to this spatio-temporal Nature and that part which does not: or, if you prefer, between those phenomena of humanity which are rigidly interlocked with all other events in this space and time and those which have a certain independence. These two parts of a man may rightly be called Natural and Supernatural: in calling the second "Super-Natural" we mean that it is something which invades, or is added to, the great interlocked event in space and time, instead of merely arising from it. On the other hand this "Super-Natural" part is itself a created being—a thing called into existence by the Absolute Being and given by Him a certain character or "nature." We could therefore say that while "supernatural" in relation to *this* Nature (this complex event in space and time) it is, in another sense, "natural," i.e. it is a specimen of a class of things which God normally creates after a stable pattern.

There is, however, a sense in which the life of this part can become *absolutely* Supernatural, i.e. not beyond *this* Nature but beyond any and every Nature, in the sense that it can achieve a kind of life which could never have been *given* to any created being in its mere creation. The distinction will, perhaps, become clearer if we consider it in relation not to men but to angels. (It does not matter, here, whether the reader believes in angels or not. I am using them only to make the point clearer.) All angels, both the "good" ones and the bad or "fallen" ones which we call devils, are equally "Supernatural" in relation to *this* spatio-temporal Nature: i.e. they are outside it and have powers and a mode of existence which it could not provide. But the good angels lead a life which is Supernatural in another sense as well. That is to say, they have, of their own free will, offered back to God in love the "natures" He gave them at their creation. All creatures of course live from God in the sense that He made them and at every moment maintains them in existence. But there is a further and higher kind of "life from God" which can be given only to a creature who voluntarily surrenders himself to it. This life the good angels have and the bad angels have not: and it is absolutely Supernatural because no creature in any world can have it by the mere fact of being the sort of creature it is.

As with angels, so with us. The rational part of every man is Supernatural in the relative sense—the same sense in which *both* angels and devils are supernatural. But if it is, as the theologians say, "born again," if it surrenders itself back to God in Christ, it will then have a life which is absolutely Supernatural, which is not created at all but begotten, for the creature is then Second Person of the Deity.

When devotional writers talk of the "spiritual life"—and often when they talk of the "supernatural life" or when I myself, in another book, talked of *Zoë*—they mean this *absolutely* Supernatural life which no creature can be given simply by being created but which every rational creature can have by voluntarily surrendering itself to the life of Christ. But much confusion arises from the fact that in many books the words "Spirit" or "Spiritual" are also used to mean the *relatively* supernatural element in Man, the element external to *this* Nature which is (so to speak) "issued" or handed out to him by the mere fact of being created as a Man at all.

It will perhaps be helpful to make a list of the sense in which the words "spirit," "spirits," and "spiritual" are, or have been, used in English.

1. The chemical sense, e.g. "Spirits evaporate very quickly."

2. The (now obsolete) medical sense. The older doctors believed in certain extremely fine fluids in the human body which were called "the spirits." As medical science this view has long been abandoned, but it is the origin of some expressions we still use; as when we speak of being "in high spirits" or "in low spirits" or say that a horse is "spirited" or that a boy is "full of animal spirits."

3. "Spiritual" is often used to mean simply the opposite of "bodily" or "material." Thus all that is immaterial in man (emotions, passions, memory, etc.) is often called "spiritual." It is very important to remember that what is "spiritual" in this sense is not necessarily good. There is nothing specially fine about the mere fact of immateriality. Immaterial things may, like material things, be good or bad or indifferent.

4. Some people use "spirit" to mean that relatively supernatural element which is given to every man at his creation—the rational element. This is, I think, the most useful way of employing the word. Here again it is important to realise that what is "Spiritual" is not necessarily good. A Spirit (in this sense) can be either the best or the worst of created things. It is because Man is (in this sense) a spiritual animal that he can become either a son of God or a devil.

5. Finally, Christian writers use "spirit" and "spiritual" to mean the life which arises in such rational beings when they voluntarily surrender to Divine grace and become sons of the Heavenly Father in Christ. It is in this sense, and in this sense alone, that the "spiritual" is always good.

It is idle to complain that words have more than one sense. Language is a living thing and words are bound to throw out new senses as a tree throws out new branches. It is not wholly a disad-

vantage, since in the act of disentangling these senses we learn a
great deal about the things involved which we might otherwise
have overlooked. What is disastrous is that any word should
change its sense during a discussion without our being aware of
the change. Hence, for the present discussion, it might be useful
to give different names to the three things which are meant by
the word "Spirit" in senses three, four, and five. Thus for sense
three a good word would be "soul": and the adjective to go with
it would be "psychological." For sense four we might keep the
words "spirit" and "spiritual." For sense five the best adjective
would be "regenerate," but there is no very suitable noun.[1] And
this is perhaps significant: for what we are talking about is not
(as *soul* and *spirit* are) a part or element in Man but a redirec-
tion and revitalising of all the parts or elements. Thus in one
sense there is nothing more in a regenerate man than in an un-
regenerate man, just as there is nothing more in a man who is
walking in the right direction than in one who is walking in
the wrong direction. In another sense, however, it might be said
that the regenerate man is *totally* different from the unregen-
erate, for the regenerate life, the Christ that is formed in him,
transforms every part of him: in it his spirit, soul and body will
all be reborn. Thus if the regenerate life is not a *part* of the man,
this is largely because where it arises at all it cannot rest till it
becomes the whole man. It is not divided from any of the parts
as they are divided from each other. The life of the "spirit" (in
sense four) is in a sense cut off from the life of the soul: the
purely rational and moral man who tries to live entirely by his
created spirit finds himself forced to treat the passions and imaginations of his soul as mere enemies to be destroyed or impris-
oned. But the regenerate man will find his soul eventually harmonised with his spirit by the life of Christ that is in him. Hence
Christians believe in the resurrection of the body, whereas the
ancient philosophers regard the body as a mere encumbrance.
And this perhaps is a universal law, that the higher you rise the
lower you can descend. Man is a tower in which the different

---

[1] Because the 'spirit' in this sense is identical with the New Man (the Christ
formed in each perfected Christian) some Latin theologians call it simply our
Novitas i.e. our 'newness'.

floors can hardly be reached from one another but all can be reached from the top floor.

N.B. In the authorised Version the "spiritual" man means what I am calling the "regenerate" man: the "natural" man means, I think, both what I call the "spirit man" and the "soul man."

APPENDIX B

On "Special Providences"

In this book the reader has heard of two classes of events and two only—miracles and natural events. The former are not interlocked with the history of Nature in the backward direction —i.e. in the time before their occurrence. The latter are. Many pious people, however, speak of certain events as being "providential" or "special providences" without meaning that they are miraculous. This generally implies a belief that, quite apart from miracles, some events are providential in a sense in which some others are not. Thus some people thought that the weather which enabled us to bring off so much of our army at Dunkirk was "providential" in some way in which weather as a whole is not providential. The Christian doctrine that some events, though not miracles, are yet answers to prayer, would seem at first to imply this.

I find it very difficult to conceive an intermediate class of events which are neither miraculous nor merely "ordinary." Either the weather at Dunkirk was or was not that which the previous physical history of the universe, by its own character, would inevitably produce. If it was, then how is it "specially" providential? If it was not, then it was a miracle.

It seems to me, therefore, that we must abandon the idea that there is any special class of events (apart from miracles) which can be distinguished as "specially providential." Unless we are to abandon the conception of Providence altogether, and with it the belief in efficacious prayer, it follows that all events are equally providential. If God directs the course of events at all then He directs the movement of every atom at every moment; "not one sparrow falls to the ground" without that direction. The "naturalness" of natural events does not consist in being somehow outside God's providence. It consists in their being interlocked with one another inside a common space-time in accordance with the fixed pattern of the "laws."

In order to get any picture at all of a thing, it is sometimes necessary to begin with a false picture and then correct it. The false picture of Providence (false because it represents God and Nature as being both contained in a common Time) would be as follows. Every event in Nature results from some previous event, not from the laws of Nature. In the long run the first natural event, whatever it was, has dictated every other event. That is, when God at the moment of creation fed the first event into the framework of the "laws"—first set the ball rolling—He determined the whole history of Nature. Foreseeing every part of that history, He intended every part of it. If He had wished for different weather at Dunkirk He would have made the first event slightly different.

The weather we actually had is therefore in the strictest sense providential; it was decreed, and decreed for a purpose, when the world was made—but no more so (though more interestingly to us) than the precise position at this moment of every atom in the ring of Saturn.

It follows (still retaining our false picture) that every physical event was determined so as to serve a great number of purposes.

Thus God must be supposed in pre-determining the weather at Dunkirk to have taken fully into account the effect it would have not only on the destiny of two nations but (which is incomparably more important) on all the individuals involved on both sides, on all animals, vegetables and minerals within range, and finally on every atom in the universe. This may sound excessive, but in reality we are attributing to the Omniscient only an infinitely superior degree of the same kind of skill which a mere human novelist exercises daily in constructing his plot.

Suppose I am writing a novel. I have the following problems on my hands: (1) Old Mr. A. has got to be dead before Chapter 15. (2) And he'd better die suddenly because I have to prevent him from altering his will. (3) His daughter (my heroine) has got to be kept out of London for three chapters at least. (4) My hero has somehow got to recover the heroine's good opinion which he lost in Chapter 7. (5) That young prig B. who has to improve before the end of the book, needs a bad moral shock to take the conceit out of him. (6) We haven't decided on B's job yet; but the whole development of his character will involve giving him a job and showing him actually at work. How on earth am I to get in all these six things? . . . I have it. What about a railway accident? Old A. can be killed in it, and that settles him. In fact the accident can occur while he is actually going up to London to see his solicitor with the very purpose of getting his will altered. What more natural than that his daughter should run up with him? We'll have her slightly injured in the accident: that'll prevent her reaching London for as many chapters as we need. And the hero can be on the same train. He can behave with great coolness and heroism during the accident—probably he'll rescue the heroine from a burning carriage. That settles my fourth point. And the young prig B? We'll make him the signalman whose negligence caused the accident. That gives him his moral shock and also links him up with the main plot. In fact, once we have thought of the railway accident, that single event will solve six apparently separate problems.

No doubt this is in some ways an intolerably misleading image: firstly because (except as regards the prig B.) I have been thinking not of the ultimate good of my characters but of the entertainment of my readers: secondly because we are simply ignoring the effect of the railway accident on all the other passengers in that train: and finally because it is I who make B. give the wrong signal. That is, though I pretend that he has free will, he really hasn't. In spite of these objections, however, the example may perhaps suggest how Divine ingenuity could so contrive the physical "plot" of the universe as to provide a "providential" answer to the needs of innumerable creatures.

But some of these creatures have free will. It is at this point that we must begin to correct the admittedly false picture of Providence which we have hitherto been using. That picture, you will remember, was false because it represented God and Nature as inhabiting a common Time. But it is probable that Nature is not really in Time and almost certain that God is not. Time is probably (like perspective) the mode of our perception. There is therefore in reality no question of God's at one point in time (the moment of creation) adapting the material history of the universe in advance to free acts which you or I are to perform at a later point in Time. To Him all the physical events and all the human acts are present in an eternal Now. The liberation of finite wills and the creation of the whole material history of the universe (related to the acts of those wills in all the necessary complexity) is to Him a single operation. In this sense God did not create the universe long ago but creates it at this minute—at every minute.

Suppose I find a piece of paper on which a black wavy line is already drawn, I can now sit down and draw other lines (say in red) so shaped as to combine with the black line into a pattern. Let us now suppose that the original black line is conscious. But it is not conscious along its whole length at once—only of each point on that length in turn.

Its consciousness in fact is travelling along that line from left to right retaining point A only as a memory when it reaches B and unable until it has left B to become conscious of C. Let us also give this black line free will. It chooses the direction it goes in. The particular wavy shape of it is the shape it wills to have. But whereas it is aware of its own chosen shape only moment by moment and does not know at point D which way it will decide to turn at point F, I can see its shape as a whole and all at once. At every moment it will find my red lines waiting for it and adapted to it. Of course: because I, in composing the total red-and-black design have the whole course of the black line in view and take it into account. It is a matter not of impossibility but merely of designer's skill for me to devise red lines which at every point have a right relation not only to the black line but to one another so as to fill the whole paper with a satisfactory design.

In this model the black line represents a creature with free will, the red lines represent material events, and I represent God. The model would of course be more accurate if I were making the paper as well as the pattern and if there were hundreds of millions of black lines instead of one—but for the sake of simplicity we must keep it as it is.[1]

It will be seen that if the black line addressed prayers to me I might (if I chose) grant them. It prays that when it reaches point N it may find the red lines arranged around it in a certain shape. That shape may by the laws of design require to be balanced by other arrangements of red lines on quite different parts of the paper—some at the top or bottom so far away from the black line that it knows nothing about them: some so far to the left that they come before the beginning of the black line, some so far to the right that they come after its end. (The black line would call these parts of the paper, "The time before I was born," and, "The time after I'm dead.") But these other parts of the pattern demanded by that red shape which Black Line wants at N, do not prevent my granting its prayer. For his whole course has been visible to me from the moment I looked at the paper and his requirements at point N are among the things I took into account in deciding the total pattern.

Most of our prayers if fully analysed, ask either for a miracle or for events whose foundation will have to have been laid before I was born, indeed, laid when the universe began. But then to God (though not to me) I and the prayer I make in 1945 were just as much present at the creation of the world as they are now and will be a million years hence. God's creative act is timeless and timelessly adapted to the "free" elements within it: but this timeless adaptation meets our consciousness as a sequence of prayer and answer.

Two corollaries follow:

1. People often ask whether a given event (not a miracle) was really an answer to prayer or not. I think that if they analyse their thought they will find they are asking, "Did God bring it

---

[1] Admittedly all I have done is to turn the tables by making human volitions the constant and physical destiny the variable. This is as false as the opposite view; the point is that it is no falser. A subtler image of creation and freedom (or rather, creation of the free and the unfree in a single timeless act) would be the *almost* simultaneous mutual adaptation in the movements of two expert dancing partners.

about for a special purpose or would it have happened anyway as part of the natural course of events?" But this (like the old question, "Have you left off beating your wife?") makes either answer impossible. In the play, *Hamlet,* Ophelia climbs out on a branch overhanging a river: the branch breaks, she falls in and drowns. What would you reply if anyone asked, "Did Ophelia die because Shakespeare for poetic reasons wanted her to die at that moment —or because the branch broke?" I think one would have to say, "For both reasons." Every event in the play happens as a result of other events in the play, but also every event happens because the poet wants it to happen. All events in the play are Shakespearian events; similarly all events in the real world are providential events. All events in the play, however, come about (or ought to come about) by the dramatic logic of events. Similarly all events in the real world (except miracles) come about by natural causes. "Providence" and Natural causation are not alternatives; both determine every event because both are one.

2. When we are praying about the result, say, of a battle or a medical consultation the thought will often cross our minds that (if only we knew it) the event is already decided one way or the other. I believe this to be no good reason for ceasing our prayers. The event certainly has been decided—in a sense it was decided "before all worlds." But one of the things taken into account in deciding it, and therefore one of the things that really cause it to happen, may be this very prayer that we are now offering. Thus, shocking as it may sound, I conclude that we can at noon become part causes of an event occurring at ten o'clock. (Some scientists would find this easier than popular thought does.) The imagination will, no doubt, try to play all sorts of tricks on us at this point. It will ask, "Then if I stop praying can God go back and alter what has already happened?" No. The event has already happened and one of its causes has been the fact that you are asking such questions instead of praying. It will ask, "Then if I begin to pray can God go back and alter what has already happened?" No. The event has already happened and one of its causes is your present prayer. Thus something does really depend on my choice. My free act contributes

to the cosmic shape. That contribution is made in eternity or "before all worlds"; but my consciousness of contributing reaches me at a particular point in the time-series.

The following question may be asked: If we can reasonably pray for an event which must in fact have happened or failed to happen several hours ago, why can we not pray for an event which we know *not* to have happened? e.g. pray for the safety of someone who, as we know, was killed yesterday. What makes the difference is precisely our knowledge. The known event states God's will. It is psychologically impossible to pray for what we know to be unobtainable; and if it were possible the prayer would sin against the duty of submission to God's known will.

One more consequence remains to be drawn. It is never possible to prove empirically that a given, non-miraculous event was or was not an answer to prayer. Since it was non-miraculous the sceptic can always point to its natural causes and say, "Because of these it would have happened anyway," and the believer can always reply, "But because these were only links in a chain of events, hanging on other links, and the whole chain hanging upon God's will, they may have occurred because someone prayed." The efficacy of prayer, therefore, cannot be either asserted or denied without an exercise of the will—the will choosing or rejecting faith in the light of a whole philosophy. Experimental evidence there can be none on either side. In the sequence M.N.O. event N, unless it is a miracle, is always caused by M and causes O; but the real question is whether the total series (say A—Z) does or does not originate in a will that can take human prayers into account.

This impossibility of empirical proof is a spiritual necessity. A man who knew empirically that an event had been caused by his prayer would feel like a magician. His head would turn and his heart would be corrupted. The Christian is not to ask whether this or that event happened because of a prayer. He is rather to believe that all events without exception are *answers* to prayer in the sense that whether they are grantings or refusals the prayers of all concerned and their needs have all been taken into account. All prayers are heard, though not all prayers are granted. We must not picture destiny as a film unrolling for the most part on its own, but in which our prayers are sometimes allowed to insert additional items. On the contrary; what the film displays to us as it unrolls already contains the results of our prayers and of all our other acts. There is no question *whether* an event has happened because of your prayer. When the event you prayed for occurs your prayer has always contributed to it. When the opposite event occurs your prayer has never been ignored; it has been considered and refused, for your ultimate good and the good of the whole universe. (For example, because it is better for you and for everyone else in the long run that other people, including wicked ones, should exercise free will than that you should be protected from cruelty or treachery by turning the human race into automata.) But this is, and must remain, a matter of faith. You will, I think, only deceive yourself by trying to find special evidence for it in some cases more than in others.

INDEX

THE CASE FOR CHRISTIANITY

Reprinted from Mere Christianity

by

C. S. Lewis

FELLOW OF MAGDALEN COLLEGE, OXFORD

THE MACMILLAN COMPANY, NEW YORK

Preface

The contents of this book were first given on the air, and then published in three separate parts as *The Case for Christianity* (1943),* *Christian Behaviour* (1943), and *Beyond Personality* (1945). In the printed versions I made a few additions to what I had said at the microphone, but otherwise left the text much as it had been. A "talk" on the radio should, I think, be as like real talk as possible, and should not sound like an essay being read aloud. In my talks I had therefore used all the contractions and colloquialisms I ordinarily use in conversation. In the printed version I reproduced this, putting *don't* and *we've* for *do not* and *we have*. And wherever, in the talks, I had made the importance of a word clear by the emphasis of my voice, I printed it in italics. I am now inclined to think that this was a mistake—an undesirable hybrid between the art of speaking and the art of writing. A talker ought to use variations of voice for emphasis because his medium naturally lends itself to that method: but a writer ought

* Published in England under the title *Broadcast Talks*.

389

not to use italics for the same purpose. He has his own, different, means of bringing out the key words and ought to use them. In this edition I have expanded the contractions and replaced most of the italics by recasting the sentences in which they occurred: but without altering, I hope, the "popular" or "familiar" tone which I had all along intended. I have also added and deleted where I thought I understood any part of my subject better now than ten years ago or where I knew that the original version had been misunderstood by others.

The reader should be warned that I offer no help to anyone who is hesitating between two Christian "denominations." You will not learn from me whether you ought to become an Anglican, a Methodist, a Presbyterian, or a Roman Catholic. This omission is intentional (even in the list I have just given the order is alphabetical). There is no mystery about my own position. I am a very ordinary layman of the Church of England, not especially "high," nor especially "low," nor especially anything else. But in this book I am not trying to convert anyone to my own position. Ever since I became a Christian I have thought that the best, perhaps the only, service I could do for my unbelieving neighbours was to explain and defend the belief that has been common to nearly all Christians at all times. I had more than one reason for thinking this. In the first place, the questions which divide Christians from one another often involve points of high Theology or even of ecclesiastical history which ought never to be treated except by real experts. I should have been out of my depth in such waters: more in need of help myself than able to help others. And secondly, I think we must admit that the discussion of these disputed points has no tendency at all to bring an outsider into the Christian fold. So long as we write and talk about them we are much more likely to deter him from entering any Christian communion than to draw him into our own. Our divisions should never be discussed except in the presence of those who have already come to believe that there is one God and that Jesus Christ is His only Son. Finally, I got the impression that far more, and more talented, authors were already engaged in such controversial matters than in the defence of what Baxter calls "mere" Christianity. That part of the line where I thought

I could serve best was also the part that seemed to be thinnest. And to it I naturally went.

So far as I know, these were my only motives, and I should be very glad if people would not draw fanciful inferences from my silence on certain disputed matters.

For example, such silence need not mean that I myself am sitting on the fence. Sometimes I am. There are questions at issue between Christians to which I do not think I have the answer. There are some to which I may never know the answer: if I asked them, even in a better world, I might (for all I know) be answered as a far greater questioner was answered: "What is that to thee? Follow thou Me." But there are other questions as to which I am definitely on one side of the fence, and yet say nothing. For I was not writing to expound something I could call "my religion," but to expound "mere" Christianity, which is what it is and was what it was long before I was born and whether I like it or not.

Some people draw unwarranted conclusions from the fact that I never say more about the Blessed Virgin Mary than is involved in asserting the Virgin Birth of Christ. But surely my reason for not doing so is obvious? To say more would take me at once into highly controversial regions. And there is no controversy between Christians which needs to be so delicately touched as this. The Roman Catholic beliefs on that subject are held not only with the ordinary fervour that attaches to all sincere religious belief, but (very naturally) with the peculiar and, as it were, chivalrous sensibility that a man feels when the honour of his mother or his beloved is at stake. It is very difficult so to dissent from them that you will not appear to them a cad as well as a heretic. And contrariwise, the opposed Protestant beliefs on this subject call forth feelings which go down to the very roots of all Monotheism whatever. To radical Protestants it seems that the distinction between Creator and creature (however holy) is imperilled: that Polytheism is risen again. Hence it is hard so to dissent from them that you will not appear something worse than a heretic—an idolator, a Pagan. If any topic could be relied upon to wreck a book about "mere" Christianity—if any topic makes utterly unprofitable reading for those who do not yet believe that the Virgin's son is God—surely this is it.

Oddly enough, you cannot even conclude, from my silence on disputed points, either that I think them important or that I think them unimportant. For this is itself one of the disputed points. One of the things Christians are disagreed about is the importance of their disagreements. When two Christians of different denominations start arguing, it is usually not long before one asks whether such-and-such a point "really matters" and the other replies: "Matter? Why, it's absolutely essential."

All this is said simply in order to make clear what kind of book I was trying to write; not in the least to conceal or evade responsibility for my own beliefs. About those, as I said before, there is no secret. To quote Uncle Toby: "They are written in the Common-Prayer Book."

The danger clearly was that I should put forward as common Christianity anything that was peculiar to the Church of England or (worse still) to myself. I tried to guard against this by sending the original script of what is now Book II to four clergymen (Anglican, Methodist, Presbyterian, Roman Catholic) and asking for their criticism. The Methodist thought I had not said enough about Faith, and the Roman Catholic thought I had gone rather too far about the comparative unimportance of theories in explanation of the Atonement. Otherwise all five of us were agreed. I did not have the remaining books similarly "vetted" because in them, though differences might arise among Christians, these would be differences between individuals or schools of thought, not between denominations.

So far as I can judge from reviews and from the numerous letters written to me, the book, however faulty in other respects, did at least succeed in presenting an agreed, or common, or central, or "mere" Christianity. In that way it may possibly be of some help in silencing the view that, if we omit the disputed points, we shall have left only a vague and bloodless H.C.F. The H.C.F. turns out to be something not only positive but pungent; divided from all non-Christian beliefs by a chasm to which the worst divisions inside Christendom are not really comparable at all. If I have not directly helped the cause of reunion, I have perhaps made it clear why we ought to be reunited. Certainly I have met with little of the fabled *odium theologicum* from convinced members of communions different from my own. Hostility has come more from borderline people whether within the Church of England or without it: men not exactly obedient to any communion. This I find curiously consoling. It is at her centre, where her truest children dwell, that each communion is really closest to every other in spirit, if not in doctrine. And this suggests that at the centre of each there is something, or a Someone, who against all divergences of belief, all differences of temperament, all memories of mutual persecution, speaks with the same voice.

So much for my omissions on doctrine. In Book III, which deals with morals, I have also passed over some things in silence, but for a different reason. Ever since I served as an infantryman in the first world war I have had a great dislike of people who, themselves in ease and safety, issue exhortations to men in the front line. As a result I have a reluctance to say much about temptations to which I myself am not exposed. No man, I suppose, is tempted to every sin. It so happens that the impulse which makes men gamble has been left out of my make-up; and, no doubt, I pay for this by lacking some good impulse of which it is the excess or perversion. I therefore did not feel myself qualified to give advice about permissable and impermissable gambling: if there is any permissable, for I do not claim to know even that. I have also said nothing about birth-control. I am not a woman nor even a married man, nor am I a priest. I did not think it my place to take a firm line about pains, dangers and expenses from which I am protected; having no pastoral office which obliged me to do so.

Far deeper objections may be felt—and have been expressed—against my use of the word *Christian* to mean one who accepts the common doctrines of Christianity. People ask: "Who are you, to lay down who is, and who is not a Christian?" or "May not many a man who cannot believe these doctrines be far more truly a Christian, far closer to the spirit of Christ, than some who do?" Now this objection is in one sense very right, very charitable, very spiritual, very sensitive. It has every amiable quality except that of being useful. We simply cannot, without disaster, use language as these objectors want us to use it. I will try to make this clear by the history of another, and very much less important, word.

The word *gentleman* originally meant something recognisable; one who had a coat of arms and some landed property. When you called someone "a gentleman" you were not paying him a compliment, but merely stating a fact. If you said he was not "a gentleman" you were not insulting him, but giving information. There was no contradiction in saying that John was a liar and a gentleman; any more than there now is in saying that James is a fool and an M.A. But then there came people who said—so rigidly, charitably, spiritually, sensitively, so anything but usefully—"Ah, but surely the important thing about a gentleman is not the coat of arms and the land, but the behaviour? Surely he is the true gentleman who behaves as a gentleman should? Surely in that sense Edward is far more truly a gentleman than John?" They meant well. To be honourable and courteous and brave is of course a far better thing than to have a coat of arms. But it is not the same thing. Worse still, it is not a thing everyone will agree about. To call a man "a gentleman" in this new, refined sense, becomes, in fact, not a way of giving information about him, but a way of praising him: to deny that he is "a gentleman" becomes simply a way of insulting him. When a word ceases to be a term of description and becomes merely a term of praise, it no longer tells you facts about the object: it only tells you about the speaker's attitude to that object. (A "nice" meal only means a meal the speaker likes.) A *gentleman,* once it has been spiritualised and refined out of its old coarse, objective sense, means hardly more than a man whom the speaker likes. As a result, *gentleman* is now a useless word. We had lots of terms of approval already, so it was not needed for that use; on the other hand if anyone (say, in a historical work) wants to use it in its old sense, he cannot do so without explanations. It has been spoiled for that purpose.

Now if once we allow people to start spiritualising and refining, or as they might say "deepening," the sense of the word *Christian,* it too will speedily become a useless word. In the first place, Christians themselves will never be able to apply it to anyone. It is not for us to say who, in the deepest sense, is or is not close to the spirit of Christ. We do not see into men's hearts. We cannot judge, and are indeed forbidden to judge. It would be wicked arrogance for us to say that any man is, or is not, a Christian in this refined sense. And obviously a word which we can never apply is not going to be a very useful word. As for the unbelievers, they will no doubt cheerfully use the word in the refined sense. It will become in their mouths simply a term of praise. In calling anyone a Christian they will mean that they think him a good man. But that way of using the word will be no enrichment of the language, for we already have the word *good*. Meanwhile, the word *Christian* will have been spoiled for any really useful purpose it might have served.

We must therefore stick to the original, obvious meaning. The name *Christians* was first given at Antioch (Acts xi. 26) to "the disciples," to those who accepted the teaching of the apostles. There is no question of its being restricted to those who profited by that teaching as much as they should have. There is no question of its being extended to those who in some refined, spiritual, inward fashion were "far closer to the spirit of Christ" than the less satisfactory of the disciples. The point is not a theological, or moral one. It is only a question of using words so that we can all understand what is being said. When a man who accepts the Christian doctrine lives unworthily of it, it is much clearer to say he is a bad Christian than to say he is not a Christian.

I hope no reader will suppose that "mere" Christianity is here put forward as an alternative to the creeds of the existing communions—as if a man could adopt it in preference to Congregationalism or Greek Orthodoxy or anything else. It is more like a hall out of which doors open into several rooms. If I can bring anyone into that hall I shall have done what I attempted. But it is in the rooms, not in the hall, that there are fires and chairs and meals. The hall is a place to wait in, a place from which to try the various doors, not a place to live in. For that purpose the worst of the rooms (whichever that may be) is, I think, preferable. It is true that some people may find they have to wait in the hall for a considerable time, while others feel certain almost at once which door they must knock at. I do not know why there is this difference, but I am sure God keeps no one waiting unless

He sees that it is good for him to wait. When you do get into your room you will find that the long wait has done you some kind of good which you would not have had otherwise. But you must regard it as waiting, not a camping. You must keep on praying for light: and, of course, even in the hall, you must begin trying to obey the rules which are common to the whole house. And above all you must be asking which door is the true one; not which pleases you best by its paint and panelling. In plain language, the question should never be: "Do I like that kind of service?" but "Are these doctrines true: Is holiness here? Does my conscience move me towards this? Is my reluctance to knock at this door due to my pride, or my mere taste, or my personal dislike of this particular door-keeper?"

When you have reached your own room, be kind to those who have chosen different doors and to those who are still in the hall. If they are wrong they need your prayers all the more; and if they are your enemies, then you are under orders to pray for them. That is one of the rules common to the whole house.

Contents

RIGHT AND WRONG AS A CLUE TO THE MEANING OF THE UNIVERSE

I.

THE LAW OF HUMAN NATURE

Every one has heard people quarrelling. Sometimes it sounds funny and sometimes it sounds merely unpleasant but however it sounds, I believe we can learn something very important from listening to the kind of things they say. They say things like this: "How'd you like it if anyone did the same to you?"—"That's my seat, I was there first"—"Leave him alone, he isn't doing you any harm"—"Why should you shove in first"—"Give me a bit of your orange, I gave you a bit of mine"—"Come on, you promised." People say things like that every day, educated people as well as uneducated, and children as well as grown-ups.

Now what interests me about all these remarks is that the man who makes them is not merely saying that the other man's behaviour does not happen to please him. He is appealing to some kind of standard of behaviour which he expects the other man to know about. And the other man very seldom replies: "To hell with your standard." Nearly always he tries to make out that what he has been doing does not really go against the standard, or that if it does there is some special excuse. He pretends there is some special reason in this particular case why the person who took the seat first should not keep it, or that things were quite different when he was given the bit of orange, or that something has turned up which lets him off keeping his promise. It looks, in fact, very much as if both parties had in mind some kind of Law or Rule of fair play or decent behaviour or morality or whatever you like to call it, about which they really agreed. And they have. If they had not, they might, of course, fight like animals, but they could not *quarrel* in the human sense of the word. Quarrelling means trying to show that the other man is in the wrong. And there would be no sense in trying to do that unless you and he had some sort of agreement as to what Right and Wrong are; just as there would be no sense in saying that a footballer had committed a foul unless there was some agreement about the rules of football.

Now this Law or Rule about Right and Wrong used to be called the Law of Nature. Nowadays, when we talk of the "laws of nature" we usually mean things like gravitation, or heredity, or the laws of chemistry. But when the older thinkers called the Law of Right and Wrong "the Law of Nature," they really meant the Law of *Human* Nature. The idea was that, just as all bodies are governed by the law of gravitation and organisms by biological laws, so the creature called man also had *his* law— with this great difference, that a body could not choose whether it obeyed the law of gravitation or not, but a man could choose either to obey the Law of Human Nature or to disobey it.

We may put this in another way. Each man is at every moment subjected to several different sets of law but there is only one of these which he is free to disobey. As a body, he is subjected to gravitation and cannot disobey it; if you leave him unsupported in mid-air, he has no more choice about falling than a stone has. As an organism, he is subjected to various biological laws which he cannot disobey any more than an animal can. That is, he cannot disobey those laws which he shares with other things; but the law which is peculiar to his human nature, the law he does not share with animals or vegetables or inorganic things, is the one he can disobey if he chooses.

This law was called the Law of Nature because people thought that every one knew it by nature and did not need to be taught it. They did not mean, of course, that you might not find an odd individual here and there who did not know it, just as you find a few people who are colour-blind or have no ear for a tune. But taking the race as a whole, they thought that the human idea of decent behaviour was obvious to every one. And I believe they were right. If they were not, then all the things we said about the war were nonsense. What was the sense in saying the enemy were in the wrong unless Right is a real thing which the Nazis at bottom knew as well as we did and ought to have practised? If they had had no notion of what we mean by right, then, though we might still have had to fight them, we could no more have blamed them for that than for the colour of their hair.

I know that some people say the idea of a Law of Nature or decent behaviour known to all men is unsound, because different civilisations and different ages have had quite different moralities.

But this is not true. There have been differences between their moralities, but these have never amounted to anything like a total difference. If anyone will take the trouble to compare the moral teaching of, say, the ancient Egyptians, Babylonians, Hindus, Chinese, Greeks and Romans, what will really strike him will be how very like they are to each other and to our own. Some of the evidence for this I have put together in the appendix of another book called *The Abolition of Man;* but for our present purpose I need only ask the reader to think what a totally different morality would mean. Think of a country where people were admired for running away in battle, or where a man felt proud of double-crossing all the people who had been kindest to him. You might just as well try to imagine a country where two and two made five. Men have differed as regards what people you ought to be unselfish to—whether it was only your own family, or your fellow countrymen, or everyone. But they have always agreed that you ought not to put yourself first. Selfishness has never been admired. Men have differed as to whether you should have one wife or four. But they have always agreed that you must not simply have any woman you liked.

But the most remarkable thing is this. Whenever you find a man who says he does not believe in a real Right and Wrong, you will find the same man going back on this a moment later. He may break his promise to you, but if you try breaking one to him he will be complaining "It's not fair" before you can say Jack Robinson. A nation may say treaties do not matter; but then, next minute, they spoil their case by saying that the particular treaty they want to break was an unfair one. But if treaties do not matter, and if there is no such thing as Right and Wrong—in other words, if there is no Law of Nature—what is the difference between a fair treaty and an unfair one? Have they not let the cat out of the bag and shown that, whatever they say, they really know the Law of Nature just like anyone else?

It seems, then, we are forced to believe in a real Right and Wrong. People may be sometimes mistaken about them, just as people sometimes get their sums wrong; but they are not a matter of mere taste and opinion any more than the multiplication table. Now if we are agreed about that, I go on to my next point, which is this. None of us are really keeping the Law of Nature. If there are any exceptions among you, I apologise to them. They had much better read some other work, for nothing I am going to say concerns them. And now, turning to the ordinary human beings who are left:

I hope you will not misunderstand what I am going to say. I am not preaching, and Heaven knows I do not pretend to be better than anyone else. I am only trying to call attention to a fact; the fact that this year, or this month, or, more likely, this very day, we have failed to practise ourselves the kind of behaviour we expect from other people. There may be all sorts of excuses for us. That time you were so unfair to the children was when you were very tired. That slightly shady business about the money—the one you have almost forgotten—came when you were very hard up. And what you promised to do for old So-and-so and have never done—well, you never would have promised if you had known how frightfully busy you were going to be. And as for your behaviour to your wife (or husband) or sister (or brother) if I knew how irritating they could be, I would not wonder at it—and who the dickens am I, anyway? I am just the same. That is to say, I do not succeed in keeping the Law of Nature very well, and the moment anyone tells me I am not keeping it, there starts up in my mind a string of excuses as long as your arm. The question at the moment is not whether they are good excuses. The point is that they are one more proof of how deeply, whether we like it or not, we believe in the Law of Nature. If we do not believe in decent behaviour, why should we be so anxious to make excuses for not having behaved decently? The truth is, we believe in decency so much—we feel the Rule or Law pressing on us so—that we cannot bear to face the fact that we are breaking it, and consequently we try to shift the responsibility. For you notice that it is only for our bad behaviour that we find all these explanations. It is only our bad temper that we put down to being tired or worried or hungry; we put our good temper down to ourselves.

These, then, are the two points I wanted to make. First, that human beings, all over the earth, have this curious idea that they ought to behave in a certain way, and cannot really get rid of it. Secondly, that they do not in fact behave in that way. They know the Law of Nature; they break it. These two facts are the foundation of all clear thinking about ourselves and the universe we live in.

2.

SOME OBJECTIONS

If they are the foundation, I had better stop to make that foundation firm before I go on. Some of the letters I have had show that a good many people find it difficult to understand just what this Law of Human Nature, or Moral Law, or Rule of Decent Behaviour is.

For example, some people wrote to me saying, "Isn't what you call the Moral Law simply our herd instinct and hasn't it been developed just like all our other instincts?" Now I do not deny that we may have a herd instinct: but that is not what I mean by the Moral Law. We all know what it feels like to be prompted by instinct—by mother love, or sexual instinct, or the instinct for food. It means that you feel a strong want or desire to act in a certain way. And, of course, we sometimes do feel just that sort of desire to help another person: and no doubt that desire is due to the herd instinct. But feeling a desire to help is quite different from feeling that you ought to help whether you want to or not. Supposing you hear a cry for help from a man in danger. You will probably feel two desires—one a desire to give help (due to your herd instinct), the other a desire to keep out of danger (due to the instinct for self-preservation). But you will find inside you, in addition to these two impulses, a third thing which tells you that you ought to follow the impulse to help, and suppress the impulse to run away. Now this thing that judges between two instincts, that decides which should be encouraged, cannot itself be either of them. You might as well say that the sheet of music which tells you, at a given moment, to play one note on the piano and not another, is itself one of the notes on the keyboard. The Moral Law tells us the tune we have to play: our instincts are merely the keys.

Another way of seeing that the Moral Law is not simply one of our instincts is this. If two instincts are in conflict, and there is nothing in a creature's mind except those two instincts, obviously the stronger of the two must win. But at those moments when we are most conscious of the Moral Law, it usually seems to be telling us to side with the weaker of the two impulses. You probably *want* to be safe much more than you want to help the man who is drowning: but the Moral Law tells you to help him all the same. And surely it often tells us to try to make the right impulse stronger than it naturally is? I mean, we often feel it our duty to stimulate the herd instinct, by waking up our imaginations and arousing our pity and so on, so as to get up enough steam for doing the right thing. But clearly we are not acting *from* instinct when we set about making an instinct stronger than it is. The thing that says to you, "Your herd instinct is asleep. Wake it up," cannot itself *be* the herd instinct. The thing that tells you which note on the piano needs to be played louder cannot itself be that note.

Here is a third way of seeing it. If the Moral Law was one of our instincts, we ought to be able to point to some one impulse inside us which was always what we call "good," always in agreement with the rule of right behaviour. But you cannot. There is none of our impulses which the Moral Law may not sometimes tell us to suppress, and none which it may not sometimes tell us to encourage. It is a mistake to think that some of our impulses— say mother love or patriotism—are good, and others, like sex or the fighting instinct, are bad. All we mean is that the occasions on which the fighting instinct or the sexual desire need to be restrained are rather more frequent than those for restraining mother love or patriotism. But there are situations in which it is the duty of a married man to encourage his sexual impulse and of a soldier to encourage the fighting instinct. There are also occasions on which a mother's love for her own children or a man's love for his own country have to be suppressed or they will lead to unfairness towards other people's children or countries.

Strictly speaking, there are no such things as good and bad impulses. Think once again of a piano. It has not got two kinds of notes on it, the "right" notes and the "wrong" ones. Every single note is right at one time and wrong at another. The Moral Law is not any one instinct or any set of instincts: it is something which makes a kind of tune (the tune we call goodness or right conduct) by directing the instincts.

By the way, this point is of great practical consequence. The most dangerous thing you can do is to take any one impulse of your own nature and set it up as the thing you ought to follow at all costs. There is not one of them which will not make us into devils if we set it up as an absolute guide. You might think love of humanity in general was safe, but it is not. If you leave out justice you will find yourself breaking agreements and faking evidence in trials "for the sake of humanity," and become in the end a cruel and treacherous man.

Other people wrote to me saying, "Isn't what you call the Moral Law just a social convention, something that is put into us by education?" I think there is a misunderstanding here. The people who ask that question are usually taking it for granted that if we have learned a thing from parents and teachers, then that thing must be merely a human invention. But, of course, this is not so. We all learned the multiplication table at school. A child who grew up alone on a desert island would not know it. But surely it does not follow that the multiplication table is simply a human convention, something human beings have made up for themselves and might have made different if they had liked? I fully agree that we learn the Rule of Decent Behaviour from parents and teachers, and friends and books, as we learn everything else. But some of the things we learn are mere conventions which might have been different—we learn to keep to the left of the road, but it might just as well have been the rule to keep to the right—and others of them, like mathematics, are real truths. The question is to which class the Law of Human Nature belongs.

There are two reasons for saying it belongs to the same class as mathematics. The first is, as I said in the first chapter, that though there are differences between the moral ideas of one time or country and those of another, the differences are not really very great—not nearly so great as most people imagine—and you can recognise the same law running through them all: whereas mere conventions, like the rule of the road or the kind of clothes people wear, may differ to any extent. The other reason is this. When you think about these differences between the morality of one people and another, do you think that the morality of one people is ever better or worse than that of another? Have any of the changes been improvements? If not, then of course there could never be any moral progress. Progress means not just changing, but changing for the better. If no set of moral ideas were truer or better than any other, there would be no sense in preferring civilised morality to savage morality, or Christian morality to Nazi morality. In fact, of course, we all do believe that some moralities are better than others. We do believe that some of the people who tried to change the moral ideas of their own age were what we would call Reformers or Pioneers—people who understood morality better than their neighbours did. Very well then. The moment you say that one set of moral ideas can be better than another, you are, in fact, measuring them both by a standard, saying that one of them conforms to that standard more nearly than the other. But the standard that measures two things is something different from either. You are, in fact, comparing them both with some Real Morality, admitting that there is such a thing as a real Right, independent of what people think, and that some people's ideas get nearer to that real Right than others. Or put it this way. If your moral ideas can be truer, and those of the Nazis less true, there must be something—some Real Morality—for them to be true about. The reason why your idea of New York can be truer or less true than mine is that New York is a real place, existing quite apart from what either of us thinks. If when each of us said "New York" each meant merely "The town I am imagining in my own head," how could one of us have truer ideas than the other? There would be no question of truth or falsehood at all. In the same way, if the Rule of Decent Behaviour meant simply "whatever each nation happens to approve," there would be no sense in saying that any one nation had ever been more correct in its approval than any other; no sense in saying that the world could ever grow morally better or morally worse.

I conclude then, that though the differences between people's ideas of Decent Behaviour often make you suspect that there is no real natural Law of Behaviour at all, yet the things we are bound to think about these differences really prove just the opposite. But one word before I end. I have met people who exaggerate the differences, because they have not distinguished between differences of morality and differences of belief about facts. For example, one man said to me, "Three hundred years ago people in England were putting witches to death. Was that what you call the Rule of Human Nature or Right Conduct?" But surely the reason we do not execute witches is that we do not believe there are such things. If we did—if we really thought that there were people going about who had sold themselves to the devil and received supernatural powers from him in return and were using these powers to kill their neighbours or drive them mad or bring bad weather, surely we would all agree that if anyone deserved the death penalty, then these filthy quislings did. There is no difference of moral principle here: the difference is simply about matter of fact. It may be a great advance in knowledge not to believe in witches: there is no moral advance in not executing them when you do not think they are there. You would not call a man humane for ceasing to set mousetraps if he did so because he believed there were no mice in the house.

3.

THE REALITY OF THE LAW

I now go back to what I said at the end of the first chapter, that there were two odd things about the human race. First, that they were haunted by the idea of a sort of behaviour they ought to practise, what you might call fair play, or decency, or morality, or the Law of Nature. Second, that they did not in fact do so. Now some of you may wonder why I called this odd. It may seem to you the most natural thing in the world. In particular, you may have thought I was rather hard on the human race. After all, you may say, what I call breaking the Law of Right and Wrong or of Nature, only means that people are not perfect. And why on earth should I expect them to be? That would be a good answer if what I was trying to do was to fix the exact amount of blame which is due to us for not behaving as we expect others to behave. But that is not my job at all. I am not concerned at present with blame; I am trying to find out truth. And from that point of view the very idea of something being imperfect, of its not being what it ought to be, has certain consequences.

If you take a thing like a stone or a tree, it is what it is and there seems no sense in saying it ought to have been otherwise. Of course you may say a stone is "the wrong shape" if you want to use it for a rockery, or that a tree is a bad tree because it does not give you as much shade as you expected. But all you mean is that the stone or tree does not happen to be convenient for some purpose of your own. You are not, except as a joke, blaming them for that. You really know, that, given the weather and the soil, the tree could not have been any different. What we, from our point of view, call a "bad" tree is obeying the laws of its nature just as much as a "good" one.

Now have you noticed what follows? It follows that what we usually call the laws of nature—the way weather works on a tree for example—may not really be *laws* in the strict sense, but only in a manner of speaking. When you say that falling stones always obey the law of gravitation, is not this much the same as saying that the law only means "what stones always do?" You do not really think that when a stone is let go, it suddenly remembers that it is under orders to fall to the ground. You only mean that, in fact, it does fall. In other words, you cannot be sure that there is anything over and above the facts themselves, any law about what ought to happen, as distinct from what does happen. The laws of nature, as applied to stones or trees, may only mean "what Nature, in fact, does." But if you turn to the Law of Human Nature, the Law of Decent Behaviour, it is a different matter. That law certainly does not mean "what human beings, in fact, do"; for as I said before, many of them do not obey this law at all, and none of them obey it completely. The law of gravity tells you what stones do if you drop them; but the Law of Human Nature tells you what human beings ought to do and do not. In other words, when you are dealing with humans, something else comes in above and beyond the actual facts. You have the facts (how men do behave) and you also have something else (how they ought to behave). In the rest of the universe there need not be anything but the facts. Electrons and molecules behave in a certain way, and certain results follow, and that may be the whole story.* But men behave in a certain way and that is not the whole story, for all the time you know that they ought to behave differently.

Now this is really so peculiar that one is tempted to try to explain it away. For instance, we might try to make out that when you say a man ought not to act as he does, you only mean the same as when you say that a stone is the wrong shape; namely, that what he is doing happens to be inconvenient to you. But that is simply untrue. A man occupying the corner seat in the

---

* I do not think it *is* the whole story, as you will see later. I mean that, as far as the argument has gone up to date, it *may* be.

train because he got there first, and a man who slipped into it while my back was turned and removed my bag, are both equally inconvenient. But I blame the second man and do not blame the first. I am not angry—except perhaps for a moment before I come to my senses—with a man who trips me up by accident; I am angry with a man who tries to trip me up even if he does not succeed. Yet the first has hurt me and the second has not. Sometimes the behaviour which I call bad is not inconvenient to me at all, but the very opposite. In war, each side may find a traitor on the other side very useful. But though they use him and pay him they regard him as human vermin. So you cannot say that what we call decent behaviour in others is simply the behaviour that happens to be useful to us. And as for decent behaviour in ourselves, I suppose it is pretty obvious that it does not mean the behaviour that pays. It means things like being content with thirty shillings when you might have got three pounds, doing school work honestly when it would be easy to cheat, leaving a girl alone when you would like to make love to her, staying in dangerous places when you could go somewhere safer, keeping promises you would rather not keep, and telling the truth even when it makes you look a fool.

Some people say that though decent conduct does not mean what pays each particular person at a particular moment, still, it means what pays the human race as a whole; and that consequently there is no mystery about it. Human beings, after all, have some sense; they see that you cannot have real safety or happiness except in a society where every one plays fair, and it is because they see this that they try to behave decently. Now, of course, it is perfectly true that safety and happiness can only come from individuals, classes, and nations being honest and fair and kind to each other. It is one of the most important truths in the world. But as an explanation of why we feel as we do about Right and Wrong it just misses the point. If we ask: "Why ought I to be unselfish?" and you reply "Because it is good for society," we may then ask, "Why should I care what's good for society except when it happens to pay *me* personally?" and then you will have to say, "Because you ought to be unselfish"— which simply brings us back to where we started. You are saying what is true, but you are not getting any further. If a man asked what was the point of playing football, it would not be much good saying "in order to score goals," for trying to score goals is the game itself, not the reason for the game, and you would really only be saying that football was football—which is true, but not worth saying. In the same way, if a man asks what is the point of behaving decently, it is no good replying, "in order to benefit society," for trying to benefit society, in other words being unselfish (for "society" after all only means "other people"), is one of the things decent behaviour consists in; all you are really saying is that decent behaviour is decent behaviour. You would have said just as much if you had stopped at the statement, "Men ought to be unselfish."

And that is where I do stop. Men ought to be unselfish, ought to be fair. Not that men are unselfish, nor that they like being unselfish, but that they ought to be. The Moral Law, or Law of Human Nature, is not simply a fact about human behaviour in the same way as the Law of Gravitation is, or may be, simply a fact about how heavy objects behave. On the other hand it is not a mere fancy, for we cannot get rid of the idea, and most of the things we say and think about men would be reduced to nonsense if we did. And it is not simply a statement about how we should like men to behave for our own convenience; for the behaviour we call bad or unfair is not exactly the same as the behaviour we find inconvenient, and may even be the opposite. Consequently, this Rule of Right and Wrong, or Law of Human Nature, or whatever you call it, must somehow or other be a real thing—a thing that is really there, not made up by ourselves. And yet it is not a fact in the ordinary sense, in the same way as our actual behaviour is a fact. It begins to look as if we shall have to admit that there is more than one kind of reality; that, in this particular case, there is something above and beyond the ordinary facts of men's behaviour, and yet quite definitely real—a real law, which none of us made, but which we find pressing on us.

4.

WHAT LIES BEHIND THE LAW

Let us sum up what we have reached so far. In the case of stones and trees and things of that sort, what we call the Laws of Nature may not be anything except a way of speaking. When you say that nature is governed by certain laws, this may only mean that nature does, in fact, behave in a certain way. The so-called laws may not be anything real—anything above and beyond the actual facts which we observe. But in the case of Man, we saw that this will not do. The Law of Human Nature, or of Right and Wrong, must be something above and beyond the actual facts of human behaviour. In this case, besides the actual facts, you have something else—a real law which we did not invent and which we know we ought to obey.

I now want to consider what this tells us about the universe we live in. Ever since men were able to think, they have been wondering what this universe really is and how it came to be there. And, very roughly, two views have been held. First, there is what is called the materialist view. People who take that view think that matter and space just happen to exist, and always have existed, nobody knows why; and that the matter, behaving in certain fixed ways, has just happened, by a sort of fluke, to produce creatures like ourselves who are able to think. By one chance in a thousand something hit our sun and made it produce the planets; and by another thousandth chance the chemicals necessary for life, and the right temperature, occurred on one of these planets, and so some of the matter on this earth came alive; and then, by a very long series of chances, the living creatures developed into things like us. The other view is the reli-

gious view.* According to it, what is behind the universe is more
like a mind than it is like anything else we know. That is to say,
it is conscious, and has purposes, and prefers one thing to another. And on this view it made the universe, partly for purposes we do not know, but partly, at any rate, in order to produce
creatures like itself—I mean, like itself to the extent of having
minds. Please do not think that one of these views was held a
long time ago and that the other has gradually taken its place.
Wherever there have been thinking men both views turn up.
And note this too. You cannot find out which view is the right
one by science in the ordinary sense. Science works by experiments. It watches how things behave. Every scientific statement
in the long run, however complicated it looks, really means something like, "I pointed the telescope to such and such a part of the
sky at 2:20 A.M. on January 15th and saw so-and-so," or, "I put
some of this stuff in a pot and heated it to such-and-such a temperature and it did so-and-so." Do not think I am saying anything
against science: I am only saying what its job is. And the more
scientific a man is, the more (I believe) he would agree with
me that this is the job of science—and a very useful and necessary
job it is too. But why anything comes to be there at all, and
whether there is anything behind the things science observes—
something of a different kind—this is not a scientific question.
If there is "Something Behind," then either it will have to remain altogether unknown to men or else make itself known
in some different way. The statement that there is any such thing,
and the statement that there is no such thing, are neither of
them statements that science can make. And real scientists do not
usually make them. It is usually the journalists and popular
novelists who have picked up a few odds and ends of half-baked
science from textbooks who go in for them. After all, it is really
a matter of common sense. Supposing science ever became complete so that it knew every single thing in the whole universe. Is
it not plain that the questions, "Why is there a universe?" "Why
does it go on as it does?" "Has it any meaning?" would remain
just as they were?

Now the position would be quite hopeless but for this. There

* See Note at end of this chapter.

is one thing, and only one, in the whole universe which we know more about than we could learn from external observation. That one thing is Man. We do not merely observe men, we *are* men. In this case we have, so to speak, inside information; we are in the know. And because of that, we know that men find themselves under a moral law, which they did not make, and cannot quite forget even when they try, and which they know they ought to obey. Notice the following point. Anyone studying Man from the outside as we study electricity or cabbages, not knowing our language and consequently not able to get any inside knowledge from us, but merely observing what we did, would never get the slightest evidence that we had this moral law. How could he? for his observations would only show what we did, and the moral law is about what we ought to do. In the same way, if there were anything above or behind the observed facts in the case of stones or the weather, we, by studying them from outside, could never hope to discover it.

The position of the question, then, is like this. We want to know whether the universe simply happens to be what it is for no reason or whether there is a power behind it that makes it what it is. Since that power, if it exists, would be not one of the observed facts but a reality which makes them, no mere observation of the facts can find it. There is only one case in which we can know whether there is anything more, namely our own case. And in that one case we find there is. Or put it the other way round. If there was a controlling power outside the universe, it could not show itself to us as one of the facts inside the universe —no more than the architect of a house could actually be a wall or staircase or fireplace in that house. The only way in which we could expect it to show itself would be inside ourselves as an influence or a command trying to get us to behave in a certain way. And that is just what we do find inside ourselves. Surely this ought to arouse our suspicions? In the only case where you can expect to get an answer, the answer turns out to be Yes; and in the other cases, where you do not get an answer, you see why you do not. Suppose someone asked me, when I see a man in a blue uniform going down the street leaving little paper packets at each house, why I suppose that they contain letters? I should

reply, "Because whenever he leaves a similar little packet for me
I find it does contain a letter." And if he then objected, "But
you've never seen all these letters which you think the other people are getting," I should say, "Of course not, and I shouldn't
expect to, because they're not addressed to me. I'm explaining
the packets I'm not allowed to open by the ones I am allowed to
open." It is the same about this question. The only packet I am
allowed to open is Man. When I do, especially when I open that
particular man called Myself, I find that I do not exist on my
own, that I am under a law; that somebody or something wants
me to behave in a certain way. I do not, of course, think that if I
could get inside a stone or a tree I should find exactly the same
thing, just as I do not think all the other people in the street get
the same letters as I do. I should expect, for instance, to find that
the stone had to obey the law of gravity—that whereas the sender
of the letters merely tells me to obey the law of my human nature, He compels the stone to obey the laws of its stony nature.
But I should expect to find that there was, so to speak, a sender
of letters in both cases, a Power behind the facts, a Director, a
Guide.

Do not think I am going faster than I really am. I am not yet
within a hundred miles of the God of Christian theology. All I
have got to is a Something which is directing the universe, and
which appears in me as a law urging me to do right and making
me feel responsible and uncomfortable when I do wrong. I think
we have to assume it is more like a mind than it is like anything
else we know—because after all the only other thing we know is
matter and you can hardly imagine a bit of matter giving instruc-
tions. But, of course, it need not be very like a mind, still less like
a person. In the next chapter we shall see if we can find out
anything more about it. But one word of warning. There has
been a great deal of soft soap talked about God for the last hundred years. That is not what I am offering. You can cut all that
out.

·   ·   ·   ·   ·

NOTE.—In order to keep this section short enough when it
was given on the air, I mentioned only the Materialist view
and the Religious view. But to be complete I ought to mention

the In-between view called Life-Force philosophy, or Creative Evolution, or Emergent Evolution. The wittiest expositions of it come in the works of Bernard Shaw, but the most profound ones in those of Bergson. People who hold this view say that the small variations by which life on this planet "evolved" from the lowest forms to Man were not due to chance but to the "striving" or "purposiveness" of a Life-Force. When people say this we must ask them whether by Life-Force they mean something with a mind or not. If they do, then "a mind bringing life into existence and leading it to perfection" is really a God, and their view is thus identical with the Religious. If they do not, then what is the sense in saying that something without a mind "strives" or has "purposes"? This seems to me fatal to their view. One reason why many people find Creative Evolution so attractive is that it gives one much of the emotional comfort of believing in God and none of the less pleasant consequences. When you are feeling fit and the sun is shining and you do not want to believe that the whole universe is a mere mechanical dance of atoms, it is nice to be able to think of this great mysterious Force rolling on through the centuries and carrying you on its crest. If, on the other hand, you want to do something rather shabby, the Life-Force, being only a blind force, with no morals and no mind, will never interfere with you like that troublesome God we learned about when we were children. The Life-Force is a sort of tame God. You can switch it on when you want, but it will not bother you. All the thrills of religion and none of the cost. Is the Life-Force the greatest achievement of wishful thinking the world has yet seen?

5.

WE HAVE CAUSE TO BE UNEASY

I ended my last chapter with the idea that in the Moral Law somebody or something from beyond the material universe was actually getting at us. And I expect when I reached that point some of you felt a certain annoyance. You may even have thought that I had played a trick on you—that I had been carefully wrapping up to look like philosophy what turns out to be one more "religious jaw." You may have felt you were ready to listen to me as long as you thought I had anything new to say; but if it turns out to be only religion, well, the world has tried that and you cannot put the clock back. If anyone is feeling that way I should like to say three things to him.

First, as to putting the clock back. Would you think I was joking if I said that you can put a clock back, and that if the clock is wrong it is often a very sensible thing to do? But I would rather get away from that whole idea of clocks. We all want progress. But progress means getting nearer to the place where you want to be. And if you have taken a wrong turning, then to go forward does not get you any nearer. If you are on the wrong road, progress means doing an about-turn and walking back to the right road; and in that case the man who turns back soonest is the most progressive man. We have all seen this when doing arithmetic. When I have started a sum the wrong way, the sooner I admit this and go back and start over again, the faster I shall get on. There is nothing progressive about being pigheaded and refusing to admit a mistake. And I think if you look at the present state of the world, it is pretty plain that humanity has been making some big mistake. We are on the wrong road. And if that is so, we must go back. Going back is the quickest way on.

Then, secondly, this has not yet turned exactly into a "religious jaw." We have not yet got as far as the God of any actual religion, still less the God of that particular religion called Christianity. We have only got as far as a Somebody or Something behind the Moral Law. We are not taking anything from the Bible or the Churches, we are trying to see what we can find out about this Somebody on our own steam. And I want to make it quite clear that what we find out on our own steam is something that gives us a shock. We have two bits of evidence about the Somebody. One is the universe He has made. If we used that as our only clue, then I think we should have to conclude that He was a great artist (for the universe is a very beautiful place), but also that He is quite merciless and no friend to man (for the universe is a very dangerous and terrifying place). The other bit of evidence is that Moral Law which He has put into our minds. And this is a better bit of evidence than the other, because it is inside information. You find out more about God from the Moral Law than from the universe in general just as you find out more about a man by listening to his conversation than by looking at a house he has built. Now, from this second bit of evidence we conclude that the Being behind the universe is intensely interested in right conduct—in fair play, unselfishness, courage, good faith, honesty and truthfulness. In that sense we should agree with the account given by Christianity and some other religions, that God is "good." But do not let us go too fast here. The Moral Law does not give us any grounds for thinking that God is "good" in the sense of being indulgent, or soft, or sympathetic. There is nothing indulgent about the Moral Law. It is as hard as nails. It tells you to do the straight thing and it does not seem to care how painful, or dangerous, or difficult it is to do. If God is like the Moral Law, then He is not soft. It is no use, at this stage, saying that what you mean by a "good" God is a God who can forgive. You are going too quickly. Only a Person can forgive. And we have not yet got as far as a personal God— only as far as a power, behind the Moral Law, and more like a mind than it is like anything else. But it may still be very unlike a Person. If it is pure impersonal mind, there may be no sense in asking it to make allowances for you or let you off, just as there is no sense in asking the multiplication table to let you off when you do your sums wrong. You are bound to get the wrong answer. And it is no use either saying that if there is a God of that sort—an impersonal absolute goodness—then you do not like Him and are not going to bother about Him. For the trouble is that one part of you is on His side and really agrees with His disapproval of human greed and trickery and exploitation. You may want Him to make an exception in your own case, to let you off this one time; but you know at bottom that unless the power behind the world really and unalterably detests that sort of behaviour, then He cannot be good. On the other hand, we know that if there does exist an absolute goodness it must hate most of what we do. That is the terrible fix we are in. If the universe is not governed by an absolute goodness, then all our efforts are in the long run hopeless. But if it is, then we are making ourselves enemies to that goodness every day, and are not in the least likely to do any better tomorrow, and so our case is hopeless again. We cannot do without it, and we cannot do with it. God is the only comfort, He is also the supreme terror: the thing we most need and the thing we most want to hide from. He is our only possible ally, and we have made ourselves His enemies. Some people talk as if meeting the gaze of absolute goodness would be fun. They need to think again. They are still only playing with religion. Goodness is either the great safety or the great danger—according to the way you react to it. And we have reacted the wrong way.

Now my third point. When I chose to get to my real subject in this roundabout way, I was not trying to play any kind of trick on you. I had a different reason. My reason was that Christianity simply does not make sense until you have faced the sort of facts I have been describing. Christianity tells people to repent and promises them forgiveness. It therefore has nothing (as far as I know) to say to people who do not know they have done anything to repent of and who do not feel that they need any forgiveness. It is after you have realised that there is a real Moral Law, and a Power behind the law, and that you have broken that law and put yourself wrong with that Power—it is after all this, and not a moment sooner, that Christianity begins to talk. When you know you are sick, you will listen to the doctor. When you have realised that our position is nearly desperate you will begin to understand what the Christians are talking about. They offer an explanation of how we got into our present state of both hating goodness and loving it. They offer an explanation of how God can be this impersonal mind at the back of the Moral Law and yet also a Person. They tell you how the demands of this law, which you and I cannot meet, have been met on our behalf, how God Himself becomes a man to save man from the disapproval of God. It is an old story and if you want to go into it you will no doubt consult people who have more authority to talk about it than I have. All I am doing is to ask people to face the facts—to understand the questions which Christianity claims to answer. And they are very terrifying facts. I wish it was possible to say something more agreeable. But I must say what I think true. Of course, I quite agree that the Christian religion is, in the long run, a thing of unspeakable comfort. But it does not begin in comfort; it begins in the dismay I have been describing, and it is no use at all trying to go on to that comfort without first going through that dismay. In religion, as in war and everything else, comfort is the one thing you cannot get by looking for it. If you look for truth, you may find comfort in the end: if you look for comfort you will not get either comfort or truth—only soft soap and wishful thinking to begin with and, in the end, despair. Most of us have got over the pre-war wishful thinking about international politics. It is time we did the same about religion.

WHAT CHRISTIANS
BELIEVE

I.

THE RIVAL CONCEPTIONS OF GOD

I have been asked to tell you what Christians believe, and I am going to begin by telling you one thing that Christians do not need to believe. If you are a Christian you do not have to believe that all the other religions are simply wrong all through. If you are an atheist you do have to believe that the main point in all the religions of the whole world is simply one huge mistake. If you are a Christian, you are free to think that all these religions, even the queerest ones, contain at least some hint of the truth. When I was an atheist I had to try to persuade myself that most of the human race have always been wrong about the question that mattered to them most; when I became a Christian I was able to take a more liberal view. But, of course, being a Christian does mean thinking that where Christianity differs from other religions, Christianity is right and they are wrong. As in arithmetic—there is only one right answer to a sum, and all other answers are wrong: but some of the wrong answers are much nearer being right than others.

The first big division of humanity is into the majority, who believe in some kind of God or gods, and the minority who do not. On this point, Christianity lines up with the majority—lines up with ancient Greeks and Romans, modern savages, Stoics, Platonists, Hindus, Mohammedans, etc., against the modern Western European materialist.

Now I go on to the next big division. People who all believe in God can be divided according to the sort of God they believe in. There are two very different ideas on this subject. One of them is the idea that He is beyond good and evil. We humans call one thing good and another thing bad. But according to some people that is merely our human point of view. These people would say that the wiser you become the less you would want to call anything good or bad, and the more clearly you would see that everything is good in one way and bad in another, and that nothing could have been different. Consequently, these people think that long before you got anywhere near the divine point of view the distinction would have disappeared altogether. We call a cancer bad, they would say, because it kills a man; but you might just as well call a successful surgeon bad because he kills a cancer. It all depends on the point of view. The other and opposite idea is that God is quite definitely "good" or "righteous," a God who takes sides, who loves love and hates hatred, who wants us to behave in one way and not in another. The first of these views—the one that thinks God beyond good and evil— is called Pantheism. It was held by the great Prussian philosopher Hegel and, as far as I can understand them, by the Hindus. The other view is held by Jews, Mohammedans and Christians.

And with this big difference between Pantheism and the Christian idea of God, there usually goes another. Pantheists usually believe that God, so to speak, animates the universe as you animate your body: that the universe almost *is* God, so that if it did not exist He would not exist either, and anything you find in the universe is a part of God. The Christian idea is quite different. They think God invented and made the universe—like a man making a picture or composing a tune. A painter is not a picture, and he does not die if his picture is destroyed. You may say, "He's put a lot of himself into it," but you only mean that all its beauty and interest has come out of his head. His skill is not in the picture in the same way that it is in his head, or even in his hands. I expect you see how this difference between Pantheists and Christians hangs together with the other one. If you do not take the distinction between good and bad very seriously, then it is easy to say that anything you find in this world is a part of God. But, of course, if you think some things really bad, and God really good, then you cannot talk that. You must believe that God is separate from the world and that some of the things we see in it are contrary to His will. Confronted with a cancer or a slum the Pantheist can say, "If you could only see it from the divine point of view, you would realise that this also is God." The Christian replies, "Don't talk damned nonsense." * For Christianity is a fighting religion. It thinks God made the world —that space and time, heat and cold, and all the colours and tastes, and all the animals and vegetables, are things that God "made up out of His head" as a man makes up a story. But it also thinks that a great many things have gone wrong with the world that God made and that God insists, and insists very loudly, on our putting them right again.

And, of course, that raises a very good question. If a good God made the world why has it gone wrong? And for many years I simply refused to listen to the Christian answers to this question, because I kept on feeling "whatever you say, and however clever your arguments are, isn't it much simpler and easier to say that the world was not made by any intelligent power? Aren't all your arguments simply a complicated attempt to avoid the obvious?" But then that threw me back into another difficulty.

My argument against God was that the universe seemed so cruel and unjust. But how had I got this idea of *just* and *unjust?* A man does not call a line crooked unless he has some idea of a straight line. What was I comparing this universe with when I called it unjust? If the whole show was bad and senseless from A to Z, so to speak, why did I, who was supposed to be part of the show, find myself in such violent reaction against it? A man feels wet when he falls into water, because man is not a water animal: a fish would not feel wet. Of course I could have given up my idea of justice by saying it was nothing but a private idea of my own. But if I did that, then my argument against God collapsed too—for the argument depended on saying that the world was really unjust, not simply that it did not happen to please my private fancies. Thus in the very act of trying to prove that God did not exist—in other words, that the whole of reality was senseless—I found I was forced to assume that one part of reality—

---

* One listener complained of the word *damned* as frivolous swearing. But I mean exactly what I say—nonsense that is *damned* is under God's curse, and will (apart from God's grace) lead those who believe it to eternal death.

namely my idea of justice—was full of sense. Consequently atheism turns out to be too simple. If the whole universe has no meaning, we should never have found out that it has no meaning: just as, if there were no light in the universe and therefore no creatures with eyes, we should never know it was dark. *Dark* would be without meaning.

2.

THE INVASION

Very well then, atheism is too simple. And I will tell you another view that is also too simple. It is the view I call Christianity-and-water, the view which simply says there is a good God in Heaven and everything is all right—leaving out all the difficult and terrible doctrines about sin and hell and the devil, and the redemption. Both these are boys' philosophies.

It is no good asking for a simple religion. After all, real things are not simple. They look simple, but they are not. The table I am sitting at looks simple: but ask a scientist to tell you what it is really made of—all about the atoms and how the light waves rebound from them and hit my eye and what they do to the optic nerve and what it does to my brain—and, of course, you find that what we call "seeing a table" lands you in mysteries and complications which you can hardly get to the end of. A child saying a child's prayer looks simple. And if you are content to stop there, well and good. But if you are not—and the modern world usually is not—if you want to go on and ask what is really happening—then you must be prepared for something difficult. If we ask for something more than simplicity, it is silly then to complain that the something more is not simple.

Very often, however, this silly procedure is adopted by people who are not silly, but who, consciously or unconsciously, want to destroy Christianity. Such people put up a version of Christianity suitable for a child of six and make that the object of their attack. When you try to explain the Christian doctrine as it is really held by an instructed adult, they then complain that you are making their heads turn round and that it is all too complicated and that if there really were a God they are sure He would have made "religion" simple, because simplicity is so beautiful, etc. You must be on your guard against these people for they will change their ground every minute and only waste your time. Notice, too, their idea of God "making religion simple": as if "religion" were something God invented, and not His statement to us of certain quite unalterable facts about His own nature.

Besides being complicated, reality, in my experience, is usually odd. It is not neat, not obvious, not what you expect. For instance, when you have grasped that the earth and the other planets all go round the sun, you would naturally expect that all the planets were made to match—all at equal distances from each other, say, or distances that regularly increased, or all the same size, or else getting bigger or smaller as you go farther from the sun. In fact, you find no rhyme or reason (that we can see) about either the sizes or the distances; and some of them have one moon, one has four, one has two, some have none, and one has a ring.

Reality, in fact, is usually something you could not have guessed. That is one of the reasons I believe Christianity. It is a religion you could not have guessed. If it offered us just the kind of universe we had always expected, I should feel we were making it up. But, in fact, it is not the sort of thing anyone would have made up. It has just that queer twist about it that real things have. So let us leave behind all these boys' philosophies— these oversimple answers. The problem is not simple and the answer is not going to be simpler either.

What is the problem? A universe that contains much that is obviously bad and apparently meaningless, but containing creatures like ourselves who know that it is bad and meaningless. There are only two views that face all the facts. One is the Christian view that this is a good world that has gone wrong, but still retains the memory of what it ought to have been. The other is the view called Dualism. Dualism means the belief that there are two equal and independent powers at the back of everything, one of them good and the other bad, and that this universe is the battlefield in which they fight out an endless war. I personally think that next to Christianity Dualism is the manliest and most sensible creed on the market. But it has a catch in it.

The two powers, or spirits, or gods—the good one and the bad one—are supposed to be quite independent. They both existed from all eternity. Neither of them made the other, neither of them has any more right than the other to call itself God. Each presumably thinks it is good and thinks the other bad. One of them likes hatred and cruelty, the other likes love and mercy, and each backs its own view. Now what do we mean when we call one of them the Good Power and the other Bad Power? Either we are merely saying that we happen to prefer the one to the other—like preferring beer to cider—or else we are saying that, whatever the two powers think about it, and whichever we humans, at the moment, happen to like, one of them is actually wrong, actually mistaken, in regarding itself as good. Now if we mean merely that we happen to prefer the first, then we must give up talking about good and evil at all. For good means what you ought to prefer quite regardless of what you happen to like at any given moment. If "being good" meant simply joining the side you happened to fancy, for no real reason, then good would not deserve to be called good. So we must mean that one of the two powers is actually wrong and the other actually right.

But the moment you say that, you are putting into the universe a third thing in addition to the two Powers: some law or standard or rule of good which one of the powers conforms to and the other fails to conform to. But since the two powers are judged by this standard, then this standard, or the Being who made this standard, is farther back and higher up than either of them, and He will be the real God. In fact, what we meant by calling them good and bad turns out to be that one of them is in a right relation to the real ultimate God and the other in a wrong relation to Him.

The same point can be made in a different way. If Dualism is true, then the bad Power must be a being who likes badness for its own sake. But in reality we have no experience of anyone liking badness just because it is bad. The nearest we can get to it is in cruelty. But in real life people are cruel for one of two reasons—either because they are sadists, that is, because they have a sexual perversion which makes cruelty a cause of sensual pleasure to them, or else for the sake of something they are going to get out of it—money, or power, or safety. But pleasure, money,

power, and safety are all, as far as they go, good things. The badness consists in pursuing them by the wrong method, or in the
wrong way, or too much. I do not mean, of course, that the people who do this are not desperately wicked. I do mean that
wickedness, when you examine it, turns out to be the pursuit of
some good in the wrong way. You can be good for the mere
sake of goodness: you cannot be bad for the mere sake of badness. You can do a kind action when you are not feeling kind
and when it gives you no pleasure, simply because kindness is
ɣight; but no one ever did a cruel action simply because cruelty is
wrong—only because cruelty was pleasant or useful to him. In
other words badness cannot succeed even in being bad in the
same way in which goodness is good. Goodness is, so to speak, itself: badness is only spoiled goodness. And there must be something good first before it can be spoiled. We called sadism a sexual perversion; but you must first have the idea of a normal sexuality before you can talk of its being perverted; and you can see
which is the perversion, because you can explain the perverted
from the normal, and cannot explain the normal from the perverted. It follows that this Bad Power, who is supposed to be on
an equal footing with the Good Power, and to love badness in
the same way as the Good Power loves goodness, is a mere bogy.
In order to be bad he must have good things to want and then to
pursue in the wrong way: he must have impulses which were
originally good in order to be able to pervert them. But if he is
bad he cannot supply himself either with good things to desire
or with good impulses to pervert. He must be getting both from
the Good Power. And if so, then he is not independent. He is
part of the Good Power's world: he was made either by the Good
Power or by some power above them both.

Put it more simply still. To be bad, he must exist and have
intelligence and will. But existence, intelligence and will are in
themselves good. Therefore he must be getting them from the
Good Power: even to be bad he must borrow or steal from his
opponent. And do you now begin to see why Christianity has always said that the devil is a fallen angel? That is not a mere story
for the children. It is a real recognition of the fact that evil is a
parasite, not an original thing. The powers which enable evil to

carry on are powers given it by goodness. All the things which enable a bad man to be effectively bad are in themselves good things—resolution, cleverness, good looks, existence itself. That is why Dualism, in a strict sense, will not work.

But I freely admit that real Christianity (as distinct from Christianity-and-water) goes much nearer to Dualism than people think. One of the things that surprised me when I first read the New Testament seriously was that it talked so much about a Dark Power in the universe—a mighty evil spirit who was held to be the Power behind death and disease, and sin. The difference is that Christianity thinks this Dark Power was created by God, and was good when he was created, and went wrong. Christianity agrees with Dualism that this universe is at war. But it does not think this is a war between independent powers. It thinks it is a civil war, a rebellion, and that we are living in a part of the universe occupied by the rebel.

Enemy-occupied territory—that is what this world is. Christianity is the story of how the rightful king has landed, you might say landed in disguise, and is calling us all to take part in a great campaign of sabotage. When you go to church you are really listening-in to the secret wireless from our friends: that is why the enemy is so anxious to prevent us from going. He does it by playing on our conceit and laziness and intellectual snobbery. I know someone will ask me, "Do you really mean, at this time of day, to re-introduce our old friend the devil—hoofs and horns and all?" Well, what the time of day has to do with it I do not know. And I am not particular about the hoofs and horns. But in other respects my answer is "Yes, I do." I do not claim to know anything about his personal appearance. If anybody really wants to know him better I would say to that person, "Don't worry. If you really want to, you will. Whether you'll like it when you do is another question."

3.

THE SHOCKING ALTERNATIVE

Christians, then, believe that an evil power has made himself for the present the Prince of this World. And, of course, that raises problems. Is this state of affairs in accordance with God's will or not? If it is, He is a strange God, you will say: and if it is not, how can anything happen contrary to the will of a being with absolute power?

But anyone who has been in authority knows how a thing can be in accordance with your will in one way and not in another. It may be quite sensible for a mother to say to the children, "I'm not going to go and make you tidy the schoolroom every night. You've got to learn to keep it tidy on your own." Then she goes up one night and finds the Teddy bear and the ink and the French grammar all lying in the grate. That is against her will. She would prefer the children to be tidy. But on the other hand, it is her will which has left the children free to be untidy. The same thing arises in any regiment, or trade union, or school. You make a thing voluntary and then half the people do not do it. That is not what you willed, but your will has made it possible.

It is probably the same in the universe. God created things which had free will. That means creatures which can go either wrong or right. Some people think they can imagine a creature which was free but had no possibility of going wrong; I cannot. If a thing is free to be good it is also free to be bad. And free will is what has made evil possible. Why, then, did God give them free will? Because free will, though it makes evil possible, is also the only thing that makes possible any love or goodness or joy worth having. A world of automata—of creatures that worked like machines—would hardly be worth creating. The happiness which God designs for His higher creatures is the happiness of being freely, voluntarily united to Him and to each other in an ecstasy of love and delight compared with which the most rapturous love between a man and a woman on this earth is mere milk and water. And for that they must be free.

Of course God knew what would happen if they used their freedom the wrong way: apparently He thought it worth the risk. Perhaps we feel inclined to disagree with Him. But there is a difficulty about disagreeing with God. He is the source from which all your reasoning power comes: you could not be right and He wrong any more than a stream can rise higher than its own source. When you are arguing against Him you are arguing against the very power that makes you able to argue at all: it is like cutting off the branch you are sitting on. If God thinks this state of war in the universe a price worth paying for free will— that is, for making a live world in which creatures can do real good or harm and something of real importance can happen, instead of a toy world which only moves when He pulls the strings —then we may take it it is worth paying.

When we have understood about free will, we shall see how silly it is to ask, as somebody once asked me: "Why did God make a creature of such rotten stuff that it went wrong?" The better stuff a creature is made of—the cleverer and stronger and freer it is—then the better it will be if it goes right, but also the worse it it will be if it goes wrong. A cow cannot be very good or very bad; a dog can be both better and worse; a child better and worse still; an ordinary man, still more so; a man of genius, still more so; a superhuman spirit best—or worst—of all.

How did the Dark Power go wrong? Here, no doubt, we ask a question to which human beings cannot give an answer with any certainty. A reasonable (and traditional) guess, based on our own experiences of going wrong, can, however, be offered. The moment you have a self at all, there is a possibility of putting yourself first—wanting to be the centre—wanting to be God, in fact. That was the sin of Satan: and that was the sin he taught the human race. Some people think the fall of man had something to do with sex, but that is a mistake. (The story in the Book of Genesis rather suggests that some corruption in our sexual nature followed the fall and was its result, not its cause.) What Satan put into the heads of our remote ancestors was the idea that they could "be like gods"—could set up on their own as if they had created themselves—be their own masters—invent some sort of happiness for themselves outside God, apart from God. And out of that hopeless attempt has come nearly all that we call human history—money, poverty, ambition, war, prostitution, classes, empires, slavery—the long terrible story of man trying to find something other than God which will make him happy.

The reason why it can never succeed is this. God made us: invented us as a man invents an engine. A car is made to run on gasoline, and it would not run properly on anything else. Now God designed the human machine to run on Himself. He Himself is the fuel our spirits were designed to burn, or the food our spirits were designed to feed on. There is no other. That is why it is just no good asking God to make us happy in our own way without bothering about religion. God cannot give us a happiness and peace apart from Himself, because it is not there. There is no such thing.

That is the key to history. Terrific energy is expended—civilisations are built up—excellent institutions devised, but each time something goes wrong. Some fatal flaw always brings the selfish and cruel people to the top and it all slides back into misery and ruin. In fact, the machine conks. It seems to start up all right and runs a few yards, and then it breaks down. They are trying to run it on the wrong juice. That is what Satan has done to us humans.

And what did God do? First of all He left us conscience, the sense of right and wrong: and all through history there have been people trying (some of them very hard) to obey it. None of them ever quite succeeded. Secondly, He sent the human race what I call good dreams: I mean those queer stories scattered all through the heathen religions about a god who dies and comes to life again and, by his death, has somehow given new life to men. Thirdly, He selected one particular people and spent several centuries hammering into their heads the sort of God He was—that there was only one of Him and that He cared about right conduct.

Those people were the Jews, and the Old Testament gives an account of the hammering process.

Then comes the real shock. Among these Jews there suddenly turns up a man who goes about talking as if He was God. He claims to forgive sins. He says He has always existed. He says He is coming to judge the world at the end of time. Now let us get this clear. Among Pantheists, like the Indians, anyone might say that he was a part of God, or one with God: there would be nothing very odd about it. But this man, since He was a Jew, could not mean that kind of God. God, in their language, meant the Being outside the world Who had made it and was infinitely different from anything else. And when you have grasped that, you will see that what this man said was, quite simply, the most shocking thing that has ever been uttered by human lips.

One part of the claim tends to slip past us unnoticed because we have heard it so often that we no longer see what it amounts to. I mean the claim to forgive sins: any sins. Now unless the speaker is God, this is really so preposterous as to be comic. We can all understand how a man forgives offences against himself. You tread on my toe and I forgive you, you steal my money and I forgive you. But what should we make of a man, himself unrobbed and untrodden on, who announced that he forgave you for treading on other men's toes and stealing other men's money? Asinine fatuity is the kindest description we should give of his conduct. Yet this is what Jesus did. He told people that their sins were forgiven, and never waited to consult all the other people whom their sins had undoubtedly injured. He unhesitatingly behaved as if He was the party chiefly concerned, the person chiefly offended in all offences. This makes sense only if He really was the God whose laws are broken and whose love is wounded in every sin. In the mouth of any speaker who is not God, these words would imply what I can only regard as a silliness and conceit unrivalled by any other character in history.

Yet (and this is the strange, significant thing) even His enemies, when they read the Gospels, do not usually get the impression of silliness and conceit. Still less do unprejudiced readers. Christ says that He is "humble and meek" and we believe Him; not noticing that, if He were merely a man, humility and meekness are the very last characteristics we could attribute to some of His sayings.

I am trying here to prevent anyone saying the really foolish thing that people often say about Him: "I'm ready to accept Jesus as a great moral teacher, but I don't accept His claim to be God." That is the one thing we must not say. A man who was merely a man and said the sort of things Jesus said would not be a great moral teacher. He would either be a lunatic—on a level with the man who says he is a poached egg—or else he would be the Devil of Hell. You must make your choice. Either this man was, and is, the Son of God: or else a madman or something worse. You can shut Him up for a fool, you can spit at Him and kill Him as a demon; or you can fall at His feet and call Him Lord and God. But let us not come with any patronising nonsense about His being a great human teacher. He has not left that open to us. He did not intend to.

4.

THE PERFECT PENITENT

We are faced, then, with a frightening alternative. This man we
are talking about either was (and is) just what He said or else a
lunatic, or something worse. Now it seems to me obvious that
He was neither a lunatic nor a fiend: and consequently, however
strange or terrifying or unlikely it may seem, I have to accept the
view that He was and is God. God has landed on this enemy-occupied world in human form.

And now, what was the purpose of it all? What did He come to
do? Well, to teach, of course; but as soon as you look into the New
Testament or any other Christian writing you will find they are
constantly talking about something different—about His death
and His coming to life again. It is obvious that Christians think
the chief point of the story lies here. They think the main thing
He came to earth to do was to suffer and be killed.

Now before I became a Christian I was under the impression
that the first thing Christians had to believe was one particular
theory as to what the point of this dying was. According to that
theory God wanted to punish men for having deserted and joined
the Great Rebel, but Christ volunteered to be punished instead,
and so God let us off. Now I admit that even this theory does not
seem to me quite so immoral and so silly as it used to; but that is
not the point I want to make. What I came to see later on was
that neither this theory nor any other is Christianity. The central
Christian belief is that Christ's death has somehow put us right
with God and given us a fresh start. Theories as to how it did this
are another matter. A good many different theories have been
held as to how it works; what all Christians are agreed on is that it
does work. I will tell you what I think it is like. All sensible peo-

ple know that if you are tired and hungry a meal will do you good. But the modern theory of nourishment—all about the vitamins and proteins—is a different thing. People ate their dinners and felt better long before the theory of vitamins was ever heard of: and if the theory of vitamins is some day abandoned they will go on eating their dinners just the same. Theories about Christ's death are not Christianity: they are explanations about how it works. Christians would not all agree as to how important these theories are. My own church—the Church of England—does not lay down any one of them as the right one. The Church of Rome goes a bit further. But I think they will all agree that the thing itself is infinitely more important than any explanations that theologians have produced. I think they would probably admit that no explanation will ever be quite adequate to the reality. But as I said in the preface to this book, I am only a layman, and at this point we are getting into deep water. I can only tell you, for what it is worth, how I, personally, look at the matter.

On my view the theories are not themselves the thing you are asked to accept. Many of you no doubt have read Jeans or Eddington. What they do when they want to explain the atom, or something of that sort, is to give you a description out of which you can make a mental picture. But then they warn you that this picture is not what the scientists actually believe. What the scientists believe is a mathematical formula. The pictures are there only to help you to understand the formula. They are not really true in the way the formula is; they do not give you the real thing but only something more or less like it. They are only meant to help, and if they do not help you can drop them. The thing itself cannot be pictured, it can only be expressed mathematically. We are in the same boat here. We believe that the death of Christ is just that point in history at which something absolutely unimaginable from outside shows through into our own world. And if we cannot picture even the atoms of which our own world is built, of course we are not going to be able to picture this. Indeed, if we found that we could fully understand it, that very fact would show it was not what it professes to be—the inconceivable, the uncreated, the thing from beyond nature, striking down into nature like lightning. You may ask what good will it be to us if we do not understand it. But that is easily answered. A man can eat his dinner without understanding exactly how food nourishes him. A man can accept what Christ has done without knowing how it works: indeed, he certainly would not know how it works until he has accepted it.

We are told that Christ was killed for us, that His death has washed out our sins, and that by dying He disabled death itself. That is the formula. That is Christianity. That is what has to be believed. Any theories we build up as to how Christ's death did all this are, in my view, quite secondary: mere plans or diagrams to be left alone if they do not help us, and, even if they do help us, not to be confused with the thing itself. All the same, some of these theories are worth looking at.

The one most people have heard is the one I mentioned before —the one about our being let off because Christ had volunteered to bear a punishment instead of us. Now on the face of it that is a very silly theory. If God was prepared to let us off, why on earth did He not do so? And what possible point could there be in punishing an innocent person instead? None at all that I can see, if you are thinking of punishment in the police-court sense. On the other hand, if you think of a debt, there is plenty of point in a person who has some assets paying it on behalf of someone who has not. Or if you take "paying the penalty," not in the sense of being punished, but in the more general sense of "standing the racket" or "footing the bill," then, of course, it is a matter of common experience that, when one person has got himself into a hole, the trouble of getting him out usually falls on a kind friend.

Now what was the sort of "hole" man had got himself into? He had tried to set up on his own, to behave as if he belonged to himself. In other words, fallen man is not simply an imperfect creature who needs improvement: he is a rebel who must lay down his arms. Laying down your arms, surrendering, saying you are sorry, realising that you have been on the wrong track and getting ready to start life over again from the ground floor—that is the only way out of a "hole." This process of surrender—this movement full speed astern—is what Christians call repentance. Now repentance is no fun at all. It is something much harder than merely eating humble pie. It means unlearning all the self-conceit and self-will that we have been training ourselves into for thousands of years. It means killing part of yourself, undergoing a kind of death. In fact, it needs a good man to repent. And here comes the catch. Only a bad person needs to repent: only a good person can repent perfectly. The worse you are the more you need it and the less you can do it. The only person who could do it perfectly would be a perfect person—and he would not need it.

Remember, this repentance, this willing submission to humiliation and a kind of death, is not something God demands of you before He will take you back and which He could let you off if He chose: it is simply a description of what going back to Him is like. If you ask God to take you back without it, you are really asking Him to let you go back without going back. It cannot happen. Very well, then, we must go through with it. But the same badness which makes us need it, makes us unable to do it. Can we do it if God helps us? Yes, but what do we mean when we talk of God helping us? We mean God putting into us a bit of Himself, so to speak. He lends us a little of His reasoning powers and that is how we think: He puts a little of His love into us and that is how we love one another. When you teach a child writing, you hold its hand while it forms the letters: that is, it forms the letters because you are forming them. We love and reason because God loves and reasons and holds our hand while we do it. Now if we had not fallen, that would be all plain sailing. But unfortunately we now need God's help in order to do something which God, in His own nature, never does at all—to surrender, to suffer, to submit, to die. Nothing in God's nature corresponds to this process at all. So that the one road for which we now need God's leadership most of all is a road God, in His own nature, has never walked. God can share only what He has: this thing, in His own nature, He has not.

But supposing God became a man—suppose our human nature which can suffer and die was amalgamated with God's nature in one person—then that person could help us. He could surrender His will, and suffer and die, because He was man; and He could do it perfectly because He was God. You and I can go through this process only if God does it in us; but God can do it only if He becomes man. Our attempts at this dying will succeed only if we men share in God's dying, just as our thinking can succeed only because it is a drop out of the ocean of His intelligence: but we cannot share God's dying unless God dies; and He cannot die except by being a man. That is the sense in which He pays our debt, and suffers for us what He Himself need not suffer at all.

I have heard some people complain that if Jesus was God as well as man, then His sufferings and death lose all value in their eyes, "because it must have been so easy for him." Others may (very rightly) rebuke the ingratitude and ungraciousness of this objection; what staggers me is the misunderstanding it betrays. In one sense, of course, those who make it are right. They have even understated their own case. The perfect submission, the perfect suffering, the perfect death were not only easier to Jesus because He was God, but were possible only because He was God. But surely that is a very odd reason for not accepting them? The teacher is able to form the letters for the child because the teacher is grown-up and knows how to write. That, of course, makes it easier for the teacher; and only because it is easier for him can he help the child. If it rejected him because "it's easy for grown-ups" and waited to learn writing from another child who could not write itself (and so had no "unfair" advantage), it would not get on very quickly. If I am drowning in a rapid river, a man who still has one foot on the bank may give me a hand which saves my life. Ought I to shout back (between my gasps) "No, it's not fair! You have an advantage! You're keeping one foot on the bank"? That advantage—call it "unfair" if you like—is the only reason why he can be of any use to me. To what will you look for help if you will not look to that which is stronger than yourself?

Such is my own way of looking at what Christians call the Atonement. But remember this is only one more picture. Do not mistake it for the thing itself: and if it does not help you, drop it.

5.

THE PRACTICAL CONCLUSION

The perfect surrender and humiliation were undergone by Christ: perfect because He was God, surrender and humiliation because He was man. Now the Christian belief is that if we somehow share the humility and suffering of Christ we shall also share in His conquest for death and find a new life after we have died and in it become perfect, and perfectly happy, creatures. This means something much more than our trying to follow His teaching. People often ask when the next step in evolution—the step to something beyond man—will happen. But on the Christian view, it has happened already. In Christ a new kind of man appeared: and the new kind of life which began in Him is to be put into us.

How is this to be done? Now, please remember how we acquired the old, ordinary kind of life. We derived it from others, from our father and mother and all our ancestors, without our consent—and by a very curious process, involving pleasure, pain, and danger. A process you would never have guessed. Most of us spend a good many years in childhood trying to guess it: and some children, when they are first told, do not believe it—and I am not sure that I blame them, for it is very odd. Now the God who arranged that process is the same God who arranges how the new kind of life—the Christ life—is to be spread. We must be prepared for it being odd too. He did not consult us when He invented sex: He has not consulted us either when He invented this.

There are three things that spread the Christ life to us: baptism, belief, and that mysterious action which different Christians call by different names—Holy Communion, the Mass, the Lord's Supper. At least, those are the three ordinary methods.

I am not saying there may not be special cases where it is spread without one or more of these. I have not time to go into special cases, and I do not know enough. If you are trying in a few minutes to tell a man how to get to Edinburgh you will tell him the trains: he can, it is true, get there by boat or by a plane, but you will hardly bring that in. And I am not saying anything about which of these three things is the most essential. My Methodist friend would like me to say more about belief and less (in proportion) about the other two. But I am not going into that. Anyone who professes to teach you Christian doctrine will, in fact, tell you to use all three, and that is enough for our present purpose.

I cannot myself see why these things should be the conductors of the new kind of life. But then, if one did not happen to know, I should never have seen any connection between a particular physical pleasure and the appearance of a new human being in the world. We have to take reality as it comes to us: there is no good jabbering about what it ought to be like or what we should have expected it to be like. But though I cannot see why it should be so, I can tell you why I believe it is so. I have explained why I have to believe that Jesus was (and is) God. And it seems plain as a matter of history that He taught His followers that the new life was communicated in this way. In other words, I believe it on His authority. Do not be scared by the word authority. Believing things on authority only means believing them because you have been told them by someone you think trustworthy. Ninety-nine per cent of the things you believe are believed on authority. I believe there is such a place as New York. I have not seen it myself. I could not prove by abstract reasoning that there must be such a place. I believe it because reliable people have told me so. The ordinary man believes in the Solar System, atoms, evolution, and the circulation of the blood on authority—because the scientists say so. Every historical statement in the world is believed on authority. None of us has seen the Norman Conquest or the defeat of the Armada. None of us could prove them by pure logic as you prove a thing in mathematics. We believe them simply because people who did see them have left writings that tell us about them: in fact, on authority. A man who jibbed at authority in other things as some people do in religion would have to be content to know nothing all his life.

Do not think I am setting up baptism and belief and the Holy Communion as things that will do instead of your own attempts to copy Christ. Your natural life is derived from your parents; that does not mean it will stay there if you do nothing about it. You can lose it by neglect, or you can drive it away by committing suicide. You have to feed it and look after it: but always remember you are not making it, you are only keeping up a life you got from someone else. In the same way a Christian can lose the Christ-life which has been put into him, and he has to make efforts to keep it. But even the best Christian that ever lived is not acting on his own steam—he is only nourishing or protecting a life he could never have acquired by his own efforts. And that has practical consequences. As long as the natural life is in your body, it will do a lot towards repairing that body. Cut it, and up to a point it will heal, as a dead body would not. A live body is not one that never gets hurt, but one that can to some extent repair itself. In the same way a Christian is not a man who never goes wrong, but a man who is enabled to repent and pick himself up and begin over again after each stumble—because the Christ-life is inside him, repairing him all the time, enabling him to repeat (in some degree) the kind of voluntary death which Christ Himself carried out.

That is why the Christian is in a different position from other people who are trying to be good. They hope, by being good, to please God if there is one; or—if they think there is not—at least they hope to deserve approval from good men. But the Christian thinks any good he does comes from the Christ-life inside him. He does not think God will love us because we are good, but that God will make us good because He loves us; just as the roof of a greenhouse does not attract the sun because it is bright, but becomes bright because the sun shines on it.

And let me make it quite clear that when Christians say the Christ-life is in them, they do not mean simply something mental or moral. When they speak of being "in Christ" or of Christ being "in them," this is not simply a way of saying that they are thinking about Christ or copying Him. They mean that Christ is actually operating through them; that the whole mass of Christians are the physical organism through which Christ acts—that we are His fingers and muscles, the cells of His body. And perhaps that explains one or two things. It explains why this new life is spread not only by purely mental acts like belief, but by bodily acts like baptism and Holy Communion. It is not merely the spreading of an idea; it is more like evolution—a biological or super-biological fact. There is no good trying to be more spiritual than God. God never meant man to be a purely spiritual creature. That is why He uses material things like bread and wine to put the new life into us. We may think this rather crude and unspiritual. God does not: He invented eating. He likes matter. He invented it.

Here is another thing that used to puzzle me. Is it not frightfully unfair that this new life should be confined to people who have heard of Christ and been able to believe in Him? But the truth is God has not told us what His arrangements about the other people are. We do know that no man can be saved except through Christ; we do not know that only those who know Him can be saved through Him. But in the meantime, if you are worried about the people outside, the most unreasonable thing you can do is to remain outside yourself. Christians are Christ's body, the organism through which He works. Every addition to that body enables Him to do more. If you want to help those outside you must add your own little cell to the body of Christ who alone can help them. Cutting off a man's fingers would be an odd way of getting him to do more work.

Another possible objection is this. Why is God landing in this enemy-occupied world in disguise and starting a sort of secret society to undermine the devil? Why is He not landing in force, invading it? Is it that He is not strong enough? Well, Christians think He is going to land in force; we do not know when. But we can guess why He is delaying. He wants to give us the chance of joining His side freely. I do not suppose you and I would have thought much of a Frenchman who waited till the Allies were marching into Germany and then announced he was on our side. God will invade. But I wonder whether people who ask God to interfere openly and directly in our world quite realise what it will be like when He does. When that happens, it is the end of the world. When the author walks on to the stage the play is over. God is going to invade, all right: but what is the good of saying you are on His side then, when you see the whole natural universe melting away like a dream and something else—something it never entered your head to conceive—comes crashing in; something so beautiful to some of us and so terrible to others that none of us will have any choice left? For this time it will be God without disguise; something so overwhelming that it will strike either irresistible love or irresistible horror into every creature. It will be too late then to choose your side. There is no use saying you choose to lie down when it has become impossible to stand up. That will not be the time for choosing: it will be the time when we discover which side we really have chosen, whether we realised it before or not. Now, today, this moment, is our chance to choose the right side. God is holding back to give us that chance. It will not last for ever. We must take it or leave it.

CHRISTIAN BEHAVIOUR

Reprinted from Mere Christianity

by

C. S. Lewis
FELLOW OF MAGDALEN COLLEGE, OXFORD

THE MACMILLAN COMPANY, NEW YORK

Contents

CHRISTIAN BEHAVIOR

I.

THE THREE PARTS OF MORALITY

There is a story about a schoolboy who was asked what he thought God was like. He replied that, as far as he could make out, God was "The sort of person who is always snooping round to see if anyone is enjoying himself and then trying to stop it." And I am afraid that is the sort of idea that the word Morality raises in a good many people's minds: something that interferes, something that stops you having a good time. In reality, moral rules are directions for running the human machine. Every moral rule is there to prevent a breakdown, or a strain, or a friction, in the running of that machine. That is why these rules at first seem to be constantly interfering with our natural inclinations. When you are being taught how to use any machine, the instructor keeps on saying, "No, don't do it like that," because, of course, there are all sorts of things that look all right and seem to you the natural way of treating the machine, but do not really work.

Some people prefer to talk about moral "ideals" rather than moral rules and about moral "idealism" rather than moral obedience. Now it is, of course, quite true that moral perfection is an "ideal" in the sense that we cannot achieve it. In that sense every kind of perfection is, for us humans, an ideal; we cannot succeed in being perfect car drivers or perfect tennis players or in drawing perfectly straight lines. But there is another sense in which it is very misleading to call moral perfection an ideal. When a man says that a certain woman, or house, or ship, or garden is "his ideal" he does not mean (unless he is rather a fool) that everyone else ought to have the same ideal. In such matters we are entitled to have different tastes and, therefore, different ideals. But it is dangerous to describe a man who tries very hard to keep the moral

457

law as a "man of high ideals," because this might lead you to think
that moral perfection was a private taste of his own and that the
rest of us were not called on to share it. This would be a disastrous
mistake. Perfect behaviour may be as unattainable as perfect gear-
changing when we drive; but it is a necessary ideal prescribed for
all men by the very nature of the human machine just as perfect
gear-changing is an ideal prescribed for all drivers by the very nature of cars. And it would be even more dangerous to think of
oneself as a person "of high ideals" because one is trying to tell no
lies at all (instead of only a few lies) or never to commit adultery
(instead of committing it only seldom) or not to be a bully (instead of being only a moderate bully). It might lead you to become a prig and to think you were rather a special person who
deserved to be congratulated on his "idealism." In reality you
might just as well expect to be congratulated because, whenever
you do a sum, you try to get it quite right. To be sure, perfect
arithmetic is "an ideal"; you will certainly make some mistakes
in some calculations. But there is nothing very fine about trying
to be quite accurate at each step in each sum. It would be idiotic
not to try; for every mistake is going to cause you trouble later
on. In the same way every moral failure is going to cause trouble,
probably to others and certainly to yourself. By talking about
rules and obedience instead of "ideals" and "idealism" we help
to remind ourselves of these facts.

Now let us go a step further. There are two ways in which the
human machine goes wrong. One is when human individuals
drift apart from one another, or else collide with one another and
do one another damage, by cheating or bullying. The other is
when things go wrong inside the individual—when the different parts of him (his different faculties and desires and so on)
either drift apart or interfere with one another. You can get the
idea plain if you think of us as a fleet of ships sailing in formation. The voyage will be a success only, in the first place, if the
ships do not collide and get in one another's way; and, secondly, if
each ship is seaworthy and has her engines in good order. As a matter of fact, you cannot have either of these two things without
the other. If the ships keep on having collisions they will not remain seaworthy very long. On the other hand, if their steering

gears are out of order they will not be able to avoid collisions. Or, if you like, think of humanity as a band playing a tune. To get a good result, you need two things. Each player's individual instrument must be in tune and also each must come in at the right moment so as to combine with all the others.

But there is one thing we have not yet taken into account. We have not asked where the fleet is trying to get to, or what piece of music the band is trying to play. The instruments might be all in tune and might all come in at the right moment, but even so the performance would not be a success if they had been engaged to provide dance music and actually played nothing but Dead Marches. And however well the fleet sailed, its voyage would be a failure if it were meant to reach New York and actually arrived at Calcutta.

Morality, then, seems to be concerned with three things. Firstly, with fair play and harmony between individuals. Secondly, with what might be called tidying up or harmonising the things inside each individual. Thirdly, with the general purpose of human life as a whole: what man was made for: what course the whole fleet ought to be on: what tune the conductor of the band wants it to play.

You may have noticed that modern people are nearly always thinking about the first thing and forgetting the other two. When people say in the newspapers that we are striving for Christian moral standards, they usually mean that we are striving for kindness and fair play between nations, and classes, and individuals; that is, they are thinking only of the first thing. When a man says about something he wants to do, "It can't be wrong because it doesn't do anyone else any harm," he is thinking only of the first thing. He is thinking it does not matter what his ship is like inside provided that he does not run into the next ship. And it is quite natural, when we start thinking about morality, to begin with the first thing, with social relations. For one thing, the results of bad morality in that sphere are so obvious and press on us every day: war and poverty and graft and lies and shoddy work. And also, as long as you stick to the first thing, there is very little disagreement about morality. Almost all people at all times have agreed (in theory) that human beings ought to be honest and kind and helpful to one another. But though it is natural to begin with all that, if our thinking about morality stops there, we might just as well not have thought at all. Unless we go on to the second thing—the tidying up inside each human being—we are only deceiving ourselves.

What is the good of telling the ships how to steer so as to avoid collisions if, in fact, they are such crazy old tubs that they cannot be steered at all? What is the good of drawing up, on paper, rules for social behaviour, if we know that, in fact, our greed, cowardice, ill temper, and self-conceit are going to prevent us from keeping them? I do not mean for a moment that we ought not to think, and think hard, about improvements in our social and economic system. What I do mean is that all that thinking will be mere moonshine unless we realise that nothing but the courage and unselfishness of individuals is ever going to make any system work properly. It is easy enough to remove the particular kinds of graft or bullying that go on under the present system: but as long as men are twisters or bullies they will find some new way of carrying on the old game under the new system. You cannot make men good by law: and without good men you cannot have a good society. That is why we must go on to think of the second thing: of morality inside the individual.

But I do not think we can stop there either. We are now getting to the point at which different beliefs about the universe lead to different behaviour. And it would seem, at first sight, very sensible to stop before we got there, and just carry on with those parts of morality that all sensible people agree about. But can we? Remember that religion involves a series of statements about facts, which must be either true or false. If they are true, one set of conclusions will follow about the right sailing of the human fleet: if they are false, quite a different set. For example, let us go back to the man who says that a thing cannot be wrong unless it hurts some other human being. He quite understands that he must not damage the other ships in the convoy, but he honestly thinks that what he does to his own ship is simply his own business. But does it not make a great difference whether his ship is his own property or not? Does it not make a great difference whether I am, so to speak, the landlord of my own mind and body, or only a tenant, responsible to the real landlord? If somebody else made me, for his own purposes, then I shall have a lot of duties which I should not have if I simply belonged to myself.

Again, Christianity asserts that every individual human being is going to live for ever, and this must be either true or false. Now there are a good many things which would not be worth bothering about if I were going to live only seventy years, but which I had better bother about very seriously if I am going to live for ever. Perhaps my bad temper or my jealousy are gradually getting worse—so gradually that the increase in seventy years will not be very noticeable. But it might be absolute hell in a million years: in fact, if Christianity is true, Hell is the precisely correct technical term for what it would be. And immortality makes this other difference, which, by the by, has a connection with the difference between totalitarianism and democracy. If individuals live only seventy years, then a state, or a nation, or a civilisation, which may last for a thousand years, is more important than an individual. But if Christianity is true, then the individual is not only more important but incomparably more important, for he is everlasting and the life of a state of a civilisation, compared with his, is only a moment.

It seems, then, that if we are to think about morality, we must think of all three departments: relations between man and man: things inside each man: and relations between man and the power that made him. We can all co-operate in the first one. Disagreements begin with the second and become serious with the third. It is in dealing with the third that the main differences between Christian and non-Christian morality come out. For the rest of this book I am going to assume the Christian point of view, and look at the whole picture as it will be if Christianity is true.

2.

THE "CARDINAL VIRTUES"

The previous section was originally composed to be given as a short talk on the air.

If you are allowed to talk for only ten minutes, pretty well everything else has to be sacrificed to brevity. One of my chief reasons for dividing morality up into three parts (with my picture of the ships sailing in convoy) was that this seemed the shortest way of covering the ground. Here I want to give some idea of another way in which the subject has been divided by old writers, which was too long to use in my talk, but which is a very good one.

According to this longer scheme there are seven "virtues." Four of them are called "Cardinal" virtues, and the remaining three are called "Theological" virtues. The "Cardinal" ones are those which all civilised people recognise: the "Theological" are those which, as a rule, only Christians know about. I shall deal with the Theological ones later on: at present I am talking about the four Cardinal virtues. (The word "cardinal" has nothing to do with "Cardinals" in the Roman Church. It comes from a Latin word meaning "the hinge of a door." These were called "cardinal" virtues because they are, as we should say, "pivotal.") They are PRUDENCE, TEMPERANCE, JUSTICE, and FORTITUDE.

Prudence means practical common sense, taking the trouble to think out what you are doing and what is likely to come of it. Nowadays most people hardly think of Prudence as one of the "virtues." In fact, because Christ said we could only get into His world by being like children, many Christians have the idea that, provided you are "good," it does not matter being a fool. But that is a misunderstanding. In the first place, most children show plenty of "prudence" about doing the things they are really interested in, and think them out quite sensibly. In the second place, as St. Paul points out, Christ never meant that we were to remain children in *intelligence:* on the contrary, He told us to be not only "as harmless as doves," but also "as wise as serpents." He wants a child's heart, but a grown-up's head. He wants us to be simple, single-minded, affectionate, and teachable, as good child are; but He also wants every bit of intelligence we have to be alert at its job, and in first-class fighting trim. The fact that you are giving money to a charity does not mean that you need not try to find out whether that charity is a fraud or not. The fact that what you are thinking about is God Himself (for example, when you are praying) does not mean that you can be content with the same babyish ideas which you had when you were a five-year-old. It is, of course, quite true that God will not love you any the less, or have less use for you, if you happen to have been born with a very second-rate brain. He has room for people with very little sense, but He wants every one to use what sense they have. The proper motto is not "Be good, sweet maid, and let who can be clever," but "Be good, sweet maid, and don't forget that this involves being as clever as you can." God is no fonder of intellectual slackers than of any other slackers. If you are thinking of becoming a Christian, I warn you you are embarking on something which is going to take the whole of you, brains and all. But, fortunately, it works the other way round. Anyone who is honestly trying to be a Christian will soon find his intelligence being sharpened: one of the reasons why it needs no special education to be a Christian is that Christianity is an education itself. That is why an uneducated believer like Bunyan was able to write a book that has astonished the whole world.

Temperance is, unfortunately, one of those words that has changed its meaning. It now usually means teetotalism. But in the days when the second Cardinal virtue was christened "Temperance," it meant nothing of the sort. Temperance referred not specially to drink, but to all pleasures; and it meant not abstaining, but going the right length and no further. It is a mistake to think that Christians ought all to be teetotallers; Mohammedanism, not Christianity, is the teetotal religion. Of course it may be the duty of a particular Christian or of any Christian, at a particular time, to abstain from strong drink, either because he is the sort of man who cannot drink at all without drinking too much, or because he wants to give the money to the poor, or because he is with people who are inclined to drunkenness and must not encourage them by drinking himself. But the whole point is that he is abstaining, for a good reason, from something which he does not condemn and which he likes to see other people enjoying. One of the marks of a certain type of bad man is that he cannot give up a thing himself without wanting every one else to give it up. That is not the Christian way. An individual Christian may see fit to give up all sorts of things for special reasons—marriage, or meat, or beer, or the cinema; but the moment he starts saying the things are bad in themselves, or looking down his nose at other people who do use them, he has taken the wrong turning.

One great piece of mischief has been done by the modern restriction of the word Temperance to the question of drink. It helps people to forget that you can be just as intemperate about lots of other things. A man who makes his golf or his motor-bicycle the centre of his life, or a woman who devotes all her thoughts to clothes or bridge or her dog, is being just as "intemperate" as someone who gets drunk every evening. Of course, it does not show on the outside so easily: bridge-mania or golf-mania do not make you fall down in the middle of the road. But God is not deceived by externals.

Justice means much more than the sort of thing that goes on in law courts. It is the old name for everything we should now call "fairness"; it includes honesty, give and take, truthfulness, keeping promises, and all that side of life. And Fortitude includes both kinds of courage—the kind that faces danger as well as the kind that "sticks it" under pain. "Guts" is perhaps the nearest modern English. You will notice, of course, that you cannot practise any of the other virtues very long without bringing this one into play.

There is one further point about the virtues that ought to be noticed. There is a difference between doing some particular just or temperate action and being a just or temperate man. Someone who is not a good tennis player may now and then make a good shot. What you mean by a good player is the man whose eye and muscles and nerves have been so trained by making innumerable good shots that they can now be relied on. They have a certain tone or quality which is there even when he is not playing, just as a mathematician's mind has a certain habit and outlook which is there even when he is not doing mathematics. In the same way a man who perseveres in doing just actions gets in the end a certain quality of character. Now it is that quality rather than the particular actions which we mean when we talk of "virtue."

This distinction is important for the following reason. If we thought only of the particular actions we might encourage three wrong ideas.

(1) We might think that, provided you did the right thing, it did not matter how or why you did it—whether you did it willingly or unwillingly, sulkily or cheerfully, through fear of public opinion or for its own sake. But the truth is that right actions done for the wrong reason do not help to build the internal quality or character called a "virtue," and it is this quality or character that really matters. (If the bad tennis player hits very hard, not because he sees that a very hard stroke is required, but because he has lost his temper, his stroke might possibly, by luck, help him to win that particular game; but it will not be helping him to become a reliable player.)

(2) We might think that God wanted simply obedience to a set of rules: whereas He really wants people of a particular sort.

(3) We might think that the "virtues" were necessary only for this present life—that in the other world we could stop being just because there is nothing to quarrel about and stop being brave because there is no danger. Now it is quite true that there will probably be no occasion for just or courageous acts in the next world, but there will be every occasion for being the sort of people that we can become only as the result of doing such acts here. The point is not that God will refuse you admission to His eternal world if you have not got certain qualities of character: the point is that if people have not got at least the begin-

nings of those qualities inside them, then no possible external conditions could make a "Heaven" for them—that is, could make them happy with the deep, strong, unshakable kind of happiness God intends for us.

3.

SOCIAL MORALITY

The first thing to get clear about Christian morality between man and man is that in this department Christ did not come to preach any brand new morality. The Golden Rule of the New Testament (Do as you would be done by) is a summing up of what everyone, at bottom, had always known to be right. Really great moral teachers never do introduce new moralities: it is quacks and cranks who do that. As Dr. Johnson said, "People need to be reminded more often than they need to be instructed." The real job of every moral teacher is to keep on bringing us back, time after time, to the old simple principles which we are all so anxious not to see; like bringing a horse back and back to the fence it has refused to jump or bringing a child back and back to the bit in its lesson that it wants to shirk.

The second thing to get clear is that Christianity has not, and does not profess to have, a detailed political programme for applying "Do as you would be done by" to a particular society at a particular moment. It could not have. It is meant for all men at all times and the particular programme which suited one place or time would not suit another. And, anyhow, that is not how Christianity works. When it tells you to feed the hungry it does not give you lessons in cookery. When it tells you to read the Scriptures it does not give you lessons in Hebrew and Greek, or even in English grammar. It was never intended to replace or supersede the ordinary human arts and sciences: it is rather a director which will set them all to the right jobs, and a source of energy which will give them all new life, if only they will put themselves at its disposal.

People say, "The Church ought to give us a lead." That is true if they mean it in the right way, but false if they mean it in the wrong way. By the Church they ought to mean the whole body of practising Christians. And when they say that the Church should give us a lead, they ought to mean that some Christians—those who happen to have the right talents—should be economists and statesmen, and that all economists and statesmen should be Christian, and that their whole efforts in politics and economics should be directed to putting "Do as you would be done by" into action. If that happened, and if we others were really ready to take it, then we should find the Christian solution for our own social problems pretty quickly. But, of course, when they ask for a lead from the Church most people mean they want the clergy to put out a political programme. That is silly. The clergy are those particular people within the whole Church who have been specially trained and set aside to look after what concerns us as creatures who are going to live for ever: and we are asking them to do a quite different job for which they have not been trained. The job is really on us, on the laymen. The application of Christian principles, say, to trade unionism or education, must come from Christian trade unionists and Christian schoolmasters: just as Christian literature comes from Christian novelists and dramatists—not from the bench of bishops getting together and trying to write plays and novels in their spare time.

All the same, the New Testament, without going into details, gives us a pretty clear hint of what a fully Christian society would be like. Perhaps it gives us more than we can take. It tells us that there are to be no passengers or parasites: if man does not work, he ought not to eat. Every one is to work with his own hands, and what is more, every one's work is to produce something good: there will be no manufacture of silly luxuries and then of sillier advertisements to persuade us to buy them. And there is to be no "swank" or "side," no putting on airs. To that extent a Christian society would be what we now call Leftist. On the other hand, it is always insisting on obedience—obedience (and outward marks of respect) from all of us to properly appointed magistrates, from children to parents, and (I am afraid this is going to be very unpopular) from wives to husbands. Thirdly, it is to be a cheerful society: full of singing and rejoicing, and regarding worry or anxiety as wrong. Courtesy is one of the Christian virtues; and the New Testament hates what it calls "busybodies."

If there were such a society in existence and you or I visited it, I think we should come away with a curious impression. We should feel that its economic life was very socialistic and, in that sense, "advanced," but that its family life and its code of manners were rather old-fashioned—perhaps even ceremonious and aristocratic. Each of us would like some bits of it, but I am afraid very few of us would like the whole thing. That is just what one would expect if Christianity is the total plan for the human machine. We have all departed from that total plan in different ways, and each of us wants to make out that his own modification of the original plan is the plan itself. You will find this again and again about anything that is really Christian: every one is attracted by bits of it and wants to pick out those bits and leave the rest. That is why we do not get much further: and that is why people who are fighting for quite opposite things can both say they are fighting for Christianity.

Now another point. There is one bit of advice given to us by the ancient heathen Greeks, and by the Jews in the Old Testament, and by the great Christian teachers of the Middle Ages, which the modern economic system has completely disobeyed. All these people told us not to lend money at interest: and lending money at interest—what we call investment—is the basis of our whole system. Now it may not absolutely follow that we are wrong. Some people say that when Moses and Aristotle and the Christians agreed in forbidding interest (or "usury" as they called it), they could not foresee the joint stock company, and were only thinking of the private moneylender, and that, therefore, we need not bother about what they said. That is a question I cannot decide on. I am not an economist and I simply do not know whether the investment system is responsible for the state we are in or not. This is where we want the Christian economist. But I should not have been honest if I had not told you that three great civilisations had agreed (or so it seems at first sight) in condemning the very thing on which we have based our whole life.

One more point and I am done. In the passage where the New Testament says that every one must work, it gives as a reason "in order that he may have something to give to those in need." Charity—giving to the poor—is an essential part of Christian morality: in the frightening parable of the sheep and the goats it seems to be the point on which everything turns. Some people nowadays say that charity ought to be unnecessary and that instead of giving to the poor we ought to be producing a society in which there were no poor to give to. They may be quite right in saying that we ought to produce that kind of society. But if anyone thinks that, as a consequence, you can stop giving in the meantime, then he has parted company with all Christian morality. I do not believe one can settle how much we ought to give. I am afraid the only safe rule is to give more than we can spare. In other words, if our expenditure on comforts, luxuries, amusements, etc., is up to the standard common among those with the same income as our own, we are probably giving away too little. If our charities do not at all pinch or hamper us, I should say they are too small. There ought to be things we should like to do and cannot do because our charitable expenditure excludes them. I am speaking now of "charities" in the common way. Particular cases of distress among your own relatives, friends, neighbours or employees, which God, as it were, forces upon your notice, may demand much more: even to the crippling and endangering of your own position. For many of us the great obstacle to charity lies not in our luxurious living or desire for more money, but in our fear—fear of insecurity. This must often be recognised as a temptation. Sometimes our pride also hinders our charity; we are tempted to spend more than we ought on the showy forms of generosity (tipping, hospitality) and less than we ought on those who really need our help.

And now, before I end, I am going to venture on a guess as to how this section has affected any who have read it. My guess is that there are some Leftist people among them who are very angry that it has not gone further in that direction, and some people of an opposite sort who are angry because they think it has gone much too far. If so, that brings us right up against the real snag in all this drawing up of blueprints for a Christian society. Most of us are not really approaching the subject in order to find out what Christianity says: we are approaching it in the hope of finding support from Christianity for the views of our own party. We are looking for an ally where we are offered either a Master or—a Judge. I am just the same. There are bits in this section that I wanted to leave out. And that is why nothing whatever is going to come of such talks unless we go a much longer way round. A Christian society is not going to arrive until most of us really want it: and we are not going to want it until we become fully Christian. I may repeat "Do as you would be done by" till I am black in the face, but I cannot really carry it out till I love my neighbour as myself: and I cannot learn to love my neighbour as myself till I learn to love God: and I cannot learn to love God except by learning to obey Him. And so, as I warned you, we are driven on to something more inward—driven on from social matters to religious matters. For the longest way round is the shortest way home.

4.

MORALITY AND PSYCHOANALYSIS

I have said that we should never get a Christian society unless most of us became Christian individuals. That does not mean, of course, that we can put off doing anything about society until some imaginary date in the far future. It means that we must begin both jobs at once—(1) the job of seeing how "Do as you would be done by" can be applied in detail to modern society, and (2) the job of becoming the sort of people who really would apply it if we saw how. I now want to begin considering what the Christian idea of a good man is—the Christian specification for the human machine.

Before I come down to details there are two more general points I should like to make. First of all, since Christian morality claims to be a technique for putting the human machine right, I think you would like to know how it is related to another technique which seems to make a similar claim—namely, psychoanalysis.

Now you want to distinguish very clearly between two things: between the actual medical theories and technique of the psychoanalysts, and the general philosophical view of the world which Freud and some others have gone on to add to this. The second thing—the philosophy of Freud—is in direct contradiction to Christianity: and also in direct contradiction to the other great psychologist, Jung. And furthermore, when Freud is talking about how to cure neurotics he is speaking as a specialist on his own subject, but when he goes on to talk general philosophy he is speaking as an amateur. It is therefore quite sensible to attend to him with respect in the one case and not in the other— and that is what I do. I am all the readier to do it because I have found that when he is talking off his own subject and on a subject I do know something about (namely, languages) he is very ignorant. But psychoanalysis itself, apart from all the philosophical additions that Freud and others have made to it, is not in the least contradictory to Christianity. Its technique overlaps with Christian morality at some points and it would not be a bad thing if every parson knew something about it: but it does not run the same course all the way, for the two techniques are doing rather different things.

When a man makes a moral choice two things are involved. One is the act of choosing. The other is the various feelings, impulses and so on which his psychological outfit presents him with, and which are the raw material of his choice. Now this raw material may be of two kinds. Either it may be what we would call normal: it may consist of the sort of feelings that are common to all men. Or else it may consist of quite unnatural feelings due to things that have gone wrong in his subconscious. Thus fear of things that are really dangerous would be an example of the first kind: an irrational fear of cats or spiders would be an example of the second kind. The desire of a man for a woman would be of the first kind: the perverted desire of a man for a man would be of the second. Now what psychoanalysis undertakes to do is to move the abnormal feelings, that is, to give the man better raw material for his acts of choice: morality is concerned with the acts of choice themselves.

Put it this way. Imagine three men who go to war. One has the ordinary natural fear of danger that any man has and he subdues it by moral effort and becomes a brave man. Let us suppose that the other two have, as a result of things in their subconsciousness, exaggerated, irrational fears, which no amount of moral effort can do anything about. Now suppose that a psychoanalyst comes along and cures these two: that is, he puts them both back in the position of the first man. Well it is just then that the psychoanalytical problem is over and the moral problem begins. Because, now that they are cured, these two men might take quite different lines. The first might say, "Thank goodness I've got rid of all those doo-dahs. Now at last I can do what I always wanted to do—my duty to the cause of freedom." But the other might say, "Well, I'm very glad that I now feel moderately cool under fire, but, of course, that doesn't alter the fact that I'm still jolly well determined to look after Number One and let the other chap do the dangerous job whenever I can. Indeed one of the good things about feeling less frightened is that I can now look after myself much more efficiently and can be much cleverer at hiding the fact from the others." Now this difference is a purely moral one and psychoanalysis cannot do anything about it. However much you improve the man's raw material, you have still got something else: the real, free choice of the man, on the material presented to him, either to put his own advantage first or to put it last. And this free choice is the only thing that morality is concerned with.

The bad psychological material is not a sin but a disease. It does not need to be repented of, but to be cured. And by the way, that is very important. Human beings judge one another by their external actions. God judges them by their moral choices. When a neurotic who has a pathological horror of cats forces himself to pick up a cat for some good reason, it is quite possible that in God's eyes he has shown more courage than a healthy man may have shown in winning the V.C. When a man who has been perverted from his youth and taught that cruelty is the right thing, does some tiny little kindness, or refrains from some cruelty he might have committed, and thereby, perhaps, risks being sneered at by his companions, he may, in God's eyes, be doing more than you and I would do if we gave up life itself for a friend.

It is as well to put this the other way round. Some of us who seem quite nice people may, in fact, have made so little use of a good heredity and a good upbringing that we are really worse than those whom we regard as fiends. Can we be quite certain how we should have behaved if we had been saddled with the psychological outfit, and then with the bad upbringing, and then with the power, say, of Himmler? That is why Christians are told not to judge. We see only the results which a man's choices make out of his raw material. But God does not judge him on the raw material at all, but on what he has done with it. Most of the man's psychological make-up is probably due to his body: when his body dies all that will fall off him, and the real central man, the thing that chose, that made the best or the worst out of this material, will stand naked. All sorts of nice things which we thought our own, but which were really due to a good digestion, will fall off some of us: all sorts of nasty things which were due to complexes or bad health will fall off others. We shall then, for the first time, see every one as he really was. There will be surprises.

And that leads on to my second point. People often think of Christian morality as a kind of bargain in which God says, "If you keep a lot of rules I'll reward you, and if you don't I'll do the other thing." I do not think that is the best way of looking at it. I would much rather say that every time you make a choice you are turning the central part of you, the part of you that chooses, into something a little different from what it was before. And taking your life as a whole, with all your innumerable choices, all your life long you are slowly turning this central thing either into a heavenly creature or into a hellish creature: either into a creature that is in harmony with God, and with other creatures, and with itself, or else into one that is in a state of war and hatred with God, and with its fellow-creatures, and with itself. To be the one kind of creature is heaven: that is, it is joy and peace and knowledge and power. To be the other means madness, horror, idiocy, rage, impotence, and eternal loneliness. Each of us at each moment is progressing to the one state or the other.

That explains what always used to puzzle me about Christian writers; they seem to be so very strict at one moment and so very free and easy at another. They talk about mere sins of thought as if they were immensely important: and then they talk about the most frightful murders and treacheries as if you had only got to repent and all would be forgiven. But I have come to see that they are right. What they are always thinking of is the mark which the action leaves on that tiny central self which no one sees in this life but which each of us will have to endure—or enjoy—for ever. One man may be so placed that his anger sheds the blood of thousands, and another so placed that however angry he gets he will only be laughed at. But the little mark on the soul may be much the same in both. Each has done something to himself which, unless he repents, will make it harder for him to keep out of the rage next time he is tempted, and will make the rage worse when he does fall into it. Each of them, if he seriously turns to God, can have that twist in the central man straightened out again: each is, in the long run, doomed if he will not. The bigness or smallness of the thing, seen from the outside, is not what really matters.

One last point. Remember that, as I said, the right direction leads not only to peace but to knowledge. When a man is getting better he understands more and more clearly the evil that is still left in him. When a man is getting worse, he understands his own badness less and less. A moderately bad man knows he is not very good: a thoroughly bad man thinks he is all right. This is common sense, really. You understand sleep when you are awake, not while you are sleeping. You can see mistakes in arithmetic when your mind is working properly: while you are making them you cannot see them. You can understand the nature of drunkenness when you are sober, not when you are drunk. Good people know about both good and evil: bad people do not know about either.

5.

SEXUAL MORALITY

We must now consider Christian morality as regards sex, what Christians call the virtue of chastity. The Christian rule of chastity must not be confused with the social rule of "modesty" (in one sense of that word); i.e. propriety, or decency. The social rule of propriety lays down how much of the human body should be displayed and what subjects can be referred to, and in what words, according to the customs of a given social circle. Thus, while the rule of chastity is the same for all Christians at all times, the rule of propriety changes. A girl in the Pacific islands wearing hardly any clothes and a Victorian lady completely covered in clothes might both be equally "modest," proper, or decent, according to the standards of their own societies: and both, for all we could tell by their dress, might be equally chaste (or equally unchaste). Some of the language which chaste women used in Shakespeare's time would have been used in the nineteenth century only by a woman completely abandoned. When people break the rule of propriety current in their own time and place, if they do so in order to excite lust in themselves or others, then they are offending against chastity. But if they break it through ignorance or carelessness they are guilty only of bad manners. When, as often happens, they break it defiantly in order to shock or embarrass others, they are not necessarily being unchaste, but they are being uncharitable: for it is uncharitable to take pleasure in making other people uncomfortable. I do not think that a very strict or fussy standard of propriety is any proof of chastity or any help to it, and I therefore regard the great relaxation and simplifying of the rule which has taken place in my own lifetime as a good thing. At its present

477

stage, however, it has this inconvenience, that people of different ages and different types do not all acknowledge the same standard, and we hardly know where we are. While this confusion lasts I think that old, or old-fashioned, people should be very careful not to assume that young or "emancipated" people are corrupt whenever they are (by the old standard) improper; and, in return, that young people should not call their elders prudes or puritans because they do not easily adopt the new standard. A real desire to believe all the good you can of others and to make others as comfortable as you can will solve most of the problems.

Chastity is the most unpopular of the Christian virtues. There is no getting away from it: the old Christian rule is, "Either marriage, with complete faithfulness to your partner, or else total abstinence." Now this is so difficult and so contrary to our instincts, that obviously either Christianity is wrong or our sexual instinct, as it now is, has gone wrong. One or the other. Of course, being a Christian, I think it is the instinct which has gone wrong.

But I have other reasons for thinking so. The biological purpose of sex is children, just as the biological purpose of eating is to repair the body. Now if we eat whenever we feel inclined and just as much as we want, it is quite true that most of us will eat too much: but not terrifically too much. One man may eat enough for two, but he does not eat enough for ten. The appetite goes a little beyond its biological purpose, but not enormously. But if a healthy young man indulged his sexual appetite whenever he felt inclined, and if each act produced a baby, then in ten years he might easily populate a small village. This appetite is in ludicrous and preposterous excess of its function.

Or take it another way. You can get a large audience together for a strip-tease act—that is, to watch a girl undress on the stage. Now suppose you came to a country where you could fill a theatre by simply bringing a covered plate on to the stage and then slowly lifting the cover so as to let every one see, just before the lights went out, that it contained a mutton chop or a bit of bacon, would you not think that in that country something had gone wrong with the appetite for food? And would not anyone who had grown up in a different world think there was something equally queer about the state of the sex instinct among us?

One critic said that if he found a country in which such strip-tease acts with food were popular, he would conclude that the people of that country were starving. He meant, of course, to imply that such things as the strip-tease act resulted not from sexual corruption but from sexual starvation. I agree with him that if, in some strange land, we found that similar acts with mutton chops were popular, one of the possible explanations which would occur to me would be famine. But the next step would be to test our hypothesis by finding out whether, in fact, much or little food was being consumed in that country. If the evidence showed that a good deal was being eaten, then of course we should have to abandon the hypothesis of starvation and try to think of another one. In the same way, before accepting sexual starvation as the cause of the strip-tease, we should have to look for evidence that there is in fact more sexual abstinence in our age than in those ages when things like the strip-tease were unknown. But surely there is no such evidence. Contraceptives have made sexual indulgence far less costly within marriage and far safer outside it than ever before, and public opinion is less hostile to illicit unions and even to perversion than it has been since Pagan times. Nor is the hypothesis of "starvation" the only one we can imagine. Everyone knows that the sexual appetite, like our other appetites, grows by indulgence. Starving men may think much about food, but so do gluttons; the gorged, as well as the famished, like titillations.

Here is a third point. You find very few people who want to eat things that really are not food or to do other things with food instead of eating it. In other words, perversions of the good appetite are rare. But perversions of the sex instinct are numerous, hard to cure, and frightful. I am sorry to have to go into all these details, but I must. The reason why I must is that you and I, for the last twenty years, have been fed all day long on good solid lies about sex. We have been told, till one is sick of hearing it, that sexual desire is in the same state as any of our other natural desires and that if only we abandon the silly old Victorian idea of hushing it up, everything in the garden will be lovely. It is not true. The moment you look at the facts, and away from the propaganda, you see that it is not.

They tell you sex has become a mess because it was hushed up. But for the last twenty years it has not been hushed up. It has been chattered about all day long. Yet it is still in a mess. If hushing up had been the cause of the trouble, ventilation would have set it right. But it has not. I think it is the other way round. I think the human race originally hushed it up because it had become such a mess. Modern people are always saying, "Sex is nothing to be ashamed of." They may mean two things. They may mean "There is nothing to be ashamed of in the fact that the human race reproduces itself in a certain way, nor in the fact that it gives pleasure." If they mean that, they are right. Christianity says the same. It is not the thing, nor the pleasure, that is the trouble. The old Christian teachers said that if man had never fallen, sexual pleasure, instead of being less than it is now, would actually have been greater. I know some muddle-headed Christians have talked as if Christianity thought that sex, or the body, or pleasure, were bad in themselves. But they were wrong. Christianity is almost the only one of the great religions which thoroughly approves of the body which believes that matter is good, that God Himself once took on a human body, that some kind of body is going to be given to us even in Heaven and is going to be an essential part of our happiness, our beauty, and our energy. Christianity has glorified marriage more than any other religion: and nearly all the greatest love poetry in the world has been produced by Christians. If anyone says that sex, in itself, is bad, Christianity contradicts him at once. But, of course, when people say, "Sex is nothing to be ashamed of," they may mean "the state into which the sexual instinct has now got is nothing to be ashamed of."

If they mean that, I think they are wrong. I think it is everything to be ashamed of. There is nothing to be ashamed of in enjoying your food: there would be everything to be ashamed of if half the world made food the main interest of their lives and spent their time looking at pictures of food and dribbling and smacking their lips. I do not say you and I are individually responsible for the present situation. Our ancestors have handed over to us organisms which are warped in this respect: and we grow up surrounded by propaganda in favour of unchastity. There are people who want to keep our sex instinct inflamed in order to make money out of us. Because, of course, a man with an obsession is a man who has very little sales-resistance. God knows our situation; He will not judge us as if we had no difficulties to overcome. What matters is the sincerity and perseverance of our will to overcome them.

Before we can be cured we must want to be cured. Those who really wish for help will get it; but for many modern people even the wish is difficult. It is easy to think that we want something when we do not really want it. A famous Christian long ago told us that when he was a young man he prayed constantly for chastity; but years later he realised that while his lips had been saying, "Oh Lord, make me chaste," his heart had been secretly adding, "But please don't do it just yet." This may happen in prayers for other virtues too; but there are three reasons why it is now specially difficult for us to desire—let alone to achieve— complete chastity.

In the first place our warped natures, the devils who tempt us, and all the contemporary propaganda for lust, combine to make us feel that the desires we are resisting are so "natural," so "healthy," and so reasonable, that it is almost perverse and abnormal to resist them. Poster after poster, film after film, novel after novel, associate the idea of sexual indulgence with the ideas of health, normality, youth, frankness, and good humour. Now this association is a lie. Like all powerful lies, it is based on a truth—the truth, acknowledged above, that sex in itself (apart from the excesses and obsessions that have grown round it) is "normal" and "healthy," and all the rest of it. The lie consists in the suggestion that any sexual act to which you are tempted at the moment is also healthy and normal. Now this, on any conceivable view, and quite apart from Christianity, must be nonsense. Surrender to all our desires obviously leads to impotence, disease, jealousies, lies, concealment, and everything that is the reverse of health, good humour, and frankness. For any happiness, even in this world, quite a lot of restraint is going to be necessary; so the claim made by every desire, when it is strong, to be healthy and reasonable, counts for nothing. Every sane and civilised man must have some set of principles by which he chooses to reject some of his desires and to permit others. One man does this on Christian principles, another on hygienic principles, another on sociological principles. The real conflict is not between Christianity and "nature," but between Christian principle and other principles in the control of "nature." For "nature" (in the sense of natural desire) will have to be controlled anyway, unless you are going to ruin your whole life. The Christian principles are, admittedly, stricter than the others; but then we think you will get help towards obeying them which you will not get towards obeying the others.

In the second place, many people are deterred from seriously attempting Christian chastity because they think (before trying) that it is impossible. But when a thing has to be attempted, one must never think about possibility or impossibility. Faced with an optional question in an examination paper, one considers whether one can do it or not: faced with a compulsory question, one must do the best one can. You may get some marks for a very imperfect answer: you will certainly get none for leaving the question alone. Not only in examinations but in war, in mountain climbing, in learning to skate, or swim, or ride a bicycle, even in fastening a stiff collar with cold fingers, people quite often do what seemed impossible before they did it. It is wonderful what you can do when you have to.

We may, indeed, be sure that perfect chastity—like perfect charity—will not be attained by any merely human efforts. You must ask for God's help. Even when you have done so, it may seem to you for a long time that no help, or less help than you need, is being given. Never mind. After each failure, ask forgiveness, pick yourself up, and try again. Very often what God first helps us towards is not the virtue itself but just this power of always trying again. For however important chastity (or courage, or truthfulness, or any other virtue) may be, this process trains us in habits of the soul which are more important still. It curses our illusions about ourselves and teaches us to depend on God. We learn, on the one hand, that we cannot trust ourselves, even in our best moments, and, on the other, that we need not despair even in our worst, for our failures are forgiven. The only fatal thing is to sit down content with anything less than perfection.

Thirdly, people often misunderstand what psychology teaches about "repressions." It teaches us that "repressed" sex is dangerous. But "repressed" is here a technical term: it does not mean "suppressed" in the sense of "denied" or "resisted." A repressed desire or thought is one which has been thrust into the subconscious (usually at a very early age) and can now come before the mind only in a disguised and unrecognisable form. Repressed sexuality does not appear to the patient to be sexuality at all. When an adolescent or an adult is engaged in resisting a conscious desire, he is not dealing with a repression nor is he in the least danger of creating a repression. On the contrary, those who are seriously attempting chastity are more conscious, and soon know a great deal more about their own sexuality than anyone else. They come to know their desires as Wellington knew Napoleon, or as Sherlock Holmes knew Moriarty; as a ratcatcher knows rats or a plumber knows about leaky pipes. Virtue —even attempted virtue—brings light; indulgence brings fog.

Finally, though I have had to speak at some length about sex, I want to make it as clear as I possibly can that the centre of Christian morality is not here. If anyone thinks that Christians regard unchastity as the supreme vice, he is quite wrong. The sins of the flesh are bad, but they are the least bad of all sins. All the worst pleasures are purely spiritual: the pleasure of putting other people in the wrong, of bossing and patronising and spoiling sport, and back-biting; the pleasures of power, of hatred. For there are two things inside me, competing with the human self which I must try to become. They are the Animal self, and the Diabolical self. The Diabolical self is the worst of the two. That is why a cold, self-righteous prig who goes regularly to church may be far nearer to hell than a prostitute. But, of course, it is better to be neither.

6.

CHRISTIAN MARRIAGE

The last chapter was mainly negative. I discussed what was wrong with the sexual impulse in man, but said very little about its right working—in other words, about Christian marriage. There are two reasons why I do not particularly want to deal with marriage. The first is that the Christian doctrines on this subject are extremely unpopular. The second is that I have never been married myself, and, therefore, can speak only at second hand. But in spite of that, I feel I can hardly leave the subject out in an account of Christian morals.

The Christian idea of marriage is based on Christ's words that a man and wife are to be regarded as a single organism—for that is what the words "one flesh" would be in modern English. And the Christians believe that when He said this He was not expressing a sentiment but stating a fact—just as one is stating a fact when one says that a lock and its key are one mechanism, or that a violin and a bow are one musical instrument. The inventor of the human machine was telling us that its two halves, the male and the female, were made to be combined together in pairs, not simply on the sexual level, but totally combined. The monstrosity of sexual intercourse outside marriage is that those who indulge in it are trying to isolate one kind of union (the sexual) from all the other kinds of union which were intended to go along with it and make up the total union. The Christian attitude does not mean that there is anything wrong about sexual pleasure, any more than about the pleasure of eating. It means that you must not isolate that pleasure and try to get it by itself, any more than you ought to try to get the pleasures of taste without swallow-

484

ing and digesting, by chewing things and spitting them out
again.

As a consequence, Christianity teaches that marriage is for
life. There is, of course, a difference here between different
Churches: some do not admit divorce at all; some allow it reluctantly in very special cases. It is a great pity that Christians should
disagree about such a question; but for an ordinary layman the
thing to notice is that Churches all agree with one another about
marriage a great deal more than any of them agrees with the outside world. I mean, they all regard divorce as something like cutting up a living body, as a kind of surgical operation. Some of
them think the operation so violent that it cannot be done at
all; others admit it as a desperate remedy in extreme cases. They
are all agreed that it is more like having both your legs cut off
than it is like dissolving a business partnership or even deserting
a regiment. What they all disagree with is the modern view that
it is a simple readjustment of partners, to be made whenever
people feel they are no longer in love with one another, or when
either of them falls in love with someone else.

Before we consider this modern view in its relation to chastity,
we must not forget to consider it in relation to another virtue,
namely justice. Justice, as I said before, includes the keeping of
promises. Now everyone who has been married in a church has
made a public, solemn promise to stick to his (or her) partner
till death. The duty of keeping that promise has no special connection with sexual morality: it is in the same position as any
other promise. If, as modern people are always telling us, the
sexual impulse is just like all our other impulses, then it ought
to be treated like all our other impulses; and as their indulgence
is controlled by our promises, so should its be. If, as I think, it is
not like all our other impulses, but is morbidly inflamed, then
we should be especially careful not to let it lead us into dishonesty.

To this someone may reply that he regarded the promise made
in church as a mere formality and never intended to keep it.
Whom, then, was he trying to deceive when he made it? God?
That was really very unwise. Himself? That was not very much

wiser. The bride, or bridegroom, or the "in-laws"? That was treacherous. Most often, I think, the couple (or one of them) hoped to deceive the public. They wanted the respectability that is attached to marriage without intending to pay the price: that is, they were impostors, they cheated. If they are still contented cheats, I have nothing to say to them: who would urge the high and hard duty of chastity on people who have not yet wished to be merely honest? If they have now come to their senses and want to be honest, their promise, already made, constrains them. And this, you will see, comes under the heading of justice, not that of chastity. If people do not believe in permanent marriage, it is perhaps better that they should live together unmarried than that they should make vows they do not mean to keep. It is true that by living together without marriage they will be guilty (in Christian eyes) of fornication. But one fault is not mended by adding another: unchastity is not improved by adding perjury.

The idea that "being in love" is the only reason for remaining married really leaves no room for marriage as a contract or promise at all. If love is the whole thing, then the promise can add nothing; and if it adds nothing, then it should not be made. The curious thing is that lovers themselves, while they remain really in love, know this better than those who talk about love. As Chesterton pointed out, those who are in love have a natural inclination to bind themselves by promises. Love songs all over the world are full of vows of eternal constancy. The Christian law is not forcing upon the passion of love something which is foreign to that passion's own nature: it is demanding that lovers should take seriously something which their passion of itself impels them to do.

And, of course, the promise, made when I am in love and because I am in love, to be true to the beloved as long as I live, commits one to being true even if I cease to be in love. A promise must be about things that I can do, about actions: no one can promise to go on feeling in a certain way. He might as well promise never to have a headache or always to feel hungry. But what, it may be asked, is the use of keeping two people together if they are no longer in love? There are several sound, social reasons; to provide a home for their children, to protect the woman (who has probably sacrificed or damaged her own career by getting married) from being dropped whenever the man is tired of her. But there is also another reason of which I am very sure, though I find it a little hard to explain.

It is hard because so many people cannot be brought to realise that when B is better than C, A may be even better than B. They like thinking in terms of good and bad, not of good, better, and best, or bad, worse and worst. They want to know whether you think patriotism a good thing: if you reply that it is, of course, far better than individual selfishness, but that it is inferior to universal charity and should always give way to universal charity when the two conflict, they think you are being evasive. They ask what you think of duelling. If you reply that it is far better to forgive a man than to fight a duel with him, but that even a duel might be better than a lifelong enmity which expresses itself in secret efforts to "do the man down," they go away complaining that you would not give them a straight answer. I hope no one will make this mistake about what I am now going to say.

What we call "being in love" is a glorious state, and, in several ways, good for us. It helps to make us generous and courageous, it opens our eyes not only to the beauty of the beloved but to all beauty, and it subordinates (especially at first) our merely animal sexuality; in that sense, love is the great conqueror of lust. No one in his senses would deny that being in love is far better than either common sensuality or cold self-centredness. But, as I said before, "the most dangerous thing you can do is to take any one impulse of our own nature and set it up as the thing you ought to follow at all costs." Being in love is a good thing, but it is not the best thing. There are many things below it, but there are also things above it. You cannot make it the basis of a whole life. It is a noble feeling, but it is still a feeling. Now no feeling can be relied on to last in its full intensity, or even to last at all. Knowledge can last, principles can last, habits can last; but feelings come and go. And in fact, whatever people say, the state called "being in love" usually does not last. If the old fairy-tale ending "They lived happily ever after" is taken to mean "They felt for the next fifty years exactly as they felt the day before they were married," then it says what probably never was nor ever could be true, and would be highly undesirable if it were. Who could bear to live in that excitement for even five years? What would become of your work, your appetite, your sleep, your friendships? But, of course, ceasing to be "in love" need not mean ceasing to love. Love in this second sense—love as distinct from "being in love" is not merely a feeling. It is a deep unity, maintrained by the will and deliberately strengthened by habit; reinforced by (in Christian marriages) the grace which both parents ask, and receive, from God. They can have this love for each other even at those moments when they do not like each other; as you love yourself even when you do not like yourself. They can retain this love even when each would easily, if they allowed themselves, be "in love" with someone else. "Being in love" first moved them to promise fidelity: this quieter love enables them to keep the promise. It is on this love that the engine of marriage *is* run: being in love was the explosion that started it.

If you disagree with me, of course, you will say, "He knows nothing about it, he is not married." You may quite possibly be right. But before you say that, make quite sure that you are judging me by what you really know from your own experience and from watching the lives of your friends, and not by ideas you have derived from novels and films. This is not so easy to do as people think. Our experience is coloured through and through by books and plays and the cinema, and it takes patience and skill to disentangle the things we have really learned from life for ourselves.

People get from books the idea that if you have married the right person you may expect to go on "being in love" for ever. As a result, when they find they are not, they think this proves they have made a mistake and are entitled to a change—not realising that, when they have changed, the glamour will presently go out of the new love just as it went out of the old one. In this department of life, as in every other, thrills come at the beginning and do not last. The sort of thrill a boy has at the first idea of flying will not go on when he has joined the R.A.F. and is really learning to fly. The thrill you feel on first seeing some delightful place dies away when you really go to live there. Does this mean it would be better not to learn to fly and not to live in the beautiful place? By no means. In both cases, if you go through with it, the dying away of the first thrill will be compensated for by a quieter and more lasting kind of interest. What is more (and I can hardly find words to tell you how important I think this), it is just the people who are ready to submit to the loss of the thrill and settle down to the sober interest, who are then most likely to meet new thrills in some quite different direction. The man who has learned to fly and becomes a good pilot will suddenly discover music; the man who has settled down to live in the beauty spot will discover gardening.

This is, I think, one little part of what Christ meant by saying that a thing will not really live unless it first dies. It is simply no good trying to keep any thrill: that is the very worst thing you can do. Let the thrill go—let it die away—go on through that period of death into the quieter interest and happiness that follow—and you will find you are living in a world of new thrills all the time. But if you decide to make thrills your regular diet and try to prolong them artificially, they will all get weaker and weaker, and fewer and fewer, and you will be a bored, disillusioned old man for the rest of your life. It is because so few people understand this that you find many middle-aged men and women maundering about their lost youth, at the very age when new horizons ought to be appearing and new doors opening all round them. It is much better fun to learn to swim than to go on endlessly (and hopelessly) trying to get back the feeling you had when you first went paddling as a small boy.

Another notion we get from novels and plays is that "falling in love" is something quite irresistible; something that just happens to one, like measles. And because they believe this, some married people throw up the sponge and give in when they find themselves attracted by a new acquaintance. But I am inclined to think that these irresistible passions are much rarer in real life than in books, at any rate when one is grown up. When we meet someone beautiful and clever and sympathetic, of course we ought, in one sense, to admire and love these good qualities. But is it not very largely in our own choice whether this love shall, or shall not, turn into what we call "being in love"? No doubt, if our minds are full of novels and plays and sentimental songs, and our bodies full of alcohol, we shall turn any love we feel into that kind of love: just as if you have a rut in your path all the rainwater will run into that rut, and if you wear blue spectacles everything you see will turn blue. But that will be our own fault.

Before leaving the question of divorce, I should like to distinguish two things which are very often confused. The Christian conception of marriage is one: the other is the quite different question—how far Christians, if they are voters or Members of Parliament, ought to try to force their views of marriage on the rest of the community by embodying them in the divorce laws. A great many people seem to think that if you are a Christian yourself you should try to make divorce difficult for everyone. I do not think that. At least I know I should be very angry if the Mohammedans tried to prevent the rest of us from drinking wine. My own view is that the Churches should frankly recognise that the majority of the British people are not Christians and, therefore, cannot be expected to live Christian lives. There ought to be two distinct kinds of marriage: one governed by the State with rules enforced on all citizens, the other governed by the Church with rules enforced by her on her own members. The distinction ought to be quite sharp, so that a man knows which couples are married in a Christian sense and which are not.

So much for the Christian doctrine about the permanence of marriage. Something else, even more unpopular, remains to be dealt with. Christian wives promise to obey their husbands. In Christian marriage the man is said to be the "head." Two questions obviously arise here. (1) Why should there be a head at all —why not equality? (2) Why should it be the man?

(1) The need for some head follows from the idea that marriage is permanent. Of course, as long as the husband and wife are agreed, no question of a head need arise; and we may hope that this will be the normal state of affairs in a Christian marriage. But when there is a real disagreement, what is to happen? Talk it over, of course; but I am assuming they have done that and still failed to reach agreement. What do they do next? They cannot decide by a majority vote, for in a council of two there can be no majority. Surely, only one or other of two things can

happen: either they must separate and go their own ways or else one or other of them must have a casting vote. If marriage is permanent, one or other party must, in the last resort, have the power of deciding the family policy. You cannot have a permanent association without a constitution.

(2) If there must be a head, why the man? Well, firstly, is there any very serious wish that it should be the woman? As I have said, I am not married myself, but as far as I can see, even a woman who wants to be the head of her own house does not usually admire the same state of things when she finds it going on next door. She is much more likely to say "Poor Mr. X! Why he allows that appalling woman to boss him about the way she does is more than I can imagine." I do not think she is even very flattered if anyone mentions the fact of her own "headship." There must be something unnatural about the rule of wives over husbands, because the wives themselves are half ashamed of it and despise the husbands whom they rule. But there is also another reason; and here I speak quite frankly as a bachelor, because it is a reason you can see from outside even better than from inside. The relations of the family to the outer world —what might be called its foreign policy—must depend, in the last resort, upon the man, because he always ought to be, and usually is, much more just to the outsiders. A woman is primarily fighting for her own children and husband against the rest of the world. Naturally, almost, in a sense, rightly, their claims override, for her, all other claims. She is the special trustee of their interests. The function of the husband is to see that this natural preference of hers is not given its head. He has the last word in order to protect other people from the intense family patriotism of the wife. If anyone doubts this, let me ask a simple question. If your dog has bitten the child next door, or if your child has hurt the dog next door, which would you sooner have to deal with, the master of that house or the mistress? Or, if you are a married woman, let me ask you this question. Much as you admire your husband, would you not say that his chief failing is his tendency not to stick up for his rights and yours against the neighbours as vigorously as you would like? A bit of an Appeaser?

7.

FORGIVENESS

I said in a previous chapter that chastity was the most unpopular of the Christian virtues. But I am not sure I was right. I believe the one I have to talk of today is even more unpopular: the Christian rule, "Thou shalt love thy neighbour as thyself." Because in Christian morals "thy neighbour" includes "thy enemy," and so we come up against this terrible duty of forgiving our enemies.

Every one says forgiveness is a lovely idea, until they have something to forgive, as we had during the war. And then, to mention the subject at all is to be greeted with howls of anger. It is not that people think this too high and difficult a virtue: it is that they think it hateful and contemptible. "That sort of talk makes them sick," they say. And half of you already want to ask me, "I wonder how you'd feel about forgiving the Gestapo if you were a Pole or a Jew?"

So do I. I wonder very much. Just as when Christianity tells me that I must not deny my religion even to save myself from death by torture, I wonder very much what I should do when it came to the point. I am not trying to tell you in this book what I could do—I can do precious little—I am telling you what Christianity is. I did not invent it. And there, right in the middle of it, I find "Forgive us our sins as we forgive those that sin against us." There is no slightest suggestion that we are offered forgiveness on any other terms. It is made perfectly clear that if we do not forgive we shall not be forgiven. There are no two ways about it. What are we to do?

It is going to be hard enough, anyway, but I think there are two things we can do to make it easier. When you start mathematics you do not begin with the calculus; you begin with simple addition. In the same way, if we really want (but all depends on really wanting) to learn how to forgive, perhaps we had better start with something easier than the Gestapo. One might start with forgiving one's husband or wife, or parents or children, or the nearest N.C.O., for something they have done or said in the last week. That will probably keep us busy for the moment. And secondly, we might try to understand exactly what loving your neighbour as yourself means. I have to love him as I love myself. Well, how exactly do I love myself?

Now that I come to think of it, I have not exactly got a feeling of fondness or affection for myself, and I do not even always enjoy my own society. So apparently "Love your neighbour" does not mean "feel fond of him" or "find him attractive." I ought to have seen that before, because, of course, you cannot feel fond of a person by trying. Do I think well of myself, think myself a nice chap? Well, I am afraid I sometimes do (and those are, no doubt, my worst moments) but that is not why I love myself. In fact it is the other way round: my self-love makes me think myself nice, but thinking myself nice is not why I love myself. So loving my enemies does not apparently mean thinking them nice either. That is an enormous relief. For a good many people imagine that forgiving your enemies means making out that they are really not such bad fellows after all, when it is quite plain that they are. Go a step further. In my most clear-sighted moments not only do I not think myself a nice man, but I know that I am a very nasty one. I can look at some of the things I have done with horror and loathing. So apparently I am allowed to loathe and hate some of the things my enemies do. Now that I come to think of it, I remember Christian teachers telling me long ago that I must hate a bad man's actions, but not hate the bad man: or, as they would say, hate the sin but not the sinner.

For a long time I used to think this a silly, straw-splitting distinction: how could you hate what a man did and not hate the man? But years later it occurred to me that there was one man to whom I had been doing this all my life—namely myself. However much I might dislike my own cowardice or conceit or greed, I went on loving myself. There had never been the slightest difficulty about it. In fact the very reason why I hated the things was that I loved the man. Just because I loved myself, I was sorry to find that I was the sort of man who did those things. Consequently, Christianity does not want us to reduce by one atom the hatred we feel for cruelty and treachery. We ought to hate them. Not one word of what we have said about them needs to be unsaid. But it does want us to hate them in the same way in which we hate things in ourselves: being sorry that the man should have done such things, and hoping, if it is anyway possible, that somehow, sometime, somewhere, he can be cured and made human again.

The real test is this. Suppose one reads a story of filthy atrocities in the paper. Then suppose that something turns up suggesting that the story might not be quite true, or not quite so bad as it was made out. Is one's first feeling, "Thank God, even they aren't quite so bad as that," or is it a feeling of disappointment, and even a determination to cling to the first story for the sheer pleasure of thinking your enemies as bad as possible? If it is the second then it is, I am afraid, the first step in a process which, if followed to the end, will make us into devils. You see, one is beginning to wish that black was a little blacker. If we give that wish its head, later on we shall wish to see grey as black, and then to see white itself as black. Finally, we shall insist on seeing everything—God and our friends and ourselves included—as bad, and not be able to stop doing it: we shall be fixed for ever in a universe of pure hatred.

Now a step further. Does loving your enemy mean not punishing him? No, for loving myself does not mean that I ought not to subject myself to punishment—even to death. If one had committed a murder, the right Christian thing to do would be to give yourself up to the police and be hanged. It is, therefore, in my opinion, perfectly right for a Christian judge to sentence a man to death or a Christian soldier to kill an enemy. I always have thought so, ever since I became a Christian, and long before the war, and I still think so now that we are at peace. It is no good quoting "Thou shalt not kill." There are two Greek words: the ordinary word to *kill* and the word to *murder*. And when Christ quotes that commandment He uses the *murder* one

in all three accounts, Matthew, Mark, and Luke. And I am told
there is the same distinction in Hebrew. All killing is not murder
any more than all sexual intercourse is adultery. When soldiers
came to St. John the Baptist asking what to do, he never remotely
suggested that they ought to leave the army: nor did Christ
when He met a Roman sergeant-major—what they called a cen-
turion. The idea of the knight—the Christian in arms for the
defence of a good cause—is one of the great Christian ideas. War
is a dreadful thing, and I can respect an honest pacifist, though I
think he is entirely mistaken. What I cannot understand is this
sort of semipacifism you get nowadays which gives people the
idea that though you have to fight, you ought to do it with a
long face and as if you were ashamed of it. It is that feeling that
robs lots of magnificent young Christians in the Services of something they have a right to, something which is the natural accom-
paniment of courage—a kind of gaiety and wholeheartedness.

I have often thought to myself how it would have been if,
when I served in the first world war, I and some young German
had killed each other simultaneously and found ourselves together
a moment after death. I cannot imagine that either of us would
have felt any resentment or even any embarrassment. I think
we might have laughed over it.

I imagine somebody will say, "Well, if one is allowed to condemn the enemy's acts, and punish him, and kill him, what difference is left between Christian morality and the ordinary view?"
All the difference in the world. Remember, we Christians think
man lives for ever. Therefore, what really matters is those little
marks or twists on the central, inside part of the soul which are
going to turn it, in the long run, into a heavenly or a hellish
creature. We may kill if necessary, but we must not hate and enjoy hating. We may punish if necessary, but we must not enjoy
it. In other words, something inside us, the feeling of resentment,
the feeling that wants to get one's own back, must be simply
killed. I do not mean that anyone can decide this moment that
he will never feel it any more. That is not how things happen. I
mean that every time it bobs its head up, day after day, year after
year, all our lives long, we must hit it on the head. It is hard
work, but the attempt is not impossible. Even while we kill and

punish we must try to feel about the enemy as we feel about ourselves—to wish that he were not bad, to hope that he may, in this world or another, be cured: in fact, to wish his good. That is what is meant in the Bible by loving him: wishing his good, not feeling fond of him nor saying he is nice when he is not.

I admit that this means loving people who have nothing lovable about them. But then, has oneself anything lovable about it? You love it simply because it is yourself. God intends us to love all selves in the same way and for the same reason: but He has given us the sum ready worked out on our own case to show us how it works. We have then to go on and apply the rule to all the other selves. Perhaps it makes it easier if we remember that that is how He loves us. Not for any nice, attractive qualities we think we have, but just because we are the things called selves. For really there is nothing else in us to love: creatures like us who actually find hatred such a pleasure that to give it up is like giving up beer or tobacco. . . .

8.

THE GREAT SIN

Today I come to that part of Christian morals where they differ most sharply from all other morals. There is one vice of which no man in the world is free; which every one in the world loathes when he sees it in someone else; and of which hardly any people, except Christians, ever imagine that they are guilty themselves. I have heard people admit that they are bad-tempered, or that they cannot keep their heads about girls or drink, or even that they are cowards. I do not think I have ever heard anyone who was not a Christian accuse himself of this vice. And at the same time I have very seldom met anyone, who was not a Christian, who showed the slightest mercy to it in others. There is no fault which makes a man more unpopular, and no fault which we are more unconscious of in ourselves. And the more we have it ourselves, the more we dislike it in others.

The vice I am talking of is Pride or Self-Conceit: and the virtue opposite to it, in Christian morals, is called Humility. You may remember, when I was talking about sexual morality, I warned you that the centre of Christian morals did not lie there. Well, now, we have come to the centre. According to Christian teachers, the essential vice, the utmost evil, is Pride. Unchastity, anger, greed, drunkenness, and all that, are mere fleabites in comparison: it was through Pride that the devil became the devil: Pride leads to every other vice: it is the complete anti-God state of mind.

Does this seem to you exaggerated? If so, think it over. I pointed out a moment ago that the more pride one had, the more one disliked pride in others. In fact, if you want to find out how proud you are the easiest way is to ask yourself, "How much do I

497

dislike it when other people snub me, or refuse to take any notice of me, or shove their oar in, or patronise me, or show off?" The point is that each person's pride is in competition with every one else's pride. It is because I wanted to be the big noise at the party that I am so annoyed at someone else being the big noise. Two of a trade never agree. Now what you want to get clear is that Pride is *essentially* competitive—is competitive by its very nature—while the other vices are competitive only, so to speak, by accident. Pride gets no pleasure out of having something, only out of having more of it than the next man. We say that people are proud of being rich, or clever, or good-looking, but they are not. They are proud of being richer, or cleverer, or better-looking than others. If every one else became equally rich, or clever, or good-looking there would be nothing to be proud about. It is the comparison that makes you proud: the pleasure of being above the rest. Once the element of competition has gone, pride has gone. That is why I say that Pride is essentially competitive in a way the other vices are not. The sexual impulse may drive two men into competition if they both want the same girl. But that is only by accident; they might just as likely have wanted two different girls. But a proud man will take your girl from you, not because he wants her, but just to prove to himself that he is a better man than you. Greed may drive men into competition if there is not enough to go round; but the proud man, even when he has got more than he can possibly want, will try to get still more just to assert his power. Nearly all those evils in the world which people put down to greed or selfishness are really far more the result of Pride.

Take it with money. Greed will certainly make a man want money, for the sake of a better house, better holidays, better things to eat and drink. But only up to a point. What is it that makes a man with £10,000 a year anxious to get £20,000 a year? It is not the greed for more pleasure. £10,000 will give all the luxuries that any man can really enjoy. It is Pride—the wish to be richer than some other rich man, and (still more) the wish for power. For, of course, power is what Pride really enjoys: there is nothing makes a man feel so superior to others as being able to move them about like toy soldiers. What makes a pretty girl spread misery wherever she goes by collecting admirers? Certainly not her sexual instinct: that kind of girl is quite often sexually frigid. It is Pride. What is it that makes a political leader or a whole nation go on and on, demanding more and more? Pride again. Pride is competitive by its very nature: that is why it goes on and on. If I am a proud man, then, as long as there is one man in the whole world more powerful, or richer, or cleverer than I, he is my rival and my enemy.

The Christians are right: it is Pride which has been the chief cause of misery in every nation and every family since the world began. Other vices may sometimes bring people together: you may find good fellowship and jokes and friendliness among drunken people or unchaste people. But Pride always means enmity—it *is* enmity. And not only enmity between man and man, but enmity to God.

In God you come up against something which is in every respect immeasurably superior to yourself. Unless you know God as that—and, therefore, know yourself as nothing in comparison —you do not know God at all. As long as you are proud you cannot know God. A proud man is always looking down on things and people: and, of course, as long as you are looking down, you cannot see something that is above you.

That raises a terrible question. How is it that people who are quite obviously eaten up with Pride can say they believe in God and appear to themselves very religious? I am afraid it means they are worshipping an imaginary God. They theoretically admit themselves to be nothing in the presence of this phantom God, but are really all the time imagining how He approves of them and thinks them far better than ordinary people: that is, they pay a pennyworth of imaginary humility to Him and get out of it a pound's worth of Pride towards their fellow-men. I suppose it was of those people Christ was thinking when He said that some would preach about Him and cast out devils in His name, only to be told at the end of the world that He had never known them. And any of us may at any moment be in this death-trap. Luckily, we have a test. Whenever we find that our religious life is making us feel that we are good—above all, that we are better than someone else—I think we may be sure that we are being acted on, not by God, but by the devil. The real test of being in the presence of God is that you either forget about yourself altogether or see yourself as a small, dirty object. It is better to forget about yourself altogether.

It is a terrible thing that the worst of all the vices can smuggle itself into the very centre of our religious life. But you can see why. The other, and less bad, vices come from the devil working on us through our animal nature. But this does not come through our animal nature at all. It comes direct from Hell. It is purely spiritual: consequently it is far more subtle and deadly. For the same reason, Pride can often be used to beat down the simpler vices. Teachers, in fact, often appeal to a boy's Pride, or, as they call it, his self-respect, to make him behave decently: many a man has overcome cowardice, or lust, or ill-temper by learning to think that they are beneath his dignity—that is, by Pride. The devil laughs. He is perfectly content to see you becoming chaste and brave and self-controlled provided, all the time, he is setting up in you the Dictatorship of Pride—just as he would be quite content to see your chilblains cured if he was allowed, in return, to give you cancer. For Pride is spiritual cancer: it eats up the very possibility of love, or contentment, or even common sense.

Before leaving this subject I must guard against some possible misunderstandings:

(1) Pleasure in being praised is not Pride. The child who is patted on the back for doing a lesson well, the woman whose beauty is praised by her lover, the saved soul to whom Christ says "Well done," are pleased and ought to be. For here the pleasure lies not in what you are but in the fact that you have pleased someone you wanted (and rightly wanted) to please. The trouble begins when you pass from thinking, "I have pleased him; all is well," to thinking, "What a fine person I must be to have done it." The more you delight in yourself and the less you delight in the praise, the worse you are becoming. When you delight wholly in yourself and do not care about the praise at all, you have reached the bottom. That is why vanity, though it is the sort of Pride which shows most on the surface, is really the least bad and most pardonable sort. The vain person wants praise, ap-

plause, admiration, too much and is always angling for it. It is a fault, but a childlike and even (in an odd way) a humble fault. It shows that you are not yet completely contented with your own admiration. You value other people enough to want them to look at you. You are, in fact, still human. The real black, diabolical Pride comes when you look down on others so much that you do not care what they think of you. Of course, it is very right, and often our duty, not to care what people think of us, if we do so for the right reason; namely, because we care so incomparably more what God thinks. But the Proud man has a different reason for not caring. He says "Why should I care for the applause of that rabble as if their opinion were worth anything? And even if their opinions were of value, am I the sort of man to blush with pleasure at a compliment like some chit of a girl at her first dance? No, I am an integrated, adult personality. All I have done has been done to satisfy my own ideals—or my artistic conscience—or the traditions of my family—or, in a word, because I'm That Kind of Chap. If the mob like it, let them. They're nothing to me." In this way real thoroughgoing Pride may act as a check on vanity; for, as I said a moment ago, the devil loves "curing" a small fault by giving you a great one. We must try not to be vain, but we must never call in our Pride to cure our vanity; better the frying-pan than the fire.

(2) We say in English that a man is "proud" of his son, or his father, or his school, or regiment, and it may be asked whether "pride" in this sense is a sin. I think it depends on what, exactly, we mean by "proud of." Very often, in such sentences, the phrase "is proud of" means "has a warm-hearted admiration for." Such an admiration is, of course, very far from being a sin. But it might, perhaps, mean that the person in question gives himself airs on the ground of his distinguished father, or because he belongs to a famous regiment. This would, clearly, be a fault; but even then, it would be better than being proud simply of himself. To love and admire anything outside yourself is to take one step away from utter spiritual ruin; though we shall not be well so long as we love and admire anything more than we love and admire God.

(3) We must not think Pride is something God forbids because

He is offended at it, or that Humility is something He demands as due to His own dignity—as if God Himself was proud. He is not in the least worried about His dignity. The point is, He wants you to know Him: wants to give you Himself. And He and you are two things of such a kind that if you really get into any kind of touch with Him you will, in fact, be humble—delightedly humble, feeling the infinite relief of having for once got rid of all the silly nonsense about your own dignity which has made you restless and unhappy all your life. He is trying to make you humble in order to make this moment possible: trying to take off a lot of silly, ugly, fancy-dress in which we have all got ourselves up and are strutting about like the little idiots we are. I wish I had got a bit further with humility myself: if I had, I could probably tell you more about the relief, the comfort, of taking the fancy-dress off—getting rid of the false self, with all its "Look at me" and "Aren't I a good boy?" and all its posing and posturing. To get even near it, even for a moment, is like a drink of cold water to a man in a desert.

(4) Do not imagine that if you meet a really humble man he will be what most people call "humble" nowadays: he will not be a sort of greasy, smarmy person, who is always telling you that, of course, he is nobody. Probably all you will think about him is that he seemed a cheerful, intelligent chap who took a real interest in what *you* said to *him*. If you do dislike him it will be because you feel a little envious of anyone who seems to enjoy life so easily. He will not be thinking about humility: he will not be thinking about himself at all.

If anyone would like to acquire humility, I can, I think, tell him the first step. The first step is to realise that one is proud. And a biggish step, too. At least, nothing whatever can be done before it. If you think you are not conceited, it means you are very conceited indeed.

9.

CHARITY

I said in an earlier chapter that there were four "Cardinal" virtues and three "Theological" virtues. The three Theological ones are Faith, Hope, and Charity. Faith is going to be dealt with in the last two chapters. Charity was partly dealt with in Chapter 7, but there I concentrated on that part of Charity which is called Forgiveness. I now want to add a little more.

First, as to the meaning of the word. "Charity" now means simply what used to be called "alms"—that is, giving to the poor. Originally it had a much wider meaning. (You can see how it got the modern sense. If a man has "charity," giving to the poor is one of the most obvious things he does, and so people came to talk as if that were the whole of charity. In some way, "rhyme" is the most obvious thing about poetry, and so people come to mean by "poetry" simply rhyme and nothing more.) Charity means "Love, in the Christian sense." But love, in the Christian sense, does not mean an emotion. It is a state not of the feelings but of the will; that state of the will which we have naturally about ourselves, and must learn to have about other people.

I pointed out in the chapter on Forgiveness that our love for ourselves does not mean that we *like* ourselves. It means that we wish our own good. In the same way Christian Love (or Charity) for our neighbours is quite a different thing from liking or affection. We "like" or are "fond of" some people, and not of others. It is important to understand that this natural "liking" is neither a sin nor a virtue, any more than your likes and dislikes in food are a sin or a virtue. It is just a fact. But, of course, what we do about it is either sinful or virtuous.

Natural liking or affection for people makes it easier to be "charitable" towards them. It is, therefore, normally a duty to encourage our affections—to "like" people as much as we can (just as it is often our duty to encourage our liking for exercise or wholesome food)—not because this liking is itself the virtue of charity, but because it is a help to it. On the other hand, it is also necessary to keep a very sharp look-out for fear our liking for some one person makes us uncharitable, or even unfair, to someone else. There are even cases where our liking conflicts with our charity towards the person we like. For example, a doting mother may be tempted by natural affection to "spoil" her child; that is, to gratify her own affectionate impulses at the expense of the child's real happiness later on.

But though natural likings should normally be encouraged, it would be quite wrong to think that the way to become charitable is to sit trying to manufacture affectionate feelings. Some people are "cold" by temperament; that may be a misfortune for them, but it is no more a sin than having a bad digestion is a sin; and it does not cut them out from the chance, or excuse them from the duty, of learning charity. The rule for all of us is perfectly simple. Do not waste time bothering whether you "love" your neighbour; act as if you did. As soon as we do this we find one of the great secrets. When you are behaving as if you loved someone, you will presently come to love him. If you injure someone you dislike, you will find yourself disliking him more. If you do him a good turn, you will find yourself disliking him less. There is, indeed, one exception. If you do him a good turn, not to please God and obey the law of charity, but to show him what a fine forgiving chap you are, and to put him in your debt, and then sit down to wait for his "gratitude," you will probably be disappointed. (People are not fools: they have a very quick eye for anything like showing off, or patronage.) But whenever we do good to another self, just because it is a self, made (like us) by God, and desiring its own happiness as we desire ours, we shall have learned to love it a little more or, at least, to dislike it less.

Consequently, though Christian charity sounds a very cold thing to people whose heads are full of sentimentality, and though it is quite distinct from affection, yet it leads to affection.

The difference between a Christian and a worldly man is not that the worldly man has only affections or "likings" and the Christian has only "charity." The worldly man treats certain people kindly because he "likes" them: the Christian, trying to treat every one kindly, finds himself liking more and more people as he goes on—including people he could not even have imagined himself liking at the beginning.

This same spiritual law works terribly in the opposite direction. The Germans, perhaps, at first ill-treated the Jews because they hated them: afterwards they hated them much more because they had ill-treated them. The more cruel you are, the more you will hate; and the more you hate, the more cruel you will become—and so on in a vicious circle for ever.

Good and evil both increase at compound interest. That is why the little decisions you and I make every day are of such infinite importance. The smallest good act today is the capture of a strategic point from which, a few months later, you may be able to go on to victories you never dreamed of. An apparently trivial indulgence in lust or anger today is the loss of a ridge or railway line or bridgehead from which the enemy may launch an attack otherwise impossible.

Some writers use the word charity to describe not only Christian love between human beings, but also God's love for man and man's love for God. About the second of these two, people are often worried. They are told they ought to love God. They cannot find any such feeling in themselves. What are they to do? The answer is the same as before. Act as if you did. Do not sit trying to manufacture feelings. Ask yourself, "If I were sure that I loved God, what would I do?" When you have found the answer, go and do it.

On the whole, God's love for us is a much safer subject to think about than our love for Him. Nobody can always have devout feelings: and even if we could, feelings are not what God principally cares about. Christian Love, either towards God or towards man, is an affair of the will. If we are trying to do His will we are obeying the commandment, "Thou shalt love the Lord thy God." He will give us feelings of love if He pleases. We cannot create them for ourselves, and we must not demand them as a right.

But the great thing to remember is that, though our feelings come and go, His love for us does not. It is not wearied by our sins, or our indifference; and, therefore, it is quite relentless in its determination that we shall be cured of those sins, at whatever cost to us, at whatever cost to Him.

10.

HOPE

Hope is one of the Theological virtues. This means that a continual looking forward to the eternal world is not (as some modern people think) a form of escapism or wishful thinking, but one of the things a Christian is meant to do. It does not mean that we are to leave the present world as it is. If you read history you will find that the Christians who did most for the present world were just those who thought most of the next. The Apostles themselves, who set on foot the conversion of the Roman Empire, the great men who built up the Middle Ages, the English Evangelicals who abolished the Slave Trade, all left their mark on Earth, precisely because their minds were occupied with Heaven. It is since Christians have largely ceased to think of the other world that they have become so ineffective in this. Aim at Heaven and you will get earth "thrown in": aim at earth and you will get neither. It seems a strange rule, but something like it can be seen at work in other matters. Health is a great blessing, but the moment you make health one of your main, direct objects you start becoming a crank and imagining there is something wrong with you. You are only likely to get health provided you want other things more—food, games, work, fun, open air. In the same way, we shall never save civilisation as long as civilisation is our main object. We must learn to want something else even more.

Most of us find it very difficult to want "Heaven" at all—except in so far as "Heaven" means meeting again our friends who have died. One reason for this difficulty is that we have not been trained: our whole education tends to fix our minds on this world. Another reason is that when the real want for Heaven is present in us, we do not recognise it. Most people, if they had really learned to look into their own hearts, would know that they do want, and want acutely, something that cannot be had in this world. There are all sorts of things in this world that offer to give it to you, but they never quite keep their promise. The longings which arise in us when we first fall in love, or first think of some foreign country, or first take up some subject that excites us, are longings which no marriage, no travel, no learning, can really satisfy. I am not now speaking of what would be ordinarily called unsuccessful marriages, or holidays, or learned careers. I am speaking of the best possible ones. There was something we grasped at, in that first moment of longing, which just fades away in the reality. I think everyone knows what I mean. The wife may be a good wife, and the hotels and scenery may have been excellent, and chemistry may be a very interesting job: but something has evaded us. Now there are two wrong ways of dealing with this fact, and one right one.

(1) The Fool's Way.—He puts the blame on the things themselves. He goes on all his life thinking that if only he tried another woman, or went for a more expensive holiday, or whatever it is, then, this time, he really would catch the mysterious something we are all after. Most of the bored, discontented, rich people in the world are of this type. They spend their whole lives trotting from woman to woman (through the divorce courts), from continent to continent, from hobby to hobby, always thinking that the latest is "the Real Thing" at last, and always disappointed.

2) The Way of the Disillusioned "Sensible Man."—He soon decides that the whole thing was moonshine. "Of course," he says, "one feels like that when one's young. But by the time you get to my age you've given up chasing the rainbow's end." And so he settles down and learns not to expect too much and represses the part of himself which used, as he would say, "to cry for the moon." This is, of course, a much better way than the first, and makes a man much happier, and less of a nuisance to society. It tends to make him a prig (he is apt to be rather superior towards

what he calls "adolescents"), but on the whole, he rubs along fairly comfortably. It would be the best line we could take if man did not live for ever. But supposing infinite happiness really is there, waiting for us? Supposing one really can reach the rainbow's end? In that case it would be a pity to find out too late (a moment after death) that by our supposed "common sense" we had stifled in ourselves the faculty of enjoying it.

(3) The Christian Way.—The Christian says, "Creatures are not born with desires unless satisisfaction for those desires exists. A baby feels hunger: well, there is such a thing as food. A duckling wants to swim: well, there is such a thing as water. Men feel sexual desire: well, there is such a thing as sex. If I find in myself a desire which no experience in this world can satisfy, the most probable explanation is that I was made for another world. If none of my earthly pleasures satisfy it, that does not prove that the universe is a fraud. Probably earthly pleasures were never meant to satisfy it, but only to arouse it, to suggest the real thing. If that is so, I must take care, on the one hand, never to despise, or be unthankful for, these earthly blessings, and on the other, never to mistake them for the something else of which they are only a kind of copy, or echo, or mirage. I must keep alive in myself the desire for my true country, which I shall not find till after death; I must never let it get snowed under or turned aside; I must make it the main object of life to press on to that other country and to help others to do the same.

There is no need to be worried by facetious people who try to make the Christian hope of "Heaven" ridiculous by saying they do not want "to spend eternity playing harps." The answer to such people is that if they cannot understand books written for grown-ups, they should not talk about them. All the scriptural imagery (harps, crowns, gold, etc.) is, of course, a merely symbolical, attempt to express the inexpressible. Musical instruments are mentioned because for many people (not all) music is the thing known in the present life which most strongly suggests ecstasy and infinity. Crowns are mentioned to suggest the fact that those who are united with God in eternity share His splendour and power and joy. Gold is mentioned to suggest the timelessness of Heaven (gold does not rust) and the preciousness of it. People who take these symbols literally might as well think that when Christ told us to be like doves, He meant that we were to lay eggs.

II.

FAITH

I must talk in this chapter about what the Christians call Faith. Roughly speaking, the word Faith seems to be used by Christians in two senses or on two levels, and I will take them in turn. In the first sense it means simply Belief—accepting or regarding as true the doctrines of Christianity. That is fairly simple. But what does puzzle people—at least it used to puzzle me—is the fact that Christians regard faith in this sense as a virtue. I used to ask how on earth it can be a virtue—what is there moral or immoral about believing or not believing a set of statements? Obviously, I used to say, a sane man accepts or rejects any statement, not because he wants or does not want to, but because the evidence seems to him good or bad. If he were mistaken about the goodness or badness of the evidence that would not mean he was a bad man, but only that he was not very clever. And if he thought the evidence bad but tried to force himself to believe in spite of it, that would be merely stupid.

Well, I think I still take the view. But what I did not see then—and a good many people do not see still—was this. I was assuming that if the human mind once accepts a thing as true it will automatically go on regarding it as true, until some real reason for reconsidering it turns up. In fact, I was assuming that the human mind is completely ruled by reason. But that is not so. For example, my reason is perfectly convinced by good evidence that anaesthetics do not smother me and that properly trained surgeons do not start operating until I am unconscious. But that does not alter the fact that when they have me down on the table and clap their horrible mask over my face, a mere childish panic begins inside me. I start thinking I am going to choke, and I am afraid they will start cutting me up before I am properly under. In other words, I lose my faith in anaesthetics. It is not reason that is taking away my faith: on the contrary, my faith is based on reason. It is my imagination and emotions. The battle is between faith and reason on one side and emotion and imagination on the other.

When you think of it you will see lots of instances of this. A man knows, on perfectly good evidence, that a pretty girl of his acquaintance is a liar and cannot keep a secret and ought not to be trusted; but when he finds himself with her his mind loses its faith in that bit of knowledge and he starts thinking, "Perhaps she'll be different this time," and once more makes a fool of himself and tells her something he ought not to have told her. His senses and emotions have destroyed his faith in what he really knows to be true. Or take a boy learning to swim. His reason knows perfectly well that an unsupported human body will not necessarily sink in water: he has seen dozens of people float and swim. But the whole question is whether he will be able to go on believing this when the instructor takes away his hand and leaves him unsupported in the water—or whether he will suddenly cease to believe it and get in a fright and go down.

Now just the same thing happens about Christianity. I am not asking anyone to accept Christianity if his best reasoning tells him that the weight of the evidence is against it. That is not the point at which Faith comes in. But supposing a man's reason once decides that the weight of the evidence is for it. I can tell that man what is going to happen to him in the next few weeks. There will come a moment when there is bad news, or he is in trouble, or is living among a lot of other people who do not believe it, and all at once his emotions will rise up and carry out a sort of blitz on his belief. Or else there will come a moment when he wants a woman, or wants to tell a lie, or feels very pleased with himself, or sees a chance of making a little money in some way that is not perfectly fair: some moment, in fact, at which it would be very convenient if Christianity were not true. And once again his wishes and desires will carry out a blitz. I am not talking of moments at which any real new reasons against Christianity turn up. Those have to be faced and that is a different matter. I am talking about moments where a mere mood rises up against it.

Now Faith, in the sense in which I am here using the word, is the art of holding on to things your reason has once accepted, in spite of your changing moods. For moods will change, whatever view your reason takes. I know that by experience. Now that I am a Christian I do have moods in which the whole thing looks very improbable: but when I was an atheist I had moods in which Christianity looked terribly probable. This rebellion of your moods against your real self is going to come anyway. That is why Faith is such a necessary virtue: unless you teach your moods "where they get off," you can never be either a sound Christian or even a sound atheist, but just a creature dithering to and fro, with its beliefs really dependent on the weather and the state of its digestion. Consequently one must train the habit of Faith.

The first step is to recognise the fact that your moods change. The next is to make sure that, if you have once accepted Christianity, then some of its main doctrines shall be deliberately held before your mind for some time every day. That is why daily prayers and religious reading and churchgoing are necessary parts of the Christian life. We have to be continually reminded of what we believe. Neither this belief nor any other will automatically remain alive in the mind. It must be fed. And as a matter of fact, if you examined a hundred people who had lost their faith in Christianity, I wonder how many of them would turn out to have been reasoned out of it by honest argument? Do not most people simply drift away?

Now I must turn to Faith in the second or higher sense: and this is the most difficult thing I have tackled yet. I want to approach it by going back to the subject of Humility. You may remember I said that the first step towards humility was to realise that one is proud. I want to add now that the next step is to make some serious attempt to practise the Christian virtues. A week is not enough. Things often go swimmingly for the first week. Try six weeks. By that time, having, as far as one can see, fallen back completely or even fallen lower than the point one began from, one will have discovered some truths about oneself. No man knows how bad he is till he has tried very hard to be good. A silly idea is current that good people do not know what temptation means. This is an obvious life. Only those who try to resist temptation know how strong it is. After all, you find out the strength of the German army by fighting against it, not by giving in. You find out the strength of a wind by trying to walk against it, not by lying down. A man who gives in to temptation after five minutes simply does not know what it would have been like an hour later. That is why bad people, in one sense, know very little about badness. They have lived a sheltered life by always giving in. We never find out the strength of the evil impulse inside us until we try to fight it: and Christ, because He was the only man who never yielded to temptation, is also the only man who knows to the full what temptation means—the only complete realist. Very well, then. The main thing we learn from a serious attempt to practise the Christian virtues is that we fail. If there was any idea that God had set us a sort of exam and that we might get good marks by deserving them, that has to be wiped out. If there was any idea of a sort of bargain—any idea that we could perform our side of the contract and thus put God in our debts so that it was up to Him, in mere justice, to perform His side—that has to be wiped out.

I think every one who has some vague belief in God, until he becomes a Christian, has the idea of an exam or of a bargain in his mind. The first result of real Christianity is to blow that idea into bits. When they find it blown into bits, some people think this means that Christianity is a failure and give up. They seem to imagine that God is very simple-minded! In fact, of course, He knows all about this. One of the very things Christianity was designed to do was to blow this idea to bits. God has been waiting for the moment at which you discover that there is no question of earning a pass mark in this exam or putting Him in your debt.

Then comes another discovery. Every faculty you have, your power of thinking or of moving your limbs from moment to moment, is given you by God. If you devoted every moment of your whole life exclusively to His service you could not give Him anything that was not in a sense His own already. So that when we talk of a man doing anything for God or giving anything to

God, I will tell you what it is really like. It is like a small child going to his father and saying, "Daddy, give me sixpence to buy you
a birthday present." Of course, the father does, and he is pleased
with the child's present. It is all very nice and proper, but only
an idiot would think that the father is sixpence to the good on the
transaction. When a man has made these two discoveries God
can really get to work. It is after this that real life begins. The
man is awake now. We can now go on to talk of Faith in the
second sense.

12.

FAITH

I want to start by saying something that I would like everyone to notice carefully. It is this. If this chapter means nothing to you, if it seems to be trying to answer questions you never asked, drop it at once. Do not bother about it at all. There are certain things in Christianity that can be understood from the outside, before you have become a Christian. But there are a great many things that cannot be understood until after you have gone a certain distance along the Christian road. These things are purely practical, though they do not look as if they were. They are directions for dealing with particular cross-roads and obstacles on the journey and they do not make sense until a man has reached those places. Whenever you find any statement in Christian writings which you can make nothing of, do not worry. Leave it alone. There will come a day, perhaps years later, when you suddenly see what it meant. If one could understand it now, it would only do one harm.

Of course all this tells against me as much as anyone else. The thing I am going to try to explain in this chapter may be ahead of me. I may be thinking I have got there when I have not. I can only ask instructed Christians to watch very carefully, and tell me when I go wrong; and others to take what I say with a grain of salt—as something offered, because it may be a help, not because I am certain that I am right.

I am trying to talk about Faith in the second sense, the higher sense. I said last week that the question of Faith in this sense arises after a man has tried his level best to practise the Christian virtues, and found that he fails, and seen that even if he could he would only be giving back to God what was already God's own.

516

In other words, he discovers his bankruptcy. Now, once again, what God cares about is not exactly our actions. What he cares about is that we should be creatures of a certain kind or quality —the kind of creatures He intended us to be—creatures related to Himself in a certain way. I do not add "and related to one another in a certain way," because that is included: if you are right with Him you will inevitably be right with all your fellow-creatures, just as if all the spokes of a wheel are fitted rightly into the hub and the rim they are bound to be in the right positions to one another. And as long as a man is thinking of God as an examiner who has set him a sort of paper to do, or as the opposite party in a sort of bargain—as long as he is thinking of claims and counterclaims between himself and God—he is not yet in the right relation to Him. He is misunderstanding what he is and what God is. And he cannot get into the right relation until he has discovered the fact of our bankruptcy.

When I say "discovered," I mean really discovered: not simply said it parrot-fashion. Of course, any child, if given a certain kind of religious education, will soon learn to *say* that we have nothing to offer to God that is not already His own and that we find ourselves failing to offer even that without keeping something back. But I am talking of really discovering this: really finding out by experience that it is true.

Now we cannot, in that sense, discover our failure to keep God's law except by trying our very hardest (and then failing). Unless we really try, whatever we say there will always be at the back of our minds the idea that if we try harder next time we shall succeed in being completely good. Thus, in one sense, the road back to God is a road of moral effort, of trying harder and harder. But in another sense it is not trying that is ever going to bring us home. All this trying leads up to the vital moment at which you turn to God and say, "You must do this. I can't." Do not, I implore you, start asking yourselves, "Have I reached that moment?" Do not sit down and start watching your own mind to see if it is coming along. That puts a man quite on the wrong track. When the most important things in our life happen we quite often do not know, at the moment, what is going on. A man does not always say to himself, "Hullo! I'm growing up."

It is often only when he looks back that he realises what has happened and recognises it as what people call "growing up." You can see it even in simple matters. A man who starts anxiously watching to see whether he is going to sleep is very likely to remain wide awake. As well, the thing I am talking of now may not happen to every one in a sudden flash—as it did to St. Paul or Bunyan: it may be so gradual that no one could ever point to a particular hour or even a particular year. And what matters is the nature of the change in itself, not how we feel while it is happening. It is the change from being confident about our own efforts to the state in which we despair of doing anything for ourselves and leave it to God.

I know the words "leave it to God" can be misunderstood, but they must stay for the moment. The sense in which a Christian leaves it to God is that he puts all his trust in Christ: trusts that Christ will somehow share with him the perfect human obedience which He carried out from His birth to His crucifixion: that Christ will make the man more like Himself and, in a sense, make good his deficiencies. In Christian language, He will share His "sonship" with us, will make us, like Himself, "Sons of God": in Book IV I shall attempt to analyse the meaning of those words a little further. If you like to put it that way, Christ offers something for nothing: He even offers everything for nothing. In a sense, the whole Christian life consists in accepting that very remarkable offer. But the difficulty is to reach the point of recognising that all we have done and can do is nothing. What we should have liked would be for God to count our good points and ignore our bad ones. Again, in a sense, you may say that no temptation is ever overcome until we stop trying to overcome it— throw up the sponge. But then you could not "stop trying" in the right way and for the right reason until you had tried your very hardest. And, in yet another sense, handing everything over to Christ does not, of course, mean that you stop trying. To trust Him means, of course, trying to do all that He says. There would be no sense in saying you trusted a person if you would not take his advice. Thus if you have really handed yourself over to Him, it must follow that you are trying to obey Him. But trying in a new way, a less worried way. Not doing these things in order to be saved, but because He has begun to save you already. Not hoping to get to Heaven as a reward for your actions, but inevitably wanting to act in a certain way because a first faint gleam of Heaven is already inside you.

Christians have often disputed as to whether what leads the Christian home is good actions, or Faith in Christ. I have no right really to speak on such a difficult question, but it does seem to me like asking which blade in a pair of scissors is most necessary. A serious moral effort is the only thing that will bring you to the point where you throw up the sponge. Faith in Christ is the only thing to save you from despair at that point: and out of that Faith in Him good actions must inevitably come. There are two parodies of the truth which different sets of Christians have, in the past, been accused by other Christians of believing: perhaps they may make the truth clearer. One set were accused of saying, "Good actions are all that matters. The best good action is charity. The best kind of charity is giving money. The best thing to give money to is the Church. So hand us over £10,000 and we will see you through." The answer to that nonsense, of course, would be that good actions done for that motive, done with the idea that Heaven can be bought, would not be good actions at all, but only commercial speculations. The other set were accused of saying, "Faith is all that matters. Consequently, if you have faith, it doesn't matter what you do. Sin away, my lad, and have a good time and Christ will see that it makes no difference in the end." The answer to that nonsense is that, if what you call your "faith" in Christ does not involve taking the slightest notice of what He says, then it is not Faith at all—not faith or trust in Him, but only intellectual acceptance of some theory about Him.

The Bible really seems to clinch the matter when it puts the two things together into one amazing sentence. The first half is, "Work out your own salvation with fear and trembling"—which looks as if everything depended on us and our good actions: but the second half goes on, "For it is God who worketh in you"— which looks as if God did everything and we nothing. I am afraid that is the sort of thing we come up against in Christianity. I am puzzled, but I am not surprised. You see, we are now trying to understand, and to separate into water-tight compartments, what exactly God does and what man does when God and man are working together. And, of course, we begin by thinking it is like two men working together, so that you could say, "He did this bit and I did that." But this way of thinking breaks down. God is not like that. He is inside you as well as outside: even if we could understand who did what, I do not think human language could properly express it. In the attempt to express it different Churches say different things. But you will find that even those who insist most strongly on the importance of good actions tell you you need Faith; and even those who insist most strongly on Faith tell you to do good actions. At any rate that is as far as I go.

I think all Christians would agree with me if I said that though Christianity seems at first to be all about morality, all about duties and rules and guilt and virtue, yet it leads you on, out of all that, into something beyond. One has a glimpse of a country where they do not talk of those things, except perhaps as a joke. Every one there is filled full with what we should call goodness as a mirror is filled with light. But they do not call it goodness. They do not call it anything. They are not thinking of it. They are too busy looking at the source from which it comes. But this is near the stage where the road passes over the rim of our world. No one's eyes can see very far beyond that: lots of people's eyes can see further than mine.